A HISTORY OF THE PRACTICE OF NAVIGATION

A HISTORY

OF THE

PRACTICE OF NAVIGATION

BY

Commander J. B. HEWSON, F.R.G.S., R.D., R.N.R. (Retired)

Extra Master, Member of the Honourable Company of Master Mariners
Of the Inner Temple, Barrister-at-Law

GLASGOW
BROWN, SON & FERGUSON, LIMITED
4–10 DARNLEY STREET

First edition 1951
Revised 1963
Second edition 1983

ISBN 0 85174 418 4
© 1983 BROWN, SON & FERGUSON LTD, GLASGOW G41 2SD
PRINTED AND MADE IN GREAT BRITAIN

INTRODUCTION

To many of those whose business is upon the sea the question may sometimes arise: How did the earlier navigators sail their ships across unknown waters and return to their homelands? What charts did they use and when did they first rely upon the compass?

To the wider world of people who follow the sea and its history in the books of those who voyaged long ago similar questions, too, must often arise.

From such thoughts and unanswered questions was this book born.

So far as possible every attempt has been made to avoid a wearisome collection of dates which, in following the history of an art, serves to confuse the broad outlines of its gradual evolution. So often is one instrument or idea the outcome of another that time and place can often be but imperfectly fixed. While the object of this book has been to trace the evolution of the art of ocean navigation, it has not been possible to ascribe all inventions and improvements to particular persons, and where names and dates have been given it must not be uncompromisingly accepted that such and such did not happen before that date or that some other unrecorded person did not attempt the same method years before. Many authorities have been consulted, though not a few unprofitably, but it cannot be too often stated that through the centuries many persons of practically every European nation and of North America contributed to the advancement of navigation. The names of many have been omitted from this book in order to keep it within reasonable limits. One of the guiding principles has been to follow the trend of the art in the books of those who wrote for seamen, and were frequently navigators of no mean order themselves, and who recommended new methods to their less gifted brethren when they had tested them at sea. When practical men begin to tell about a new method or advocate some improvement which they have tried themselves on the unstable sea, then is the time to speak of its introduction and not when the philosopher first conceived the idea on the firm earth. This rule has been followed when doubts have arisen, but let it not detract from the deep and sincere admiration and gratitude which seamen feel for the mathematicians and men of science who, from the first, have laboured and still labour for the benefit of all who use the sea.

The evolution of ocean navigation, or proper pilotage, as it was called in Elizabethan days, is the story of the application of mathematical theory to sea-going practice. The Norse voyages to Greenland and Labrador ten centuries ago were not undertaken with a knowledge of navigation as the term was understood in the fifteenth century when Prince Henry the Navigator established his academy of navigation at Sagres. The seamanship of the Norsemen, the ingenious art employed by certain Pacific islanders and the methods of other Eastern peoples have no place in this study, as they contributed little to the general advancement of the art but rather contented themselves with their own domestic, coastal or seasonal navigation, adding little to the practical solution of the problems which beset the Western navigator.

The birth of British maritime enterprise coincided with the beginning of scientific ocean navigation but her navigators were, at first, slow to emulate the methods of its first successful exponent, Columbus. There were, doubtless, many earlier unrecorded navigators who ventured far from land and found their way back, but due honour must be given to Columbus who first loosed the flood of gathering confidence in the compass, the use of heavenly bodies to find the latitude, parallel sailing and dead reckoning.

During the century which followed the discovery of America British navigators gradually learned the art of proper pilotage and assimilated all their more Southern brethren had to teach. By virtue of her geographical position Britain was well situated for voyages across the North Atlantic and into the Arctic Seas, and it was in those waters that her navigators practised and evolved their art. From that time, their methods and progress give a substantially correct picture of the practice of ocean navigation among all Western nations whose sons belonged to the brotherhood of the sea.

J. B. H.

CONTENTS

CONTENTS

PART I

CHAPTER I.

CHARTS AND SAILING DIRECTIONS.

THE evolution of the art of chart-making began later than the making of maps which had its beginning centuries before the Christian era.

Ancient geographers, philosophers and land measurers were more concerned about caravan routes and trading centres, the size and shape of the earth or the limits of private properties and the extent of kingdoms. They had little interest in the way by sea to places beyond the horizon where no landmarks were to be found. When they viewed the sea it was from the land, whereas the mariner viewed the land and its approaches from the sea.

In the course of time seamen and merchants coasted further and further away from their native ports in search of trade, increasing their knowledge and experience, but their voyages were essentially coastal until the introduction and adoption of the compass during the Middle Ages. There were exceptions but these were forced upon the unhappy mariner by ill winds or unexpected storms and contributed little to the gradual development of scientific navigation.

The cradle of modern navigation was the Mediterranean Sea and in it the first sea maps or charts were made.

The more intelligent and venturesome shipmaster must have felt the lack of some pictorial representation of the coasts along which he sailed. The urge to transport his cargoes in quicker time than others, and the desire to accomplish as many voyages as possible during the navigable season must have led him to draw rough charts annotated with important data to assist him in his future voyages.

Few voyages were undertaken during the winter, between November and March, for the Mediterranean was virtually closed to navigation during the more boisterous months. In classical times navigation was in principle suspended from some time in November till the beginning of March. What in Roman times was a rule of prudence became in the Middle Ages a rule of law. The Pisan Constitutum Usus laid down that, if a ship were in harbour after the kalends of November, the owners were not to leave before the kalends of March without the consent of the merchants who had goods on board, or of the majority of them. The maritime statute of Ancona (c.77) fixed dates at which ships returning to Ancona from abroad were to leave the outport. When a ship failed to leave at the prescribed time, and was compelled to winter on the way, the mariners were entitled to their full pay during the winter.[1]

The merchants usually voyaged with their goods and were frequently as experienced in weather lore and coastal identification as the shipmaster. Thus, there was every reason why they should decide whether undue risks should be run with their goods.

The bad weather was not solely responsible for these prohibitions. The seamen of those days were just as capable of handling their ships as the seamen of later days, but their trading ships were of clumsier build and made more leeway. The single mast with its enormous square sail put a terrific strain on the timbers and the labouring ships were too prone to start their seams. Apart from this danger, the early seamen had no compasses to guide them and this, too, contributed to their unwillingness to venture far from a safe haven during the winter. While the sun shone by day and the moon and the stars passed across the heavens at night, the mariner could keep some semblance of a course and find his way back to land when he lost it. In the winter, when no celestial bodies might be seen for days, he was helpless.

Whether through prudence, desire for profit, or intelligent interest, there is no doubt that rough charts were drawn and from them the Greeks compiled forms of coastal sailing directions known as peripli. Whether such collected information was widely distributed among seamen is doubtful, and it is more probable that its significance was political.

The seeds of chart-making were sown, however, and the trading master went his way with little regard for the theories of others ashore. He cared little about the size or shape of the earth. His concern was what lay round the next point of land and, later, what lay beyond the horizon. He wanted to know what the coast looked like and from what point he should expect the wind in the different seasons. Having drawn his rough chart the next problem was how to shorten the sailing distance between two points of land. To accomplish this he realised that he must evolve some way of finding his course out of sight of land, otherwise corners could only be cut at the hazard of losing his way. Even the least observant knew that the sun ran its course daily from some easterly point through south to the west and, by experience, no doubt, learned that by keeping the sun on different bearings during the day he could steer in a more or less constant direction.

All progressive mariners were, consciously or subconsciously, looking or hoping for something that would enable them to sail with confidence in any given direction. For want of the magic stone that was in the course of time to appear they studied the heavens more closely. Some heard from the

---

[1] *The Rhodian Sea Law*—Ashburner, 1909.

more learned ashore, and others doubtless discovered for themselves that the constellations of the Great and Little Bears circled round a fixed point in the north, and that the moon followed the sun's daily movement, within limits, at night. Strabo, a Greek traveller and geographer who lived in the days of Augustus Caesar and Tiberius Caesar, remarked that the Phoenicians specially designated the Little Bear and employed it in navigation, probably some 600 years before the beginning of the Christian era.[1] The Phoenicians were the finest and most scientific navigators of the Ancients and it was from them that the Greeks learned the application of astronomy to navigation.

A learned ecclesiastic, Huet, Bishop of Avranches, who studied this question, in the seventeenth century, wrote in his history of the Commerce and Navigation of the Ancients, "Many of these Grecian People have disputed the invention of divers sorts of ships . . . . but how could they attribute to themselves the first invention of these things when they saw so frequently the Phoenician and Egyptian ships upon their coasts and even their own authors agree and confess that they had learned the Art of Navigation from the Egyptians, and that the Sydonians had taught them the necessary sciences to put that Art in Practice, viz., Arithmetick and Astronomy. Now the custom of guiding their ships according to the course of the Great Bear is so different from that of the Phoenicians, who were guided at sea by the course of the Little Bear, that it is very plain these last were much superior to the former in the skill and practice of navigation . . . besides all the voyages that were made by the Greeks were chiefly confined to the Mediterranean Sea."

For short distances out of sight of land some experienced seamen doubtless kept their course by the wind during the day and by night, too, when they had reason to expect that the wind was constant. The finest example of this was the use made of the monsoons by early seamen in their trading voyages from Arabia to India. It is recorded that an ancient pilot named Hippalus sailed from Arabia for the Indies (India) not minding to coast it along as they used to do before, and being driven by a South West wind safely performed the voyage by a much shorter passage. His example was followed with so much success that this South West wind was called Hippalus.

This use of the monsoon in the Indian Ocean and the claims of the Arabians to be called the first navigators has been discussed as follows: "It was infinitely easier to the Arabians to cross this sea to India or to Ceylon than it was for the Tyrians (Phoenicians) to run over the different parts of the Mediterranean. The first had fine weather to choose at their pleasure and the winds were fixed and regular: by which they might securely perform their voyages with

---

[1]Strabo, Book 1. Chapter 1. s.6. Also Book XVI., C.11, s.24.

as much exactness, rectitude and speed as they had occasion for, and always in a manner equal in the same seasons: advantages which the Tyrians had but very rarely: they never had fine weather at a certain point on which they might depend; so that these had more need of ability in the marine than the former on account of the variableness of the winds, cloudy weather and tempests which often reign in the Mediterranean . . . Many nations among the Indians have always crossed these seas by the favour of these winds. The dry monsoons, periodically renewed by the N.E. wind assist their sailing to the westward; and the wet monsoons formed in like manner by the opposite wind of S.W. serve them also for sailing eastwards. One monsoon serving them to go and the other to return, and those always certain and regular. The Arabians washed by the same sea ought therefore to do the same thing: and it is what they have always done according to the Indian nations who regarded them as the masters of the navigation of the seas until the arrival of the Portuguese among them, who ruined entirely the vast commerce of Arabia which had been of so long duration.

". . . . It is therefore seen by the exactness of these two seasons and the regular winds of the Indies that it was not anything difficult to the Arabians happily to succeed in their navigation for passing the sea, not only to the Isle of Ceylon but also to that of Sumatra or to Malacca . . . They yet make to this very day these traverses in a great measure without using the compass, at least very rarely: for the wind being once fixed and invariable serve them for guide and rules the direction of their route almost as well and even in some manner more exact than they would do by the help in the stars in serene weather. What is it then that should have hindered them performing the same in ancient times? This is what the modern historians have not thought of in speaking of the ancient navigation of India. It is probable had they been on the spot as I have been they would have thought as I do."[1]

The watchful shipmaster must have noted when he steered a more or less constant course with the help of the wind, sun or other celestial body, whether the sun at its highest reached about the same height in the heavens as on the previous day. From point to point as he so steered he may have remarked that at some places on the same short voyage or at the same time of year the altitude of the sun at noon was the same. He may have heard of the use of the gnomon[2] ashore and then watched the length of shadow of some upright across his deck planks and counted the planks in the shadow. These were small beginnings but they enabled the early mariner to form some idea of the comparative latitudes of the places at which he touched.

---

[1]Wyndham Beame, *Lex Mercatoria*, 1813.

[2]A vertical rod which cast a shadow along a graduated horizontal scale and used for comparing the latitudes of places on land.

A strange ship would be something of an event in every port to persons of enquiring turns of mind and who made it their business to talk to and learn from the seamen and merchants. Some of these may have collated such information and observations and recorded them. There is no limit to the conjectures as to how the early sea maps gradually grew or when they started. It is left to us to admire the patient work of hardy adventurers, enquiring landsmen and, above all, the observant mariner who, unknown, gave his mite to geographical knowledge and went his way.

Portolan Charts.—There is evidence that various catalogues of places and distances appeared from time to time. Among the early peripli is the periplus of Scylax of Caryanda, it dates from the 12th century, the earliest codex is preserved in the Bibliotheque Nationale in Paris. The original sailing directions were compiled by a navigator named Scylax, he produced a comprehensive set for the Mediterranean and Black Seas in 500 B.C. These directions were, of course, brought up to date by later navigators. They showed their appreciation by retaining the original author's name.

During the 4th century A.D., Marcianus of the Italian city of Heraclea produced sailing directions for the same area. The forerunner of this work was a guide book published by Menippus of Pergamos in the 3rd century A.D. This earlier work appears to be based on Ptolemy's maps of the Mediterranean. Maps of varying accuracy no doubt accompanied them or were drawn from them at some later time. For hundreds of years before and after the dawn of Christianity the Mediterranean seaman went about his business traversing the same sea ways and checking his distances. Reliable information gradually accumulated and during the fourteenth century A.D., if not before, hand-drawn charts of commendable accuracy made their appearance. These were the famous Portolan charts, drawn by draughtsmen and map-makers of Italy and, with variations at a later date, of Spain and Portugal. Earlier sea maps must have existed for it is unlikely that the excellence of those of the fourteenth century was achieved suddenly. It is recorded in a work by Guillaume de Nangis in describing the crusade of Saint Louis (Louis IX. of France) in 1270, that, in the voyage from Aiguesmortes to Cagliari, in Sardinia, the fleet was overtaken by a storm and at the end of the sixth day, as Cagliari had not yet been reached, the King expressed a wish to know the exact location of the ship. Thereupon, we are told, the pilots brought to him their charts, and showed him that the port was not far distant[1].

The oldest Portuguese sailing directions are contained in a manuscript dated 1506 by Valentim Fernandes. They show many of the characteristics of earlier Italian sailing directions. The early Portuguese used the term 'roteiro'

---

[1]Sir George Fordham, *Maps, Their History, Characteristics and Uses.*

for their sailing directions, they were mainly for coastal work but in 1535 the navigator Diogo Alfonso compiled the earliest 'ocean roteiro' for a voyage from Lisbon to India. By 1550, the Portuguese had considerable knowledge of the winds and currents of the Atlantic. Consider the information given in the roteiro 'Livro de Marinharia' . . . "be careful, even if the wind is favourable, not to get to close to Cape Palmas, because if you are caught by calms you will be carried away by the waters that run from there to the Mina coast" . . . "When you have passed the equinoctial line and reached the trade winds, south east, you ought to go with them while it is possible: they will be going on the quarter little by little and you will increase in latitude till you are at 30°. And from there go on, because the winds will be turning to west, west-south-west, south-south-west, and with them you will reach the Cape of Good Hope."

The Portolan charts were at first issued to illustrate the sailing directions or portolani, of the time and, like all other similar compilations, were not the productions of the practical navigators, though they were designed to assist them. As the years progressed more of these charts were compiled without the companion text. It is certain that very few of these charts found their way into the hands of the more humble shipmaster. Printing was still unknown and every chart was drawn by hand. Lucky, indeed, must have been the mariner who possessed one. On organised expeditions financed by wealthy patrons, for it was an age of patronage, in trading ventures of the merchant princes and in fleets fitted out by aspiring kings, these charts would be part of the navigational aids supplied to the leaders. The pilots of such fleets would use them, but the remainder would, to a great extent, lodge in the greater security of the libraries and homes of the imperially or commercially minded ashore. Scientific navigation was advancing beyond the resources of the individual trading shipmaster. It was not he who brought about the great navigational developments that began in the Middle Ages, though it was he who, unlettered, had piecemeal supplied much information and found his precarious way by the sun and stars. It was the wealthy patron, the learned geographer and the scientifically-minded navigator who rubbed shoulders with the mathematician ashore, who brought about the development in charts, as in every other branch of navigation.

In these Portolan charts the curvature of the earth was discounted, though it was known to philosophers many hundreds of years before, and must have been apparent to the seaman very early in history. Strabo remarked, at the beginning of the Christian era, that the convexity of the sea was proof of the spheroidal shape of the earth to those who have sailed, for they could not perceive lights at a distance when placed at the same level as their eyes and sailors, as they approached their destination, beheld the shore continually raising itself to their view. It is most unlikely that the

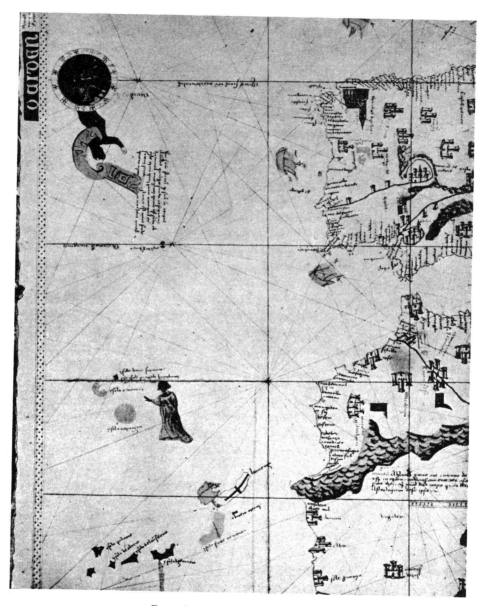

Part of a 14th century Portolano.

Reproduced by kind permission of the Royal Geographical Society.

plane projection disturbed the mariner, for the compass was so primitive that the niceties of projection with their accompanying refinements in the laying off of courses would have seemed unnecessary. He was at this time chiefly concerned with the Mediterranean which embraced comparatively low latitudes where errors in course and distance were not so apparent. It was not until the sixteenth century that the deficiencies of the plane projection seriously hampered the navigator, for it was then that intelligent attempts were made to penetrate the higher latitudes where the convergency of the meridians calls for the most diligent attention.

There is much argument as to whether the introduction of the compass was responsible for the appearance of the Portolan charts or not. It is at least arguable that the evolution of the compass had a good deal to do with the advent of the other. Both were of gradual growth and no arbitrary date can be given to either. It has already been noticed that charts and the keeping of a rough course with the help of the wind or celestial objects were known to seamen long before the introduction of the compass. But before the compass came into general use the art of navigation had reached a standstill. It is known that a form of compass was used about a century before the earliest extant Portolan. Though this proves nothing, it may indicate that the compass was in use to assist in chart making before the Portolan charts were drawn.

It is not difficult to imagine the more inspired navigators of those earlier years to whom the lodestone had been available, supporting it on water with the native cork of the Mediterranean, or pivoting it on a pin, to find the north. This was what they had been waiting for, something that would indicate a constant direction by day or by night, whether the sky was clear or overcast. It is reasonable to say that their advance was delayed when they had to wait for the sun at noon or for the Pole Star or some other celestial body at night to correct their somewhat doubtful ideas of direction. Crude and imperfect at first, misleading at times, the compass improved until the mariner trusted it and voyaged abroad with ever growing confidence in its uncanny power.

Even in many of the earliest Portolans rhumb lines were drawn to indicate every point of the compass, though some showed no more than the 16 principal points. This would seem to imply that the navigator in the fourteenth century could steer a course to within 2 points and that the time was fast approaching when he could rely on his compass to within 1 point. It is more than likely that he used the compass at first as a complement to his knowledge of the movements of the celestial bodies and that the two together created the need for and made possible the production of the Portolan chart. As the compass improved, and confidence in it developed, greater accuracy in course keeping became possible. Thus, the later charts contained rhumb lines for the 32 points of the compass. The improvement in the compass, with its resultant improvement in the making and keeping of courses in a ship, is apparent at this day. Comparatively few years ago a chart was deemed adequate when its compass rose indicated every quarter of a point and this was so long after the advent of steam. When the magnetic compass was still further improved a circle, divided into 360°, was added to the compass rose and, with the modern magnetic compass and the mechanical gyro compass, courses are laid and often steered to within a degree.

The relation between the compass and the chart is too intimate to admit of contemporary existences in separate compartments. There is little difference between the Portolan of the fourteenth century and that of the seventeenth century so far as the detail of the Mediterranean coasts is concerned. It is not easy to see how such accuracy could have been obtained without the aid of the compass or why more detail was not given in the later charts if the earlier ones were compiled without its aid.

The earlier charts were confined to the Mediterranean and Black Seas, part of the West Coast of Africa, Spain, France, the British Isles and the North Sea. The outline of the British Isles and the North Sea countries left much to be desired, but the remainder was drawn with remarkable accuracy. They were drawn on parchment and both the sea and the land were left uncoloured. The coast line was usually drawn in black and the names of places were neatly inscribed inland at right angles to it. Small islands were usually coloured red, and, in many of the later charts, they were very prominently shown in green, gold, red, blue or orange. Large outlying rocks were marked by a cross or a dot and sometimes by a combination of both in a manner very similar to that in use on charts at the present time. Soundings were not shown, nor were they to be expected, on small scale charts or on any charts in their infancy. There were not the facilities for fixing positions to run lines of soundings and the use of the lead in those days was, consequently, confined to indicating the nearness to land rather than as a guide to any particular position.

The production of these charts was, of course, restricted as they were all hand drawn, but those who had need of them would copy what they wanted from them. By the beginning of the seventeenth century the Portolan charts embraced the entire coasts of the Atlantic, most of the Pacific coasts of the Americas and the Eastern seas from the Cape of Good Hope to China.[1]

The earlier Portolans were innocent of lines of latitude and longitude, though most of them were divided into either squares or rectangles by the rhumb lines which indicated the cardinal points of the compass. The only lines of latitude that even many of the later charts could boast were the

---

[1]British Museum, Egerton MS. 819.

Equator and the tropic lines of Cancer and Capricorn. There were exceptions, of course, notably a chart of the world in three parts by Battista Agnese in 1554. He showed the Equator and the Tropics and along the Equator he marked the longitude for every 5° from the meridian of Ptolemy, with both an easterly and westerly denomination. The usual practice at this time when longitude was shown at all was to mark it from 0° to 360° in an easterly direction. The latitude was also marked by him for every 5° along the north and south rhumb in the centre of the chart. The same craftsman also produced some beautiful large scale charts of the principal islands in the Mediterranean, as well as a chart of the British Isles in which both latitude and longitude were marked along the border.

A scale of distance was always given on the charts though it was often drawn carelessly and suffered in comparison with the delicacy of the coast and rhumb lines, giving the impression that distance was a secondary consideration or that the chart-maker was not very certain of it. The unit of distances is what has been called the Portolano mile, which was equal to about two-thirds of the present-day nautical mile, and 5 Portolano miles was generally the smallest graduation on the scale.[1]

The Prime Meridian.—It has already been remarked that the Portolan charts paid scant attention to longitude. This is not surprising because of the impossibility of finding it at sea until the introduction of the accurate timepiece. It is necessary, therefore, to turn to the early maps to discover the origin and development of the prime meridian, which in later years was to become so essential for the determining of longitude.

From the Greek geographer, Strabo, we learn of early attempts to compile a map of the known world. He tells us, amongst others, of the attempts of Eratosthenes, 276-196 B.C., who was keeper of the library at Alexandria. The meridian upon which he built the whole edifice of his map was the meridian of Alexandria. It was by measuring an arc of this meridian that he computed the circumference of the earth. To call it a prime meridian in those early days would be an exaggeration, but it was the principal meridian from which his conception of the earth grew. It was like the trunk of a tree that gave birth to the unevenly spaced branches which spread horizontally as lines of equal latitude. Nothing was more natural than the adoption of this meridian. Alexandria in those days was a hub of the trade routes and a great seat of learning. It must have been the clearing house of a vast amount of geographical knowledge. In fact, Strabo writes[2] "These things Eratosthenes advances

---

[1]For further information on Portolan Charts, *vide Periplus*: an essay on the early history of Charts, by Nordenskiold A.E., 1897.

[2]Strabo, Book II., Chapter 1, Bohn Edition MDCCCLIV.

on the testimony of men who had been on the spot, and from the study of those numerous memoirs which he had for reference in that noble library[1] which Hipparchus himself acknowledges to be gigantic". From the common factors sifted from the reports of travellers and seamen it was deduced that Rhodes and Byzantium lay on the meridian of Alexandria (though, in fact, there is over 2° difference of longitude between Rhodes and Alexandria). Strabo himself believed this for he wrote ,"Again, everyone is agreed that the voyage from Alexandria to Rhode, and thence by Caria and Ionia to the Troad, Byzantium, and the Dnieper, is in a straight line with the course, of the Nile".[2]

Rhodes, the largest island on the eastern fringe of the Grecian Archipeligo was of considerable maritime importance in those days and its history is of interest. Lying half way between Alexandria and Athens it was at once the centre and turning point of seaborne trade. By virtue of its size and position it became the rendezvous of the coastal traffic. Ships going in and out of the Archipeligo coasting from Alexandria to Byzantium, Athens or Rome, would touch at Rhodes. This one time powerful maritime community equipped and maintained a strong fleet with which it kept down piracy and, later, assisted Rome in her conquests. From the common customs of the sea, of which there were no people better placed to judge, the Rhodians compiled the early sea laws of the Mediterranean, which was added to by the later Roman Emperors in Byzantium, and is known as the Rhodian Sea Law.

It was through Rhodes that Eratosthenes drew one of his lines of equal latitude. The line ran east and west through Gibraltar, to the Taurus mountains in Asia Minor, dividing the Mediterranean Sea into two parts. According to the knowledge of that time, this parallel of Rhodes (36°N.) divided the habitable world into what were called the northern and southern divisions. Another parallel was drawn through Marseilles and Byzantium.[3] No attempt was made by him to divide the map into regular divisions of latitude and longitude which is the common practice to-day. There was no pretence at geometrical precision and no measuring of degrees east and west of the principal meridian, or north and south of the dividing parallel, but rather a drawing

---

[1] The Alexandrian.

[2] Book II., Chapter 5.

[3] Strabo, Book II., Chapter 1. See also Book I., Chapter 4. "Since that (parallel of latitude) of Byzantium and Marseilles are the same. The degree of shadow from the gnomon which Pytheas states he observed at Marseilles being exactly equal to that which Hipparchus says he found at Byzantium; the periods of observation being in both cases similar." In fact, their latitudes differ by about 2°.

Marseilles was founded by the Phoenicians (Strabo, Book IV., Chapter 1) several centuries before Christ. Pytheas, a native of Marseilles was probably of Phoenician extraction and lived during the fourth century B.C. He was one of the earliest scientific navigators and voyaged as far as Thule. (Iceland)—Strabo, Book II., Chapter 5.

of lines through places which were judged to lie on the same meridians or parallels.

In the second century A.D. Ptolemy, an Egyptian astronomer, compiled his Geographia, a treatise on mathematical geography, which also contained tables of positions of several thousand places. During the Dark Ages which followed, little, if any, advance was made in map-making. In 1475, however, Ptolemy's work, with accompanying maps, was printed from manuscripts of uncertain origin. It may be that monkish mathematicians compiled the maps from the data left to the world by Ptolemy and kept their treasures hidden from the unlettered whose chief occupation was war and rapine. Suffice for our purpose to say that, with the advent of the printing press, editions of Ptolemy poured out in a constant stream. In each succeeding edition the maps were added to and amended by the publishers as their information grew.

The prime meridian of Ptolemy was taken about 2° west of the Fortunate Isles, now known as the Canaries, and the longitude was measured from there in an easterly direction. This placed London in about 21° E. of the prime meridian. In the Venice edition of Ptolemy, 1511, the prime meridian was still placed about 2° W. of the Fortunate Isles, but Britain, France and the West African Coast were drawn with greater accuracy, and moved a few degrees further west, which placed London in a longitude of about 17° E. Considering the difficulties in those days of finding longitude, it is surprising to find how near the truth these map-makers reached. For many years the prime meridian was moved about the Atlantic very much according to the whim of the map-maker.

Through the leadership of Prince Henry the Navigator, the Portuguese sailed further and further south along the west coast of Africa, mapping as they went. To the Portuguese, more than any other nation at this time, navigation was becoming more methodical and, by the beginning of the sixteenth century, they produced admirable sailing directions for the west coast of Africa. Their progression southwards was marked by careful observation for latitude which appeared in their sailing directions. Though the Prince died in 1460 his inspiration remained and in 1488 Bartholomew Diaz reached the Cape of Good Hope, and showed his successors the sea way to the Far East.

In 1492 Columbus, under the patronage of Spain, pointed the way to the East by sailing west, and placed the Spanish flag in the Indies. This did not escape the jealous eyes of the Portuguese, who felt they were about to be robbed of the fruits of their labours of many years. Both countries submitted their dispute to the Pope, Alexander VI., in 1493. He divided the map of the known world into two parts by drawing a meridian through the middle of the Atlantic, 100 leagues west of the Azores and Cape Verde

Islands. This Papal line became the prime meridian of many Spanish and Portuguese maps.[1]

In 1492, also, Martin Behaim of Nuremburg, constructed his globe of the world with the prime meridian passing through the Canaries, and this was followed by Mercator about 50 years later. Ortelius, a Dutch cartographer, in his atlas in 1570, placed the meridian through the most eastern of the Cape Verde Islands, which gave London a longitude of about 21° E.

The whole situation was summed up in *Cosmography and Geography*, 1693, by Varenus and Sanson,[2] where they wrote, "But all have not taken the same place for the first meridian, but divers. Ptolemy hath taken that near to the Fortunate Isles . . . but in process of time America was discovered, the same geographers promoted the beginning of numeration of longitude towards the W. Some made it the first meridian at the Isle of St. Nicholas adjacent to Cape Verde in Africa, but Hondius chose the Isle of St. James for his maps. Some chose the meridian of one of the islands of the Azores which is called Del Corvo for the first meridian because that in this isle and the adjoining sea the magnetic needle is found to have no declination from the meridian line. But seeing that there are other places in the earth where the magnetic needle doth the same neither doth it do it in all the meridians of this place, therefore other geographers have not thought that cause sufficient, and some have placed the first meridian in the Brazilian Shore,[3] the more modern, especially the Hollanders, having gone back to the Fortunate or Canary Isles, have chosen in one of them called Teneriffe, a mountain which is thought to be the highest in the whole world . . . and from the meridian of this mountain they judge the numeration of longitude . . . because they think fit that a famous durable place for all ages may be best chosen for this purpose. The French at this day (1693) from the year 1634 observe that for the first meridian which passeth through the western part of the Isle of Fez,[4] one of the Canaries, which beginning Louis XIII. of France commanded his mariners and geographers to observe."[5]

John Davis, the Navigator, wrote in his *Seaman's Secrets*, 1594,[6] that longitude was that portion of the Equator contained between the meridian of St. Michels, one of the Azores, and the meridian of the place whose longitude was desired. The reason why the reckoning began at St. Michels was that

---

[1] The line of Pope Alexander VI. was first shown in a map by Cantino in 1502. A facsimile of the original is in the British Museum. By the Treaty of Tordesillas, 1494, the line of demarcation was moved to 370 leagues west of the Cape Verde Islands.

[2] Famous French Cartographer and Geographer to the King of France.

[3] The Papal Line.

[4] Hierro in 18° W. of Greenwich.

[5] Whether this command of Louis XIII. was strictly observed may be open to question for in some French maps of America in 1683 the prime meridian of the Azores was used.

[6] Hakluyt Society, 1880, edited by A. H. Markham.

there was no variation there.   That there were other places in the world where the variation was nil is borne out in his account of a voyage to the East Indies in 1598.   On this occasion he was serving as Chief Pilot[1] to a Dutch expedition, and when he doubled Cape Agulhas he found there was no variation there.   In spite of his definition of longitude he repeatedly referred it to London when logging his position on his voyages of discovery.   For example, in 1586, on an expedition to find the North West passage he wrote, "On the 15th of June I discovered land in the latitude of 60 degrees and in longitude from the meridian of London westward 47 degrees".   This method was all the more interesting because the maps and charts of his day, when they numbered the degrees of longitude at all, did so in an easterly direction from the prime meridian somewhere in the Atlantic.

Up to the end of the seventeenth century the prime meridian was, in general, placed either in the Canaries or the Azores.   Often enough the seaman navigated without reference to any specific meridian for, at that time, there was no satisfactory method of finding longitude.   He recorded his position from some important point of departure which varied as the voyage progressed; for example, "In latitude no degrees fifty minutes South and longitude from the Cape of Good Hope seventy seven degrees forty minutes East".   Another method was by bearing and distance from some well-known port; for example, "In latitude 38° 30′ N. and 60 leagues from Lisbon westwards".[2]   A later example of adopting a different prime meridian to accommodate another stage of a long voyage is found in a table of variations of the compass compiled during a voyage to the East Indies in 1673.[3]   On the outward voyage the longitude was referred at first to the meridian of St. Jago and later to the Cape of Good Hope.   On the homeward voyage the meridian of Bombay was used, and, later in the voyage, Cape Aghullas.

Whatever charges may be preferred against Charles II. of England, his interest in and the encouragement he gave to navigation cannot be disputed. It was through him that Greenwich Observatory was founded in 1675 as a step towards helping the navigator to find the longitude at sea.   Shortly after the foundation of Greenwich Observatory the meridian of London (not Greenwich) was used by English map-makers and about the end of the

---

[1] Pilot was the title given in Elizabethan times to the navigator. The following definitions are taken from *The Observations of Sir Richard Hawkins*, 1622, edited by J. A. Williamson, 1933.

Office of the Master: For in matter of guide and disposing of the saylers, with the tackling of the Shippe, and the workes which belong thereunto, within board and without, all is to be committed to the master's charge.

Office of the Pilote: The Pilote is to looke carefully to the Sterridge of the Shippe, to be watchfull in taking the heights of Sunne and Starre; to note the way of his Shippe, with the augmenting and lessening of the winde.

[2] Edward Wright's account of the 3rd voyage of the Right Hon. George, Earl of Cumberland to the Azores, Vol. II., Hakluyt, 2nd Edition, 1599.

[3] *Seller's English Pilot*, 1671. The table was probably added to the volume at a later date.

eighteenth century, over 100 years later, the meridian of Greenwich was generally adopted by them.[1] Sir George Fordham, after extensive research in maps, tells us that the initial meridian in England had three stages: (i) the old vague meridian in the Atlantic, which ended with adoption of London about 1676; (ii) of the meridian of London itself 1676 to 1794, and (iii) of that of Greenwich, which has now received the sanction of the international convention for the preparation of the World Map.

All seamen will be familiar with the tables of positions at the end of modern nautical tables. Such tables were invariably added to all earlier books on navigation; in fact, Ptolemy did it in the second century A.D. In a book on the theory of navigation published in 1706 we find a collection of 150 places whose longitudes were measured from Her Majesty's Observatory deduced from celestial observations. English authors of works on navigation were, however, not in agreement about the prime meridian until long after the adoption of London by the land map-makers. This may have been on account of the conservatism of seamen, but it is more likely that it was due to the lack of adequate means of finding longitude at sea, and the impossibility of joining one position at sea to another by the shore method of triangulation. Until the perfecting of the chronometer it mattered little to the navigator which prime meridian was used. The divergence of opinion in the middle of the eighteenth century on the position of the prime meridian is well illustrated in two books on navigation written by different authors. In the one, written in 1754, the longitudes of places were given from London, the position of Greenwich being 51° 28′ N., 0° 05′ E. and the 0° to 360° method was dropped in favour of 180° E. and W., the longitude of Havana being given as 81° 11′ W. from London. It is interesting to note that the author, in his preface, suggested that one reason why the art of navigation had improved so little during the last 150 years was because writers on the subject were content, for the most part, to copy from one another.

In the other book, published in 1764, the author, in referring to the table of positions, wrote, "The longitude is reckoned from the Canaries, as anciently or from the westernmost part of the continent of Africa: that whimsical humour

---

[1]The following is taken from *Maps, Their History, Characteristics and Uses*, by Sir H. G. Fordham, Cambridge University Press, 1927.

"In John Seller's map of Hertfordshire, dated 1676, the meridian of London first appears in use, as far as I have been able to ascertain. It was from that date uniformly used on English maps, until about the end of the next century, and, when fixed more exactly, the meridian is drawn through St. Paul's Cathedral. This was displaced in its turn by Greenwich Observatory. John Cary, in his county atlas of 1787, and the second edition of 1793, bases all his maps on the meridian of London, but in the year following the latter date, on June 11, 1794, he issued his New Map of England and Wales, with part of Scotland in 81 sheets, drawn on a scale of 5 miles to the inch, and upon this map, for, it seems, the first time, appears the meridian of Greenwich, associated, no doubt, with the fact that the Ordnance Survey triangulation, commenced in 1783 had then made substantial progress."

of many modern geographers of counting the longitude from the metropolis of their own country has brought all into confusion". His table of longitude was reckoned from the meridian of the westernmost of the Canary Islands and the position of London was given as 51° 32′ N., 17° 54′ E., and of Greenwich 51° 29′ N., 18° 00′ E. He still reckoned his longitudes by the 0° to 360° method and placed Havana in longitude 294° 40′. It is more than likely that this author was one of those contented to copy from earlier writers, for he went on to say that if the much desired method of finding longitude by some observation or other could be found, it would not be necessary to correct the reckoning, and added that he doubted if such a method ever would be found. Yet, three years before this, in 1761, John Harrison had succeeded in making a chronometer which brought the solution of the problem within sight.

John Hamilton Moore, Hydrographer to His Royal Highness the Duke of Clarence, whose *Epitome of Navigation* ran into very many editions, gave a table of latitudes and longitudes of the Principal Harbours of the World in his work. In the edition published in 1800 he used the meridian of London whose position was given as 51° 32′ N., 0° 00′ E., and that of Greenwich 51° 29′ N., 0° 05′ E. In the edition published in 1814, however, he used the meridian of Greenwich and from that time onwards all reputable books on navigation, published in England, used it.

Whatever the opinions of the text-book writers, the practical navigator at sea often referred his longitude to London. It has already been remarked that, at the end of the sixteenth century, John Davis, who wrote that longitude was measured from the Azores, referred his own longitude to London when writing the journal of his second voyage to discover the North West Passage. The captain of a privateer, writing to his owners in 1757, gave his longitude as 10° 57′ from London, and in the instructions from the owners to another privateer captain in 1779, we read "Don't keep too near the coast of Ireland, and be sure to gain the longitude of 20° west from London".[1]

Whatever differences of opinion existed between English navigators and text-book writers, it is evident that there was unanimity between them in the early years of the nineteenth century that the meridian of Greenwich should be used as the prime meridian for their accounting of longitude. The factors which contributed to this were (a) the ever-growing improvements in the chronometer; (b) the publication of the first official Nautical Almanac in 1767; (c) the increasing accuracy and handiness of navigational instruments; and (d) the command of the seas by the British fleets and the enterprise of British merchants and merchant seamen.

Rutters.—Long before the Christian Era, ships from Gaul, as well as those

---

[1]*History of the Liverpool Privateers*, by Gomer Williams, 1897.

of the Phoenician traders, visited the southern shores of England. During those early days and in the years that followed the seamen of Gaul learned a lot about the coasts of the Channel, its dangers and its tides, and handed down their sea lore to their children. These more northern seamen had greater cause to observe the tides and tidal streams than the seamen of the almost tideless Mediterranean. The Race of Alderney, the high tides in the Channel ports and the alternating tidal streams up and down the Channel were as real to them as they are to us to-day. It is not surprising, therefore, to find that their sailing directions contained a fair amount of tidal information and of the Moon's effect upon the waters. How soon they committed their knowledge to paper must, as in all similar cases, be a matter of speculation, but it is certain that by the beginning of the sixteenth century books of sailing directions for the Channel were printed at Rouen. So far as we know, there were no accompanying charts, though it is quite possible that charts of the relevant area were already in existence. In these books we see the successors of the Greek peripli and the Italian portolani; in fact, it may be truly said that sailing directions are about the oldest form of intelligent guide to seamen that have come down to us in an almost unbroken line from the dawn of navigation.

There is, in the British Museum, a manuscript by an English scribe of the fifteenth century which gives sailing directions for the Circumnavigation of England and for a voyage to the Straits of Gibraltar. It begins, "Berwick lieth south and north of Golden Stonys, the Thonde and Berwick haven lien west north west and east south east. And for Vanborugh to the poynt of the Thond the cours lieth north and south . . ." The Directions contain some soundings and a little tidal information.[1]

The contributions of the Portuguese to maritime knowledge must not be forgotten. By the beginning of the sixteenth century a book of sailing directions for the West Coast of Africa had been compiled by Duarte Pacheco under the title of *Esmeraldo de Situ orbis*. The route from point to point is described, and landmarks, soundings, tides, anchorages and latitudes are given.[2]

The name given by the French authors to these books was Routier which may be translated as wayfinder or guide for seamen. This word was corrupted by the English translators into Rutter, and during the sixteenth century many Rutters were published in England. The first English translator and printer of such works of which we have record was Robert Copland, who translated the Grant Routier of Pierre Garcie, which was first printed at Rouen about 1521.[3] It seems that these books were widely used, for the

[1] A copy of this manuscript is to be found at the end of *Tractatus de Globis*, by Robt. Hues, Hakluyt Society.

[2] Hakluyt Society, Series II., Vol. LXXIX.

[3] *Dictionary of National Biography* 1887 Vol. XII.

English translation ran through several editions within a few years. Their object was to assist the merchant seaman in his carrying trade between England and France. All the earlier Rutters contained a copy of the laws of Oleron, the code of sea law associated with the isle of that name since the twelfth century.[1] The code appended to these books was vouched as follows:

> "Witnesse the seale of the Yle of Auleron establyshed by the contractes of the saide Ile, the Tuesday after the feast of Saint Andrew in the yeare of our Lorde MCCLXVI."

That Robert Copland was a man of good principle will be seen from the following extracts from the prologue to his translation, in which he also tells us how the Routier came to his hands.

". . . But the sure, wise and enured master mariner or lodesman, not ignorantly trusting his own . . . reason diligently for the safegarde of his his doinges and assurance of his practise considereth if his vessel be sure and decked at all points, and with great solicitude seeketh, enquireth and getteth such necessary instruments as behoveth to the industry of his practise as the Carde (chart), compass, rutter, . . . and other, which by speculate practise sheweth the plat (plan), that is to say, the costes (coasts), havens, roodes (roads), soundings, dangers, floodes, ebbes, windes, kennynges[2], courses and passages from land to land.   And to be more sure in the conducting of his voyage he busyly pursueth for all tacklings and store thereto behoofful as cables, ropes, ankers, mastes, sayles, ores (oars), artyllery, vitaille (victuals), fresh water, fewel (fuel) and other necessaries.   All these discreetly pondered by a . . . ingenious and circumspect mariner of the Citie of London beeing in the towne of Bourdewes (Bordeaux) bought a pretty booke imprinted in the French language called the Rutter of the Sea containing many proper feates of his science, and considering that it was expedient and necessary for all Englishmen of his faculty to have it in their own language to the erudition and safegarde of our merchants and other haunting the sea, not knowing the contents thereof.   The which booke he instantly requested me to translate into English.   Which oversene (looked over) methought it very difficult to me not knowing the terms of mariners and names of the coastes and havens, for I never came on the sea nor by no coast thereof. But following my copye by

---

[1] The Laws of Oleron probably had their origin in the earlier Rhodian Sea Law (p. 10) and were introduced to regulate the sea trade of Bordeaux and the North West coast of France during the time of the Crusades.   They were later adopted, amended and altered by the more northern nations, including England, to form the foundation of their maritime law.

The Isle of Oleron, which lies a little to the northward of Bordeaux had been known to British shipmasters for many years before this Rutter was published. The Bordeaux wine trade was one of their earliest regular trades.

[2] See later pp. 18 and 19.

the advice and oversight of certayne cunning men of science, which boldened me and informed me in many doubts, I did undertake in doing my diligence as a blind horse in a myl (mill) turning the querne ignorantly, yet safely by conducting of the miller that setteth him to worke. Desiring all expert masters to correct this and make some other for the common utilitie and safe-garde of these our native countrymen and their goods, sayling in divers regions. In the which dooing they shall not onely obtaine thankes, laude and be praised for in this world, but also in the other world shall be fully rewarded of Almighty God which is cheef master and lodesman of and to every streame and coast. To whom be given all laud prayse honour and glory in the world of worldes now and ever, Amen".

Then followed a further admonition addressed by him to all sailors, in verse, exhorting them to godliness, and to use his book.

"Gentle Mariners, move upon a boune voyage
Hoyse up your sayles and let Christ our Lord stere,
Let not cursing and swearing bee your usage
But thank God for all weathers be they black or cleare.
Then need ye not in dangers dread nor feare
For sure trust in Christ Jesu and godly lyfe
Bee great comfortes when death draweth neare
And in heaven wyll place you from all stormes and stryfe
Now mates, then forward and take this booke
And for your profit thereon often looke".

These books were very small and the information in them was by no means exhaustive. They gave courses and distances between the south coast of England and the coast of France, and certain information on the tides, soundings and the nature of the bottom[1]. It is in the Rutters that the word kennynge or kenning is used as a measure of distance, though league or mile is used to denote shorter distances. For example, we are told that the distance between Silley and the Longshippes is one kenning, and it meant that the one was in sight of the other, that is within the range of ordinary vision which was usually taken to be a distance of 20 miles.

In the British Museum there is a fine example of a late sixteenth century Rutter, or "Book of the Sea Carte" in manuscript[2]. It is in four parts and covers the coasts of the British Isles and the Continental coast of the Channel. Each part contains a small hand-drawn map on the plane projection, which is more for illustration than navigational use. It is worthy of note that in

---

[1]Sailing directions for the east coast of England were also added to these books on the same lines, under the title of the *Rutter of the North*, in 1541, by Richard Proude.

[2]Add. MS. 37024.

the first part of the book, which deals principally with the east coast of Scotland, from Leith to the Humber, the word kenning denotes a distance of only 14 miles, whereas in the other parts its measure of distance is 20 miles.[1]

The following extracts are taken from this book to give an idea of the information with which the sixteenth century navigators were supplied:—

(1) Nigh Portlande we shall have 15 fadoms and stones like beanes.

(2) To enter Falmouth ye shall fynde a rocke in the myddle of the entrynge, leve it on the larborde syde and go towarde east by those and when ye be past it go streight in for the baye is . . . large, anker where ye will at 5 or 6 fadoms amyd the baye and if ye will go at the tournynge of the full sea, for there is a banke to passe which ye shall finde at lowe water at two fadoms and a halfe.

(3) From Dodman to the Lizarde—one kennynge and three mile.

In 1590 a printed Rutter appeared in England from a different source. It was called *The Safegarde of Saylers* or the *Great Rutter* translated from the Dutch into English by Robert Norman, Hydrographer. It contained sailing directions for the British Isles, Spain, France, Flanders and Denmark, and, in common with the other books of such directions, which were copied from the Dutch, many views of the coast, similar to but cruder than those which are found in present-day charts and books of sailing directions, to assist the mariner in its identification.

Sir H. G. Fordham in *Maps, Their History, Characteristics and Uses* writes, "Generally coast line panoramic views have been used as adjuncts to charts and in support of sailing directions . . . I should like to draw attention to the discovery some few years back of the sketch book used on Drake's last voyage, in which a long series of coast outlines and views is recorded to enable future expeditions to successfully locate the Spanish ports and towns for purposes of attack. It was, it appears, the custom of that time to carry draughtsmen on the expeditions fitted out to harry the Spaniard and this book is a beautiful example of the art so applied.

At the foot of the twenty-third drawing is a note of the death of the famous navigator and commander of the expedition, which has a profound sentimental and some historical interest.

'This morninge when the discription noted or taken of this Lande beinge the 28 of Januarie 1595 beinge wedens daie in the morninge. Sr Frauncis

---

[1] In Bourne's *Regiment of the Sea*, 1596, 8th Chapter, A kenne is given as 5 or 7 leagues, the distance at which high land may be seen.

Dracke Died of the bludie flix righte of the Ilande de Buena Ventura, som 6 Leagues at see whom now resteth with the Lorde.'"

The Rutter was more particularly the forerunner of the Admiralty Tide Tables, though it served in those days as a coastal guide as well. The coming of a separate book of tide tables was foreshadowed by Blundeville, a writer on navigation at this time, in *His Exercises* (1613) in the following words, "William Bourne doth set down what moon makes a full sea, as well as in most parts of our English Coasts as in some other parts of France and Spain, and so do many others, whose tables touching the tides are called Rutters. But such Rutters do serve but for a few particular places. I would wish that some learned Pilot that both sailed many and sundry long voyages to make a general Rutter that might serve for all places if it were possible . . . and I would wish such a general Rutter to be made in manner of an alphabet. And that every place might have his true latitude and longitude added thereunto, to the intent that every place might be the more easily found out in any map or chart that is graduated with degrees of longitude and latitude and then to show what moon doth make a full sea in every such place, which thing whosoever would perform he should in my opinion deserve great commendation."

Engraved Charts and Atlases.—During the latter half of the sixteenth century the more northern nations of Europe, Holland in particular, played an ever increasing part in the production of charts for seamen. More and more ships were sailing to the East by the Cape of Good Hope and to the New World and the Pacific. England was realising the importance of maritime trade and her seamen were in need of charts, and instruction in the art of navigation.[1] At this time the Spaniards, Portuguese, Italians and Dutch were ahead of England in cartography and the art of sailing in deep water. During this period the Dutch cartographers and engravers produced hundreds of maps of the known parts of the world, which, however, were not principally for the use of seamen, in that they were not on the plane projection and lacked the radiating rhumbs necessary for the laying off of courses. Outstanding among the Dutch cartographers were Mercator, Ortelius, and Hondius.

---

[1]See Appendix A (an enumeration of the works on the art of navigation previous to and during the Age of Elizabeth) in *The Voyages and Works of John Davis*, Hakluyt Society, 1880, edited by Capt. A. H. Markham, R.N. "England, when her sons first began to undertake voyages of discovery, was obliged to look to other more advanced countries for the needful knowledge. The first works enumerated in this list are little more than paraphrases of Ptolemy. Muller (or Regiomontanus) began to take independent observations, and soon the Spaniards and Portuguese produced works for the use of mariners. The English were at first dependent on translations of Spanish books, but discoveries and improvements in the art of navigation followed rapidly on the first voyage of discovery, and all through the reign of Elizabeth books with new inventions or improved methods continued to supply an ever increasing demand. When a good work on navigation was published, edition followed edition in rapid succession."

Mercator completed his map of the world in 1569 wherein the distances between the degrees of latitude were increased from the Equator towards the Poles, but chartmakers as a whole did not follow this method of projection until many years later.[1]

In 1583, Lucas Janszoon Waghenaer, a Dutch navigator, published a collection of sea charts on the plane projection, together with a treatise on navigation and sailing directions, for the use of seamen, under the title of *The Mariner's Mirror*. The first part of this collection contained charts and directions for France, England, Ireland, Scotland, Spain and Portugal. It was so well received that, three years later, he added a second part to it embracing the North and Baltic Seas. The encouragement he received from England is best described in his own words in the preface where he says, "Moreover I was enformed by many Pilots of good credit, with how great good liking these Sea Cardes were received in many other countries and kingdoms: namely by these most famous and learned men Io, Dowza Baron of Nortwick and M. Doctor Maelson, who this last year (1585) were Embassadors for the States of the United Provinces of the low countries unto the most renowned Queene of England, where a booke of these Sea Cardes was presented at the Councell table by the Most Noble Lorde, My Lorde Charles Howard, Baron of Effingham, Lorde Admirall of England, and was esteemed by the chief personages of that grave Councell worthy to be translated and printed into a language familiar to all Nations that it might bee both read and understood of all."[2]

This volume contains information which indicates the state of nautical science at the close of the sixteenth century. There is a table of New Moons,[3] tables of the Sun's declination, a catalogue of the more important fixed stars, 93 in number, set out in the following manner:

	Longitude		Declination		R.A.		Mag.
	Deg.	Min.	Deg.	Min.	Ho.	Min.	
Mirach—Andromeda Girdle	25°	8	33°	57 N.	0	48	3

Then follows a table of the Sun's Right Ascension. Instructions are also given for making a cross staff, how to find latitude by a meridian altitude of a star and how to trace a copy of an existing chart.

Instructions for copying charts were commonly given in navigational books about this time though the methods varied. Navigators doubtless for reasons of economy, for charts were usually published in atlas form,

---

[1]Further on this see p. 31.

[2]It was translated into English in 1588. It may have been that the ever growing power of Spain at sea and her threats to England sharpened the interest of the English ministers, who caused it to be translated without delay.

[3]In the English translation, for the meridian of London.

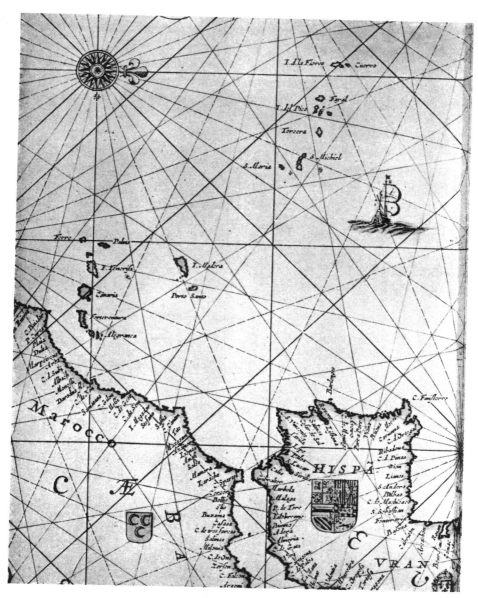

Part of a 17th century engraved chart.

copied such charts or portions of them as they needed for their particular purposes. The following are the instructions given by Wagenhaer: "First with a large pair of compasses you must draw a circle: then divide it with two diameters in 4 even quarters, every one of which is to be subdivided into 4 equal parts to represent the sixteen points of the compass. This done draw first the lines of E. W. S. and N.: next of S.E., N.W., S.W. and N.E. Then of WSW, ENE, SSE, NNW, ESE, SSW, WNW, NNE, and lastly the bywinds as West and by S., South and by West and so forth which must from point to point be extended until all the points be drawn. Your sea card in this sort drawn get in readiness a perfect pattern of some sea carde and fasten it under yours in such a manner that the lines of the one may answer the lines of the other, which done, set the both upon some table of glass against the light and draw your card with black lead that ye may after perfect it with your pen. For so shall you have an absolute and authentical sea card."

In the section devoted to sailing directions there are tables showing the course and distance between points of land, tidal information, and the soundings and shoals round the coast.

The latter half of the book contains the maps and plans, upon which three scales of distance are given, the English measurement of 20 leagues to a degree,[1] the Dutch which was 15 leagues to a degree, and the Spanish, which allowed $17\frac{1}{2}$ leagues to a degree. Latitude and Longitude are marked in degrees and thirds of a degree along the margins of the charts, and longitude is measured from 0° to 360° from the prime meridian passing through the Canaries. The rhumb lines are drawn across the charts from the compass roses, as in the earlier Portolans, to facilitate the finding of the course from one point to another.

All the charts of this and earlier times were a meshwork of rhumb lines radiating from selected positions to every point of the compass to enable the navigator, to whom parallel rulers were unknown, to lay off his course. To find the course between two points, he judged by inspection which rhumb line ran in the required direction, or parallel to that direction, and to test it, placed one leg of his dividers on the point of departure and the other on the selected rhumb line which, unless it happened to join the two points, would be somewhere to the northward or southward. Keeping the leg of the dividers on that rhumb line, he then moved the dividers towards the objective, and if the other leg ran through it, then that rhumb line was his course. If it did not run through, he repeated the operation on another line until he achieved the desired result.

---

[1]Also followed by the French.

Title Page of a Volume of Charts and Sailing Directions published in the seventeenth century. (Note the navigational instruments depicted thereon.)

C

The plans and large scale charts, which were drawn by different draughts
men, showed the soundings in fathoms. Sandbanks were marked by a system
of dots similar to that in use to-day; the anchor denoted anchorages; beacons
were shown by the symbol ø and rocks by a cross.

All these charts were very clearly engraved and were a great advance
on the earlier hand drawn Portolan in both detail and distinctness. After
engraving, the coastlines were lightly coloured in green, blue or yellow to
distinguish the seaboard of one country from another.

In 1612, a translation from the Dutch of Blaeu's *Licht der Zeevaert*
was published in England under the title *Light of Navigation*. This book
is worthy of mention in that, *inter alia*, it contains an explanation of
refraction and gives tables for its correction to be applied to the altitudes
of the sun and the stars. The table for the correction to the altitude of the
sun is for altitudes up to 32° and for the star, only to 15°. For some unexplained
reason the correction to the stars' altitudes is about 4' less than that to be
applied to the sun, which is not sufficient to take account of the sun's semi-
diameter. The corrections are fairly accurate, and were to be subtracted
from the observed altitudes, so that if they were applied by any seamen in
those days they would have minimised the error of the observation.
In explaining the cause of the refraction error he says that it will probably
be rejected by some because they have never heard of it, and advises such
disbelievers to conduct the familiar experiment of partly immersing a staff
in a tub of water. He then goes on to describe other methods of proving
the same thing and concludes thus, " . . . and in such sort the heavenly
lights that are near the horizon, by means of the vapours and exhalations,
are lifted up."

In 1619, an account of the voyage of Van Speilbergen round the world,
1614-1617, and the South Pacific navigations of Jacob Le Maire, were printed
in Holland, under the name of *The East and West Indian Mirror*.[1] It was not,
strictly speaking, a book of sailing directions, but in the fairly full description
of the voyage there was given an appreciable amount of navigational information such as the positions of places, soundings and weather information,
which would be of assistance to other ships. Included in the book was a
number of pictorial plans of islands and channels, including the Straits of
Magellan. There were also two very good plane charts of the East Indies
and the Straits of Manila.

In 1643, another compilation of engraved charts together with a treatise
on navigation, published in Amsterdam by William Janszoon Blaeu,

---

[1]Reproduced by the Hakluyt Society.

was translated into English.[1] These charts were large scale maps, on the plane projection, of the coasts of Holland and the adjacent countries and were devoid of any colouring. The number of soundings shown was an advance on anything that had hitherto been published, and the nature of the bottom was indicated by letters, a key to whose meaning was engraved on the chart. It is to be noted that by this time many channels were buoyed and the buoys were indicated very much the same as they are to-day.

As in the previous collections, the text of the sailing directions was illustrated by many drawings of views of the coast; and the whole denoted a vast amount of careful and detailed labour.

The Dutch cartographers continued to publish atlases of engraved charts, and held their place ahead of all others during the whole of the seventeenth century.[2] The charts were amended from the information supplied by Dutch and English seamen and others, but differed little in the essentials from the earlier Dutch charts.

Towards the end of the seventeenth century the dependence of the English seamen upon the Dutch Waggoners[3] was checked by John Seller, Hydrographer to the King, who in 1671 published *The English Pilot*, of which further volumes were published during the next few years. This was the first Pilot Book to be published in England, and although the copper plates necessary for its compilation were obtained from Holland, certain additions were made from native sources, and the seeds of English Hydrography were sown. There were charts of the British Isles, the North and Baltic Seas, Greenland, Africa, India and the coasts to Japan. There was also an appendix containing a particular description of the sands, shoals, buoys, beacons, roads, etc., on the coast of England from South Foreland to Orfordness by Captains Crane and Brown, Elder Brethren of Trinity House.

The English Pilot was dedicated to James, Duke of York, who with his brother Charles II., did much at this time to further the art of navigation in England. Seller, in his preface to the readers indicated the commendable sentiment, that caused him to labour so industriously in the following words which indicated the state of English cartography at that time—"As the honour and reputation of his Country every man ought highly to regard so I conceive none are more generally concerned in England's Renown than such as are or have been employed in maritime affairs, especially since our

---

[1]Named *The Sea Beacon*.

[2]For example see *Sea Atlas*, by Van Keulan, Amsterdam, 1682. *Atlas Maritimes*, by Jacob Robyn, Amsterdam, 1686. *Atlas* Maritime Section , De Witt, 1690.

[3]English corruption of Waghenaer.

credit hath been, as it were, lessened by the industry of others, without any just reason, being our own Discoveries, Voyages and Experiences have been as great, and our improvement in the Noble Art of Navigation no ways inferior to any other nation whatsoever: yet for want of a public collection of those remarks which able men of our nation have observed and written for their private informations as to the descriptions of the Sea Coasts . . . we have made use of the Dutch Waggoners and charts in many of our navigations, wherewith (for want of better) we have been sometimes constrained to accept of many errors and impertinences to our dishonour and their great interest and advantage. According therefore to my promise not long since made in a book entitled Practical Navigation, I have endeavoured (to my ability) to supply this defect in the following treatise . . ."

He then went on to apologise for its similitude to the Waggoners, which could not be avoided in all respects, and urged all mariners to assist in keeping the charts up to date.

The charts in this book, like so many others of that time, indicated the latitude but showed no longitude. One of the most interesting in the collection is a chart of the North Sea, which shows the principal shoals in the Thames Estuary and off the Dutch coast, and also the Broad Fourteens Bank, which, along with other banks in the North Sea, has retained its name to the present day.

Another example of the increasing interest in navigation which was being shown by Englishmen at this time is *Sharp's South Sea Waggoner*, which has been called the "Buccaneers' Atlas."[1] It was a book of 135 manuscript drawings of islands, anchorages, havens, and the coast line of South America, and was prefaced by a hand-drawn chart on the plane projection of the West Indies and South America. The book was made by William Hack, and dedicated by B.S., presumably Sharp, to the High and Mighty Monarch Charles the Second.

The drawings are a compromise between plans and pictorial views, the low lying coast is coloured pale green and the higher hills and points of land are painted in darker shades of green, presumably to give an idea of their comparative heights. They are devoid of scales of latitude or longitude, but the latitude is usually written in at the principal haven or anchorage depicted by each drawing. A brief description of the place and sailing directions for it is given on each page. The following is a fair example of the information given in this book.

"The Isle of Callao lyes in 12d. 20′ S., and E. and W. with the Mount of the Said Isle—where the anchor is drawn is 2 leagues, which is Callao Road.

---

[1] Sloane MS. 44, British Museum.

You may come to anchor in any part of the bay in what depth of water you please—the ships that come from Arica, or any port to the Southward, to

Isle of Callao at E b N appears thus

Lima saile between this Isle and the main in 4 fathom and 1/2 water, along the Isle untill you are as far as the spring makes the mount at West, then haull the Bowline and sett her head toward the town steering straight to the port keeping allways in 8 fathom water com to anchor where it is drawn."

For the purpose of comparison the following directions for approaching Callao Bay from the Southward are given from the *South American Pilot*, Part iii. (1915). "After making Isla Fronton steer so as to keep its southern end about a point open on the port bow until Callao Castle is seen . . . then steer for that castle, bearing 10° True, until the scar on the eastern slope of Isla San Lorenzo is in line with the large house bearing 297° True: this will lead through in not less than $5\frac{3}{4}$ fathoms . . . when the western martello tower in the castle (Lat. 12° 04′ S., Long 77° 10′ W.) comes in line with Callao Point haul gradually round to the northward till that tower opens clear of the breakers on the spit, when a course may be shaped for the anchorages, taking care not to come nearer the Whales Back than the depth of 6 fathoms."

It was by means of the drawings and information contained in the journals of navigators, and the more detailed surveys made by those expert in hydrography, that the English cartographers, led by John Seller, were able to vie with Holland and France during the eighteenth century and later, to take the lead in chart-making.

It is no part of this book to trace in detail the growth of the private firms of publishers of nautical charts, books, and sailing directions in England from the seventeenth century to the present time. It is sufficient to say that about the year 1700 several firms were established which, by purchase or family connection, eventually became merged into the well-known House of Imray, Laurie, Norie and Wilson. The history of this House has been written and the following extract from it shows briefly how private publishers fared in later days.[1]

"It was not until 1795 that the Government, having purchased a small collection of charts from the East India Company, founded, with these as its basis, a Hydrographic Department at the Admiralty. During the next half century, however, the private chart publisher was still entrusted with the production of charts, which were compiled from information supplied by Lords Commissioners of the Admiralty, or Commanders of the Royal Navy, to whom such publications were, by permission, individually dedicated.

"In more recent years, however, the great increase in navigation generally has caused the chief maritime powers, Britain not excepted, to realise the necessity of forming Government departments officially to survey its own coasts and harbours, and upon these various authoritative sources the private chart producer must now rely."

The only chart known to the ocean voyagers of the sixteenth and earlier centuries was the plane chart, upon which the courses run by ships were assumed to be upon a flat surface. This could not lead to great accuracy in deep water navigation although, doubtless, it served well enough, even in fairly high latitudes, when the voyages were coastal, or never long out of sight of land. It was a convenient and easy method of representing the earth's surface and it enabled the seaman to draw his course, for what it was worth, as a straight line. The errors in this projection probably mattered little at first in an art where the accuracy of every process, instrument and astronomical table was doubtful. In some cases a good landfall would be made through the errors cancelling out and, in others, the seaman would be far out of his reckoning because of an accumulation of errors.

The Plane Chart.—The navigator who purposed to voyage far abroad stood in need of something better than the plane chart from which, on account of its construction, he could not obtain the true course. In the plane chart the distances between the meridians at every latitude were equal to their

---

[1]*The Story of the Blue Back Chart*, 1937, compiled from Notes collected from various sources by Elena Wilson. Published by Messrs. Imray, Laurie, Norie & Wilson Ltd.

distances apart at the Equator, *i.e.*, a degree of longitude in any latitude was shown as large as it was at the Equator. No allowance was made for the convergency of the meridians towards the Poles and, consequently, each degree of longitude, north and south of the Equator, was increased on the plane chart, beyond its proper proportion. In order to preserve the correct proportion between the degrees of longitude and latitude when represented on a flat surface, in which the meridians were parallel, a proportionate elongation had to be given to the distance between every degree of latitude which increased as the Poles were approached. It was most convenient for the seaman to have a chart upon which the meridians were parallel so that he could, with ease and certainly, lay off the correct course, or rhumb line, between any two points, which would cut all the meridians at a constant angle. It was convenient, too, that he should, at the same time, be able to measure the distance, in any latitude, with accuracy.

Earlier editors of Ptolemy had suggested the way in which the navigator's difficulty could be solved but it was not until 1569, when Mercator published his map of the world, that any geographer seriously attempted a practical solution. He did not, however, publish a number of charts of various parts of the world on his projection and so make it possible for the more enlightened seamen to take advantage of his work. His map was more of an exposition and example of his theory than a chart for the practical seaman. He did not preserve the true proportion, for in the higher latitudes there were noticeable errors, nor did he explain fully in what manner or on what mathematical principle he constructed his chart. This attempt to aid the seaman in his difficulties received little recognition but, towards the end of the sixteenth century, the more learned writers on navigation began to show the mariner the errors of his ways, though with little immediate effect. In a work on on navigation first printed in England in 1569, which was translated from the writings of a Spaniard, Martin Cortes, and which ran into many editions, the current use of the plane chart was summed up at the end of the sixteenth century as follows. "The Plane Cardes are Imperfect. The Pilots and Mariners neither use nor have the knowledge to use other Cardes than onely these that are playne, I have sayde the which because they are not Globus, Spherical or rounde (they) are imperfect, and faile to shewe the true distances. For in howe much they depart from the Equinoctiall towards whyche soever of the Poles the Meridian lynes are contracte(d) narrower and narrower. In such manner that if two cities or poyntes in the Equinoctiall should be distant of longitude 60 leagues and in the selfsame meridian(s) at 60 degrees from the Equincotiall toward eyther Pole shoulde bee other two Cities or Poyntes they shoulde bee distant in longitude but only 30 leagues. And for the better declaration and understanding hereof I say that if two shyppes shoulde departe from the **Equinoctiall,** the one distant from the other 100 leagues by **East** and **West** and that eyther of them shoulde sayle directly by his meridian towarde the **North** then when either of them hath the pole over his horizon 60 degrees, the one shall be distaunt from the other onely 50 leagues by the paralelle of **East** and **West,** as appeareth by the playne cardes that they have the selfe-same hundred leagues. And besides these considerations one errour bringeth in another, so another an other: whereof to speake any more heere it shall be to certeyne Pilots (as ye proverbe saith) not onely to give musyke to the deafe or to paynt a house for blinde men, but shall also be an endlesse confusion." Other writers at about the same time wrote in similar strain, and one, Robert Hues, an English student of navigation, remarked that "the common sort of mariners do greatly err in attributing to each degree of every parallel an equal measure with a degree of the Equator."[1]

Cortes' opinion was that good charts ought to show the coasts and ports in their correct bearings one from the other and not with relation to their compass bearings which did not allow for the variation of the compass. He thought, however, that such a refinement was unnecessary in charts of the Mediterranean Sea and of the Channel of Flanders (called the Narrow Seas) where the mariners sailed from one port to another by compass course, and paid little heed to their correct geographical positions or the true courses between them. He stressed the importance of giving to every port its correct latitude and urged the King of Spain, Charles V., to command certain learned cosmographers, expert in the art of sailing, to verify the latitudes of ports, capes and islands, especially in the West Indies, "where it had pleased God that so many nations and people had received the water of Holy Baptism". In another part of his book he advised that the spaces between the parallels of latitude should be increased more and more towards the Poles, but omitted to explain upon what principle this should be done.

The Mercator Chart.—It was a Cambridge mathematician, Edward Wright, who investigated Mercator's principles and put them on a sound mathematical basis. Before publishing his results, he imparted his reasoning to Jodocus Hondius, a Dutch engraver and map-maker who brought out new editions of Mercator's works after his death in 1594. Wright delayed publishing his work for some years, with the result that Hondius produced a chart on the new projection before Wright's investigations were generally

---

[1]*Tractatus de Globis,* by Robt. Hues, 1592. See also *The Seaman's Secrets,* by John Davis, 1594, where he describes the charts then in use as "bearing no proportionate agreement with the globe".

known.[1] Few charts were engraved on this projection by Hondius, and fewer still found their way into the hands of navigators. Hondius and all the other chart-makers of the time seem to have been slow in following the lead set by Mercator. Whether it was on account of their unwillingness to scrap their existing plates and engrave their charts anew or because the majority of them were ignorant of the principles of the new projection, or whether it was due to the conservatism of the seamen is a matter for speculation. The fact remains that it was not until the end of the seventeenth century that the so-called Mercator's Projection came into its own.

In 1599 Wright published his *Certain Errors in Navigation* and in a long preface to the reader pointed out the gross errors in the plane chart, whereby, said he· "the mariner may miss one, two, yea three whole points of the compass (and more sometimes in a far Northerly or Southerly navigation) in finding the course from place to place . . . and for finding the distances of places he may err twice yea thrice so much as the whole distance cometh to and more sometimes in those Northern parts in taking the distance to be twice, thrice, yea four times greater than indeed it is."

In order to illustrate his method of depicting the surface of a globe on a plane Wright urged the reader to suppose a rectangular plane rolled about a globe until it formed a cylinder enclosing the globe and touching it at the Equator. Then to imagine the globe to swell like a bladder when blown up until every part of its surface (except the Poles, of course) touched the sides of the cylinder, and left upon them the impress of its meridians and parallels. Upon unrolling the cylinder it would be found that all lines would be straight lines, and that every degree of latitude along the meridians would be lengthened in the same proportion as the parallels of latitude had expanded to meet the sides of the cylinder. The ratio between a unit of longitude and a unit of latitude (in any latitude) was based on the following reasoning.

1. The proportion between the distance apart of two meridians at the Equator:

> Is to their distance apart in any parallel of latitude
>
> As the radius of the Equator
>
> Is to the radius of the small circle of latitude

---

[1]E. M. Tenison in his work *Elizabethan England*, Vol. IV. 1933, has brought to light a hitherto unpublished English Chart showing the Azores in relation to the coasts of Portugal, Spain, France, South of England and Ireland. It is a manuscript chart on vellum, in the possession of the Marquis of Salisbury, K.G., and Mr. Tenison puts forward a good argument for its date being about 1581. It is not a plane chart, and its projection very closely resembles Mercator's, before Wright's improvements. Upon it are drawn lines of soundings off the approach to the English Channel between the Scillies and Ushant; and the variation of the Compass is shown in many places in the following manner: V.C. 5° 0′ occ: *i.e.*, variation of the compass 5° 0′ West. Between the islands of Flores and Fayal the variation is nil.

YD : XA :: DC : AB (Because the circumferences of circles, and hence similar arcs, are in proportion to their radii).

Because DC = AC (radii)

YD : XA :: AC : AB

$$\frac{YD}{XA} = \frac{AC}{AB}$$

$$= \text{Cosec ACB}$$

$$= \text{Sec ACD}$$

$$= \text{Sec Latitude}$$

∴ YD = XA Secant Latitude

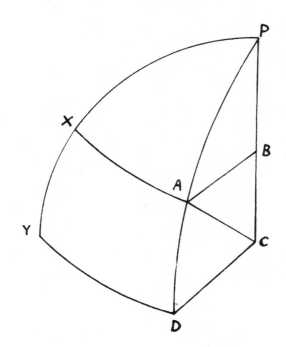

2. Because the meridians are parallel in this projection the longitude YD remains constant (when it ought to decrease) in any latitude. That is, the longitude scale increases in proportion to the secant of the latitude.

Therefore, in order to preserve the correct proportion, the latitude scale must also increase proportionately to the secant of the latitude.

3. Taking 1′ of longitude as the unit of the scale:

1′ latitude = 1′ longitude × Secant latitude,

and the distance of any parallel of latitude from the Equator, on this projection, is expressed by the sum of the secants of all the arcs of 1′ between the Equator and that parallel.

On this principle Wright constructed his table of meridional parts, in units of 1′, which for all practical purposes of navigation was accurate enough. He went on to say that "He that listeth to be more precise may make a like table to tenths of seconds."

The following is a comparison between the *Table of Meridional Parts* calculated by Wright and the values given in *Norie's Nautical Tables*. The meridional parts for the sphere have now been deleted but they show a remarkable resemblance to the values calculated in 1599. Mariners now use the meridional parts for a terrestial spheroid. These values take into account the compression of the polar radius being $\dfrac{1}{293 \cdot 465}$

			NORIE'S TABLES
Lat. 52°	Wright 1599	Sphere	Terrestial Spheroid
0′	3665·3551	3665·19	3646·74
1′	3666·9799	3666·82	3648·36
2′	3668·6053	3668·44	3649·98
3′	3670·2313	3670·07	3651·60
4′	3671·8579	3671·70	3653·22
5′	3673·4852	3673·32	3654·84
6′	3675·1131	3674·95	3656·47

About a year after the publication of *Certain Errors in Navigation*, a map of the world was engraved in England on Wright's projection, to which the name of the "New Map" has been given.[1] This map, or chart as it really was, had the following instructions engraved upon it:

"Thou hast here (gentle reader) a true hydrographical description of so much of the world as hath beene hetherto discovered, and is comme to our knowledge: which we have in such sort performed, all places herein set downe have the same positions and distances that they have in the globe, being therein placed in same longitudes and latitudes which they have in this chart, which by the ordinarie sea chart can in no wise be performed. The way to find the position, or course from any place to other herein described differeth nothing from that which is used in the ordinarie sea chart. But to finde the distance: if both places have the same latitude, see how many degrees of the meridian taken at that latitude are contayned betweene the two places, for so many score leagues is the distance. If they differ in latitude, see howe many degrees of the meridian taken about the midst of that difference are conteyned betweene them and so many score leagues is the distance."

Similar instructions for the measurement of distance were given on many

---

[1]See the *Map of the World* A.D. 1600, (Hakluyt Society 1880) and *The Voyages and Works of John Davis* (Hakluyt Society 1880) at p. LXXXV.

of the charts engraved on this projection until the latter half of the eighteenth century. This is some indication that many navigators were unfamiliar with the principle and not conversant with its use. Throughout the seventeenth century Dutch and English map-makers continued to produce an ever increasing number of charts on the plane projection, but few troubled to construct them upon Wright's principles. Notable among the exceptions were two Dutch engravers Jansson and Van Loon, who produced uncoloured charts on the new projection. In 1659 Jansson published a Marine Atlas in Amsterdam. His charts were on Mercator's projection,[1] shoals and banks were denoted as they are to-day, and the soundings were shown in figures. At the end of the seventeenth century the first of several editions of a marine atlas on the same projection was published by the French under the title of *Le Neptune Francois*. The charts were engraved by Van Loon and were more exhaustive in detail and extent than those of Jansson.

During the early years of the eighteenth century the balance between the plane and Mercator chart was about equal. It was quite usual for marine atlases to be published containing charts of the same areas on both projections, and this period probably saw the gradual adoption of Mercator's projection by seamen in general.[2] That this adoption was slow is indicated by the amount of space given to plane sailing in the treatises on navigation at the time; and more particularly, by the words of Doctor Halley, the Astronomer Royal in his preface to a marine atlas published in 1728[3] where he wrote: "It is well known that many of our sailors, and some that would be accounted artists are at this day obstinate in the use of the Plain Chart . . . and many of our masters that teach navigation teach what they call plain sailing (and many times that only) to such as are designed to take charge of ships . . . and this they do for no other reason but because they think they can measure distances thereon by a scale of equal parts, rejecting the truly Nautical Chart, commonly called Mercator, because one single scale cannot be fitted to all its parts . . ." Later on, he remarked that those who would be thought fit to be entrusted with the navigation of a ship ought to be able to calculate the true course and distance between any two places provided they knew their correct latitudes and longitudes.

During the eighteenth century the entire known world was mapped on the Mercator projection, and by degrees the charts became little different in appearance from those in use to-day. More accurate observations were

---

[1]In order to avoid confusion Mercator's Projection will be used to denote the new projection on Wright's principles as it does to-day.

[2]For examples of this type of Marine Atlas see *Sea Atlas*, by John Thornton 1700; *Sea Atlas*, by Mount and Page 1708; *West India Navigation*, 1759, King's Library, Brit.Mus.

[3]*Atlas Maritimus et Commercialis*, Trade and Navigation, containing also an account of Commerce and Sailing Directions.

taken of the variation of the compass, and tides and currents and winds received careful attention. In a large scale chart of the English Channel, published by Mount and Page, 1708, the following advertisement appears, "The smaller figures show the depths of water in fathoms, and the Roman figures show the hour of High Water, or how long the stream will run to the Eastward on the day of New or Full Moon, therefore if you add the time of the Moon's Southing or Northing to the hour found near the place of your ship the sum will show you how long the tide will run to the East, but if it exceed 12 subtract 12 therefrom."

Arrows were used, as they are to-day, to show the set of the tide, views of the coast were engraved on the chart, and the variation of the compass was shown at intervals.

The eighteenth century was an era of exploration, and the scientific investigation of both the known and the lesser known seas and their coasts was encouraged by the Governments of the maritime nations. Great assistance was given by the learned societies of these nations, among which should be mentioned the Royal Society of England and the Royal Academy of Sciences in France. The navigators of the King's ships and merchantmen alike carried out careful surveys and took accurate observations of all that was of importance in the art of navigation. The result of this encouragement and care was that during the Napoleonic wars the fleets of Britain and her well found trading ships were equipped with comparatively accurate charts on Mercator's projection. The information on them was much more detailed and exact: the longitudes of places were nearer the truth, though it was not until the next century that such were generally determined with the exactness that is essential for the safety of ships at sea.

No part of the world had been more visited by ships of all classes during the preceding 300 years than the West Indies. At first by Columbus and the Spanish treasure fleets, then by the Elizabethan seamen, who were followed by the Dutch in their war against Spain, and by traders, pirates, and the fleets of Britain and France during the Napoleonic wars. All these, and many more, contributed to the knowledge of the Western Ocean, and it is not surprising that the charts of this part of the World are good examples of the state of the best chart-making practice at the close of the eighteenth century. The following information is gathered from a set of charts published between the years 1787 and 1792 by Robert Sayer, a forerunner of the House of Imray, Laurie, Norie & Wilson, under the the title of a *Complete Pilot for the West Indies*, "based on surveys and observations of most experienced navigators in the King's as well as in the Merchants' Service." From a large scale chart of the English Channel and its approaches we find that, by this time, detailed lines of soundings had been taken all over this area and the nature of the bottom discovered and noted. One sounding, about 20 miles W.N.W. of the Scilly Isles, just north of Jones's Bank is distinguished with a bottom of "Thin and Black Ooze, that won't stick to the lead, but when you make use of butter instead of Tallow. It is the only ground of the kind near the Chops of the Channel."[1]

Tidal streams had been observed with an accuracy never before attained and large scale plans had been made of the important harbours along the coast.

From the next chart in the set, which is of the Bay of Biscay and the southern approach to the Channel, we find that similar careful surveys had been made. The most interesting additional feature of this chart is that along six different parallels of latitude a different longitude is shown on each, measured from the following prime meridians:

(1) Longitude East from the Pike of the Azores.
(2) Longitude East from the Isle of Ferro, taken from Western side.
(3) Longitude East from the Pike of Teneriffe.
(4) Longitude West from the Lizard.
(5) Longitude West from the Meridian of London.
(6) Longitude West from the Meridian of Paris.

The third chart was a large general chart of the North Atlantic from which it is seen that data was being collected to show the best outward and homeward tracks for ships, and that observations of the limits of the Trade Winds and of the set of the ocean currents were being taken by seamen.

The usual tracks taken by ships, together with numerous soundings and contemporary observations for variation were also shown on the remainder of the charts, which consisted of a general chart of the West Indies, and several larger scale charts of the individual islands, or groups of them, and the Central American coast, in greater detail. One of these, the chart of Panama to Cartagena, bears the notice "An engineer has lately proposed to the Court of Spain to open a water communication between the Bay of Panama and the Gulf of Mexico (i.e., between the Atlantic and Pacific Oceans) by means of a canal 7 or 8 leagues in length, dug from Rio Grande near Panama to Rio de Chagres, or from Rio del Caymito to the Embarcadero of Rio de la Trinidad which falls into Rio de Chagres. This very ingenious and useful prospect has been discountenanced by the Spanish Cabinet."

Admiralty Charts.—It has been mentioned that during the eighteenth century the private firms of chart-makers and the Admiralty had been taking

---

[1]How early in history the "Chops of the Channel" was used to signify the sea immediately to the westward of the English Channel it is impossible to say. The expression was certainly in vogue during the eighteenth century; it was used by Richard Walter, the compiler of Anson's Voyage, in 1748.

an increasing interest in the production of improved charts on Mercator's projection. Most maritime nations were similarly employed, and they were beginning, with some exceptions (notably the Spaniards with regard to the route across the Pacific from Manila to Mexico) to divulge their secrets and pool their information for the benefit of seamen in general. Large trading companies had been collecting information for many years, and the East India Company in particular had maintained its own hydrographic staff to produce charts for its own use. The examination of coasts and harbours was calling for the skilled services of experienced surveyors who could devote their whole time and attention to the work. Artists had occasionally been carried on voyages of exploration for the last two centuries, but nautical science was demanding more than running surveys illustrated with panoramic views of the coast. The naval wars of the eighteenth century compelled the Governments concerned to concentrate on accurate detail to an extent hitherto unknown. The advisability of providing trained surveyors to assist the British fleets was strongly urged upon the Admiralty both by the naval policy of the time and by individual writers qualified to express their opinions. The case was very clearly put by the author of Anson's Voyage round the World[1] when he wrote in his Introduction, "I cannot finish this Introduction without adding a few reflections on a matter very nearly connected with the present subject: and, as I conceive, neither destitute of utility, nor unworthy the attention of the Public; I mean, the animating my countrymen both in their public and private stations, to the encouragement and pursuit of all kinds of geographical and nautical observations, and of every species of mechanical and commercial information. It is by a settled attachment to these seemingly minute particulars, that our ambitious neighbours have established some part of that power, with which we are now struggling. And as we have the means in our hands of pursuing these subjects more effectually, than they can, it would be a dishonour to us longer to neglect so easy and beneficial a practice: For, as we have a Navy much more numerous than theirs, great part of which is always employed in very distant stations, either in the protection of our colonies and commerce, or in assisting our allies against the common enemy, this gives us frequent opportunities of furnishing ourselves with such kind of materials, as are here recommended, and such as might turn greatly to our advantage either in war or peace. For, not to mention what might be expected from the officers of the Navy, if their application to these subjects was properly encouraged, it would create no new expence to the Government to establish a particular regulation for this

---

[1] *A Voyage round the World in the years* 1740, 1, 2, 3, 4, *by George Anson, Commander in Chief of a Squadron of H.M. Ships, sent upon an expedition to the South Seas."* Compiled by Richard Walter, M.A., Chaplain of H.M. Ship *Centurion*, in that expedition. Published 1748.

purpose; since all that would be requisite, would be constantly to embark on board some of our men of war, which are sent on these distant cruises, a person, who with the character of an engineer, and the skill and talents necessary to that profession, should be employed in drawing such coasts, and planning such harbours, as the ship should touch at, and in making such other observations of all kinds, as might either prove of advantage to future Navigators, or might any ways tend to promote the Public service. Besides persons habituated to this employment (which could not fail at the same time of improving them in their proper business) would be extremely useful in many other lights, and might serve to secure our Fleets from those disgraces, with which their attempts against places on shore have been often attended. And, in a Nation like ours, where all sciences are more eagerly and universally pursued, and better understood than in any other part of the world, proper subjects for such employments could not long be wanting, if due encouragement were given to them. This method here recommended is known to have been frequently practised by the French, particularly in the instance of Monsieur Frezier, an engineer, who has published a celebrated voyage to the South Seas. For this person in the year 1711, was properly sent by the French King into that country on board a merchantman, that he might examine and describe the coast, and take plans of all the fortified places, the better to enable the French to prosecute their illicit trade, or, in case of a rupture with the Court of Spain, to form their enterprises in those seas with more readiness and certainty. Should we pursue this method, we might hope, that the emulation amongst those who were thus employed, and the experience, which even in time of peace, they would hereby acquire, might at length procure us a proper number of able Engineers, and might efface a national scandal, which our deficiency in that species of men has sometimes exposed us to. And surely, every step to encourage and improve this profession is of great moment to the Public; as no persons, when they are properly instructed, make better returns in war, for the encouragement and emoluments bestowed on them in time of peace. Of which the advantages the French have reaped from their dexterity (too numerous and recent to be soon forgot) are an ample confirmation . . . If what has been said merits the attention of Travellers of all sorts, it is, I think, more particularly applicable to the Gentlemen of the Navy; since, without drawing and planning, neither charts nor views of land can be taken; and without these it is sufficiently evident, that navigation is at a full stand. It is doubtless from a persuasion of the utility of these qualifications, that his Majesty has established a drawing Master at Portsmouth, for the instruction of those, who are presumed to be hereafter intrusted with the command of his Royal Navy. And though some have been so far misled, as to suppose that the perfection of Sea-officers consisted in a turn of mind and temper resembling the boisterous element they had to deal with, and have condemned all literature and science as effeminate, and derogatory to that ferocity, which, they would falsely persuade us was the most unerring characteristic of courage: Yet it is to be hoped, that such absurdities as these have at no time been authorised by the Public opinion, and that the belief of them daily diminishes . . ."

There is no doubt that interest in surveying was being aroused and encouraged in a much more general way than previously. A book on the theory and practice of navigation published in 1754 for the use of the Royal Mathematical School at Christ's Hospital, and the Gentlemen of the Navy, contained a section on the surveying of coasts and harbours.[1] The survey work of James Cook, and other masters in the British Fleet in North America, in the St. Lawrence, which so materially helped in the capture of Quebec in 1759, is now almost legendary. The British Government, at last alive to the necessity for accurate charts of her possessions overseas kept Cook almost continuously engaged for the next seven years in surveying Newfoundland and the Belle Isle Straits, and then sent him further afield to continue this work, amongst other labours, in the Pacific.[2] A few years later, in 1778, a large collection of charts compiled from systematic surveys was published, under the directions of the Lords Commissioners of the Admiralty, by Mr J. F. W. Des Barres. This collection went under the title of the Atlantic Neptune, and its four volumes contained numerous charts, plans and views, of the North American seaboard from the River St. Lawrence to the West Coast of Florida, covering in all about 2000 miles of coastline.

The day was fast approaching when the British Admiralty was to take over the systematic charting of almost the entire world, and in August, 1795, the Hydrographers' Department was established by Order in Council. The Order referred to the great inconveniences constantly felt by the officers of H.M. Ships, especially when ordered abroad, from the want of sufficient information of the parts of the world to which they were sent. Upon an examination of the plans and charts, which from time to time were deposited in the Admiralty, it appeared that, provided the information contained in them was properly digested, the results would prove of the greatest utility to His Majesty's Service. In looking into the practice of all other countries less dependent upon Naval operations than Great Britain it was found that they had very wisely provided considerable establishments for the collection of such information, and the Lords Commissioners thought it expedient

---

[1] *The Elements of Navigation*, by J. Robertson, F.R.S., Mathematical Master at Christ's Hospital.

[2] For examples of Cook's work in the Pacific see *Charts, Plans, Views and Drawings taken on board H.M. Bark "Endeavour" in the years* 1768-69-70." by Lieut. James Cook, Commander. Brit. Mus. ADD. 7085.

D

for them to adopt a similar plan. For this purpose a Hydrographer to the Board of Admiralty was appointed, at a salary of £500 per annum, "to be intrusted with the custody and care of such plans and charts as now are, or may hereafter be deposited in this office . . . to be charged with the duty of selecting and compiling all such information as may appear to be requisite for the purpose of improving the navigation, and for the guidance and direction of the Commanders of Your Majesty's ships, in all cases wherein any knowledge in this respect may be found to be necessary."

The first Hydrographer to the Admiralty was Alexander Dalrymple who, for some years had held the office of Hydrographer to the East India Company, and, as such, had published sailing directions for the China Seas and Philippines, Upon his death, in 1808, he was succeeded by Captain Thomas Hurd, R.N. and from then onwards the office has always been held by officers of the Royal Navy. Captain Hurd instituted a regular system of nautical surveys and, in 1811, there was published a series of charts of the English Channel, compiled in the Hydrographic Office from original surveys for the use of the Royal Navy. Shortly afterwards, charts of the west coast of France and the coast of Spain were published from the same source.

Little was heard of the Hydrographic Department, until, in 1848, it presented a report to Parliament on its work for the preceding 10 years.[1] From the year of its creation until that time it had been gradually pursuing its course, and causing charts to be published as and when the data for them was completed. The Report indicated what measures were required to bring the surveys, charts and sailing directions hitherto made by the East India Company into proper connection with each other; and what was necessary to verify existing charts, to correct known errors, to make surveys of places unsurveyed and "to render the whole useful for the benefit of navigation and the saving of life." The increase in the work undertaken by this Department was indicated by the number of ships and personnel engaged. In the year 1837-8, 13 ships, including 2 steam, were used and 796 officers and men were actively employed in surveying: whereas by 1846-7 the number of ships had risen to 19, including 7 steam, and 1227 Officers and men were similarly employed. During the 10 years referred to large sections of the coasts of the British Isles were surveyed, and surveys were conducted (and some completed) in the Mediterranean, West Coast of Africa, West Indies, North America, West Coast of South America, the N.W. Coast of Australia, Great Barrier Reef, Falkland Islands, Azores, Madeira and the China Coast.

The Report then dealt in detail with the parts of the world that still

---

[1]Parliamentary Papers 1847-48, Vol. XLI., p. 293. A Return of the amount expended for and of surveys undertaken by the Hydrographic Dept. of the Admiralty in each of the ten years 1837-8 to 1846-7; and statements of all surveys undertaken by the department and of home and foreign surveys urgently requisite.

required thorough investigation, and in which it was proposed to carry on the work. It is a little surprising to find that the greater part of the South Coast of England was still very roughly laid down "with none of that accurate detail which is absolutely necessary in considering the value of the numberless projects that are brought before the Admiralty." The surveys necessary abroad included practically the remainder of the world that had not previously been mentioned in the Report, with the exception of certain work being undertaken in India by the East India Company, part of the North African coast which the French had undertaken, and the Coasts of the United States of America which were being elaborately surveyed by their own Service.

For the sale of the charts the Admiralty employed a general agent, R. B. Bate, 21 Poultry, London, the sub-agents in the other ports of the United Kingdom being appointed by him. When alterations were made in any plate, correct impressions were supplied in exchange for all the copies which the agent had on hand, and which were immediately cancelled in the Hydrographic Office. The report was signed by Rear Admiral Beaufort, the Hydrographer, whose name will always be remembered by seamen as the originator of the Beaufort Wind Scale, and as a keen investigator of the problems which confronted them in marine meteorology.

The work of the Hydrographic Department has gone on unceasingly, making the oceans safer for all, improving upon its previous work and searching still for the unseen dangers that have beset the navigator since man first took to the Sea.

Apart from a small office in Whitehall, the whole of the Admiralty chart organization is established at Taunton, Somerset. The move from London began in 1940 when it was necessary to move the printing works to a new location so that thousands of charts could be printed for wartime use.

Nowadays, between 30,000 and 40,000 charts are despatched each week to Admiralty Chart Agents around the world. Since the late 1960's the Hydrographic Department have been heavily involved in the production of metric charts to replace the 'old' fathom charts. When the decision was made to metricate, it involved fundamental changes in the style and appearance of Admiralty charts. Metric charts use a large amount of colour and a more open style of soundings which gives a clearer appearance. In addition to metrication, the Hydrographic Department have been heavily involved in the production of New Editions to take account of the new IALA System 'A' buoyage. In 1969, only eleven charts had been metricated, but by 1978 over 700 charts were metric editions. The Hydrographic Department publish some 3,500 charts so it is anticipated that complete metrication will be completed by the end of this century. Since World War Two, there has been an explosion in the gathering of hydrographic data. This has resulted from the application of electronic fixing aids to the ancient art of surveying, this allows surveying to proceed by day and night regardless of the visibility. The importance of this task is recognized on a wide scale, many maritime nations have banded together to exchange survey data under the leadership of the International Hydrographic Bureau. The exchange of data should avoid wasteful duplication. An International Chart Commission is looking into the possibility of producing international charts so that various hydrographic offices can produce charts on a regional basis.

CHAPTER II.

THE COMPASS.

THE power of the magnet to attract iron was known in Europe for several centuries before the Christian era. It has been said by some that the word magnet was derived from Magnesia, a town in Asia Minor, in which the mineral was found in ancient times. This is probably true, though it is noteworthy that Strabo (60 B.C.-24 A.D.), in his detailed Geography, made no mention of this ore in his description of Magnesia. The reasons for this omission may be that little commercial use was made of it, and its future importance in the art of navigation was wholly unsuspected.

Legend has credited the origin of the word to a shepherd of Crete, named Magnus who, resting one day, upon a rock of magnetic ore, found his iron shod feet immovable. It matters little, however, where magnetic ore was first discovered, suffice for our purpose to remark that the properties of lodestone, as it was called by the northern peoples of Europe, were known for many centuries before the crudest form of compass was known to European seamen.

It is difficult to say by whom the compass was invented. Nearly every country where lodestone was found in ancient times has, at some time or another, been given the credit. There are good reasons to suppose that the Chinese were the first to use the magnetic needle to indicate direction. Pere Du Halde, in his *General History of China*, in recording the incidents of the reign of Hoang Ti (Third Millenium B.C.) wrote as follows:— "He was," says the History, "a wonderful child, he had scarcely left the breast but he could speak . . . Tchi Yeou . . . was a restless prince whose boundless ambition was the cause of great troubles. Hoang Ti attacked him and gave him battle three times. He perceiving that thick fogs saved the enemy from his pursuit and that the soldiers rambled out of the way and lost the course of the wind, he made a carr which showed them the 4 cardinal points, by this method he overtook Taki Yeou, made him prisoner and put him to death. Some say there were engraved in this carr on a plate the characters of a rat and a horse, and underneath was placed a needle to determine the 4 points of the world. This would amount to the use of the compass or something very near it, being of great antiquity and well attested. 'Tis pity this contrivance is not explained, but the interpreters knowing only the bare fact dare not venture

45

on conjectures."[1] Further on, in the same book, in dealing with the Third Dynasty called Tcheou (Second Millenium B.C.) we find that after the ambassadors from Cochin China had had their audience of leave, Tcheou gave them an instrument which on one side pointed towards the north and on the opposite side to the south. The gift was made to direct them better on their way home than they had been directed in going to China. The author added:— "This instrument was called Tchi Nan, which is the same name as the Chinese now call the sea compass by." Though this interpretation of the record of events is not now accepted the Chinese were apparently among the first to use a form of compass at sea. Humboldt, one of the prominent investigators into magnetism during the nineteenth century, found that Chinese ships guided by compasses visited the ports of India and the eastern coast of Africa during the fourth century A.D.[2]

It was Humboldt's opinion that the compass was introduced to Europe from the East after its use had become general throughout the Indian Seas and the coasts of Persia and Arabia. Such introduction was effected either directly by the influence of the Arabians or through the medium of the Crusaders who since 1096 had been in contact with Egypt and the Levant.

On the other hand it is not improbable that the property of the magnetised needle to indicate direction was discovered in various parts of the world at widely different times. When the inhabitants of the several regions reached a certain stage of intelligence or inventiveness, or when, by chance, some observant person noted the apparent attraction of the Northern Lights for a suspended bar which had been wrought from lodestone, the compass in its crudest form was born. News travelled slowly in those early days, and it is quite possible that compasses were developed in several parts of the world before the people of one knew of the other. Sir William Thomson in his address on Terrestial Magnetism, some years after Humbolt said, "The earliest trace we now have of the mariner's compass in Europe is contained, according to Professor Hansteen ("Inquiries concerning the Magnetism of the Earth") in an account of the discovery of Iceland by the Norwegian historian Ara Frode, who is cited as authority for the following statement:—"Flocke Vilgerdersen, a renowned viking, the third discoverer of the island, departed from Rogaland in Norway to seek Gadersholm (Iceland), some time in the year 868. He took with him three ravens to serve as guides; and in order to consecrate them to his purpose he offered up a great sacrifice in Smarsund, where his ship lay ready to sail; for in those times seamen had no loadstone (leidarstein) in the northern countries. In Icelandic, *lied* signifies region, and on this account the polestar is named Leidstjerna, consequently Leiderstein

[1]*General History of China* (1736) Vol. I. p. 273. *The Annals of the Chinese Monarchy.*
[2]*Cosmos. A Sketch of a physical description of the Universe,* by Alexander Von Humboldt, Vol. IV., Part I. Sabine's Translation, 1858 .

signifies guiding stone. According to the testimony of Suarro Sturleson, Ara Frode was born in the year 1068. This account was therefore probably written about the end of the eleventh century. We have this very strong evidence that the mariner's compass became known in the northern countries of Europe between the years 868 and 1100."[1]

Lodestone.—The principal regions from which lodestone was obtained for the touching of compass needles, long before the introduction of electrically produced magnets, were, according to writers of the sixteenth and seventeenth centuries, as follows:—[2] The best stones, which were of a bluish colour, came from the coasts of China and Bengal. Such stones were large and heavy and would hold up to twenty times their own weight of iron in suspension. They were usually sold for their own weight in silver and were eagerly sought for. Another sort, of a reddish colour, was found in Arabia along the coast of the Red Sea. Such stones were often broad and flat like tiles and were almost as good as the stones from China. Inferior qualities of lodestone were also found in Asia Minor, Macedonia, Spain, Denmark, while Germany produced lodestone, full of holes like honeycombs, of a fairly good quality. Stones of indifferent force were found in Norway in the iron mines in Long Sound and other parts, and also in the west of England.

It is not surprising that this stone, which possessed so rare a natural quality, should also have been endowed by the early philosophers with properties which it did not possess. It was popularly supposed during the Middle Ages that the lodestone if placed upon a woman's head while she slept would make her confess her adulteries; if held in the hand it would cure gout; that it would make its possessor eloquent, and that through its virtue he would find favour with princes. In those days there was supposed to exist an antidote for every substance and for this purpose the lodestone was favoured with garlic. So much so that even in 1694 John Seller wrote as follows: "There is a common received opinion that if the lodestone be rubbed over with garlick or onions that it will obstruct the virtue thereof; or if a knife being touched upon the lodestone and afterwards cut an onion or garlick it will immediately lose its virtue. This conceit hath also been countenanced by the Ancients, but if you are pleased to make a trial you will find it to be but a mere fallacy. It is also false that the diamond doth hinder the virtue of it while it is near it."

The Introduction of the Compass.—We have already seen that before the compass became a reality the mariner kept a rough course by the bearing

---

[1] *Popular Lectures and Addresses by Sir William Thomson* (Macmillan & Co., 1891.)

[2] Cortes, *Art of Navigation*, 1596. Gilbert, *De Magnete*, 1600. *Seller's Navigation*, 1694. *Blundville's Exercises*, 1613.

of some celestial body or by using his slowly increasing knowledge of the prevailing or seasonal winds. We are told that the natives of Southern India did not use the stars and planets to guide them, but that they carried birds which they released at intervals to discover in which direction the land lay.[1] It is not easy to believe that any seaman who ventured from the land did not make use of the sun and stars to guide him. The more probable explanation of the carrying and releasing of birds is that the Eastern seamen used this method to discover in which direction the nearest land lay, like our Viking forebears of a thousand years ago, and, indeed, like Noah in Old Testament times.

The date of the introduction of the magnetic needle into Europe or the evolution of the compass within the confines of the Continent must remain speculative and its inventors nameless. Certain it is, however, that a form of compass was used by French mariners towards the end of the twelfth century, as appears from some verses in a French tract entitled, *La Bible de Guyot de Provins*. Guy de Provins, in a satirical poem, expressed the wish that the Pope were like the polar star, which remained fixed and by which the mariners regulated their courses. He then proceeded to show how they knew in which direction the polar star lay when it was not visible, by touching a needle with lodestone and floating it on the surface of water in a vessel until it came to rest, when it pointed to the North Star. A translation of the material lines runs as follows:[2]

> There is a star that never moves,
> And an art that never deceives,
> By virtue of the magnet,
> An ugly brownish stone
> Which always attracts iron,
> And which always points straight,
> With this a needle they touched,
> And on a bit of straw they set it,
> Along the middle they put it,
> And the straw supports it.
> Then its point it turns,
> Towards this star without doubt,
> When the night is so extremely dark,
> That neither stars nor moon can be seen,
> Then looking at the needle with a light,
> Are they not certain,
> To see it pointing towards that star?
> Upon this the mariners depend
> For the right or proper course to keep.
> This is an art that never deceives.

---

[1] *Huet's History of Commerce and Navigation*, 1717.
[2] *The Theory and Practice of Finding the Longitude*, by Andrew Mackay, LL.D., 3rd Edition, 1810. Another translation appears in *Chronicles and Memorials of Great Britain and Ireland during the Middle Ages* in the volume *De Naturis Rerum*, edited by Thos. Wright, 1863, from which much of the information on the early compass is taken.

There is little doubt that by the beginning of the thirteenth century the use of the magnetised needle to find the north point at sea was becoming well known. Alexander Neckham (1157-1217), an Englishman of science, who was for some time a professor in Paris and who, in 1213, became Abbot of Cirencester, wrote in his *De Naturis Rerum*, chapter 98, "The sailors, moreover, as they sail over the sea, when in cloudy weather, they can no longer profit by the light of the sun or when the world is wrapped up in the darkness of the shades of night and they are ignorant to what point of the compass their ship's course is directed, they touch the magnet with a needle, which (the needle) is whirled round in a circle until, when its motion ceases its point looks direct to the north." Another contemporary writer, Jacques de Vitry, also wrote in the same strain and pointed out how very necessary the magnetic needle was to those who navigated the sea, while an anonymous poet, in a love song at this time, after comparing his lady to the polar star, described how the mariner directed himself when he could no longer see it From this poet we learn that some mariners stuck the needle through a piece of cork and placed it in a vessel of water "and letting it swim, as soon as it becomes at rest it points invariably to the polar star" Another somewhat similar account of the early compass was also given some years later by Brunetto Latini, the preceptor of Dante, in a letter written in England after a visit to Roger Bacon, the English scientist.[1]

Early Development.—The crude method of floating the needle upon water was soon displaced by mounting it upon a pivot, so that it could swing freely in a horizontal plane, until it came to rest in the direction of the polar star. We learn this also from Alexander Neckham, in his *De Utensilibus* where he enumerates among the stores which a ship should carry, "a needle mounted on a pivot, which will oscillate and turn until the point looks to the north and the sailors will thus know how to direct their course when the polar star is concealed through the troubled state of the atmosphere; for it (the pole star) never disappears under the horizon on account of the smallness of the circle it describes.[2]

Slowly the idea formed in the minds of those concerned of mounting a card upon the needle, showing the points of the compass, and enclosing the whole in a wooden box to protect it from the wind so that the steersman or lodesman could have recourse to it at all times, and during the fourteenth century a compass was evolved which differed little in its essentials from

---

[1]Roger Bacon (1214-1292 C.) spent many years in Paris, where he probably heard the current talk about the magnetic needle and its use.

[2]*De Utensilibus*—In a volume of vocabularies illustrating the condition and manners of our forefathers, etc., from tenth century to fifteenth. Edited by Thos. Wright, 1857.
See also the *Epistola de Magnete* of Petrus Peregrinus de Maricourt, written at Lucera, 1269.

the dry compass of the present day. Chaucer, in his *Conclusions of the Astrolabe*, c. 1390, speaks of the zodiac of the astrolabe, a circular net which was fitted to the instrument, "as shapen as an compasse," in a way which indicates that the circular compass card was well established in his day.

The making of a compass in the sixteenth century was well described by the Spanish writer, Martin Cortes, in his work *The Art of Navigation*. He wrote, " . . . forasmuch as the compass is so necessary we intend to show the order and manner how it ought to be made, for it may chance to fail or be lost in the voyage." It is probable that this advice was addressed to the masters of small or ill-equipped ships which only carried one compass, for upon long voyages of exploration it was more usual for the ships to be supplied with a number of compasses and all instruments of navigation in use at that time. Cortes instructed the mariner to take a piece of the paper of which charts were made and cut from it a circle of the diameter of about a span. It is interesting to note that the size of compass card recommended about 100 years ago is the same as that in use to-day, *i.e.*, from 8 to 10 inches, large enough to be read by the steersman and yet not too unwieldy for use. During the years which followed there was much controversy as to the correct size of the card, and during the last century a larger card 10 to 12 inches was generally used in the British Merchant Service because it was found to be steadier than the smaller one in a heavy sea. In some of the large ocean, going steamships, a card of 15 inches diameter was by no means unusual, but, with the adoption of the liquid compass, the great improvement in the magnets and cards in general, and the investigations into periods of vibration—the smaller card advocated by Cortes has been reverted to.[1]

The card being cut to the requisite size had to be marked with the thirty-two points of the compass, the north point being distinguished with a fleur de lys and the east point with a cross.[2] The fleur de lys was evolved from the Italian word "Tramontana" (North) which in the mediaeval portolan charts was usually abbreviated to T. The Middle Ages was an era of elaborate decoration which is reflected in the ornamental manuscript charts and in the bright painting of the ships. It was not long before the highly ornamental capital T developed into the shape of the heraldic fleur de lys, probably through the influence of the French seaman of Aquitaine. The symbol of the cross to denote the east is readily understandable in an Age of deep

---

[1]Further on this, see *Popular Lectures and Addresses*, Vol. iii., by Sir W. Thomson (Lord Kelvin) 1891, p. 286.

[2]It must be remembered that direction was indicated by the point from which the wind blew long before the compass was invented. In classical times direction was indicated by a wind rose in the form of an octagon, which was later developed into a twelve and then a sixteen-sided figure and that these sides were named before the compass was used. Further on this see Imago Mundi, Vol. ii., 1937, p. 23.

religious feeling and ecclesiastical influence which was in its earlier years marked by the Crusades and pilgrimages to the Holy Sepulchre.

The next step in the construction of the compass was to "take a wire of iron or steel of the largeness of a great pin and fix it on the underside of the card and touch it with lodestone." It will be seen that only one needle was used at this time, which was placed under the north and south line of the card, and it was retouched or fed as Cortes described it, with the lodestone when its directive force diminished.

A cap of laton[1] was fitted into the centre of the card, which was then poised upon a pivot of laton of a height about half the diameter of the card. The whole was contained in a round box of wood whose diameter was slightly in excess of that of the compass. The box was fitted with a glass lid to protect the card from the wind and the needle from dampness, and was then put within a second box, in which it was supported upon two concentric circles of laton, which were so pivoted as to keep the compass perpendicular when the ship laboured. The mariner was specially warned to see that the cap and pivot were upright, and was told to make the pivot blunter if the compass swung too quickly.

From this it is evident that the mariners of the sixteenth century, and doubtless of the century before, were equipped with dry compasses, capped and pivoted, slung in gimbals, and even provided with a crude though misguided method of damping the oscillations.

Magnetism.—It was during the sixteenth century that serious enquiries were made into the reasons why the magnetic needle pointed towards the north. It is impossible to say for how long before this men had pondered on the phenomenon, but some no doubt, ascribed it to heavenly causes unknown, while others said there was a magnetic stone under the tail of the Great Bear. As we have already seen, lodestone and its powers had been known for centuries in many parts of the world, and it was natural for the more practical minds to conjecture on the existence of a large deposit of powerful lodestone somewhere in the north. It was said that there were mountains in the north of such great powers of attraction that ships were built with wooden pegs to hold their planks together. It is of interest to note that the Arabs spoke of certain rocks off the Indian coast which had a magnetic power capable of drawing the nails out of ships, but such a fable was probably designed to discourage others from venturing into their sphere of trade and maritime interest rather than as a serious contribution to magnetic inquiry.

Martin Cortes, in his *Art of Navigation*, considered the matter and hinted

---

[1]Laton or Latten, a mixed metal of yellow colour, closely resembling brass. During the Middle Ages many ecclesiastical vessels and ornaments were made of this metal.

that there was some fixed point of attraction which did not lie in the same point or direction as the geographical pole and that this caused the easterly or westerly variation of the compass according to its position on the earth's surface. He said that the attractive point was somewhat distant from the pole of the world and inclined to the belief that it lay somewhere in Space.

In 1581, Robert Norman, an Elizabethan compass maker, published his theories on magnetism and, what was probably more important, his fortuitous discovery of the Dip of the needle. In his treatise, the *Newe Attractive*, he mentioned that others believed in a large mass of lodestone near the northern pole of the earth but he denied its existence. He argued that if such were the case, why was the compass not sensitive to lesser attractions when sailing in areas where deposits of lodestone were known to exist. He said that experience had shown that when ships passed close to the Isle of Elba, Porto Feraro and various places in Norway, the compass was not drawn towards these points. From this it would appear that the existence of areas of local attraction had not been discovered, indeed, having regard to the imperfect compasses and the laborious method of observing its error, it is not surprising that small variations of the needle from the magnetic meridian passed undetected. Even to-day, unless the compass is sensitive and a constant watch is kept on it and frequent observations are made for its error, it is easy to miss a transitory variation through local attraction, and the earlier seamen must be excused for failing to note something which they imperfectly understood. Norman would not admit the existence of a point of attraction in the North and he carried out several experiments to prove his contention. His simplest experiment was to float a magnetised needle in a bowl of water, free from wind or other disturbance. When the needle came to rest along the magnetic meridian he watched closely to see if it was then drawn towards the Northern edge of the bowl and, upon finding no movement, he concluded that there was no attractive force acting upon the needle. He contended that the power and virtue was wholly in the lodestone and not in any point on the earth's surface. When the needle was touched by the stone it received some of this virtue and then had power to point to what he called the Point Respective, which others called the Point Attractive. Norman's theory was well expressed by William Gilbert in 1600 when he said that Robert Norman found a point respective not attractive to which the magnet was collimated, but was not itself attracted. It was left to William Gilbert, who was a doctor of medicine, to lay the true foundations of our knowledge of magnetism. This he did in 1600 in a lengthy work entitled *De Magnete, magneticisque corporibus*, in which he reviewed the many theories regarding the attraction of the magnet to the north point, and gave a full account of his experiments, together with a chapter on the medicinal properties of the lodestone.

He fashioned a piece of lodestone into a sphere, which he called a terrella, and carried out numerous experiments upon it. As a result of his researches he came to the conclusion that the earth itself was a large magnet, with two opposite magnetic poles, and that magnetic bodies were governed and regulated by the earth and were subject to it in all their movements. This was the answer to Norman's query why the floating needle was not drawn to the North end of the bowl. There were two opposite forces, and not just one force in the north, which exerted a turning movement, or couple, on the lesser magnet until it was in the magnetic meridian, when the opposite forces, creating a magnetic field, held it motionless in the meridian.

Gilbert also answered the question why the compass did not incline specially when sailing near Elba, by saying that the energy of minor lodestones were very localised in their effects, and that such would not bear comparison with the largest magnet of all, the Earth itself.[1]

Dip.—Before leaving these two diligent searchers into the truth of magnetism, some description should be given of the discovery of the Dip of magnetic needle in 1576. This is most clearly set out by the discoverer, Norman, in his *Newe Attractive* (1581), in the following words:— "Having made many and divers compasses, and using alwaies to finish and end them before I touched the needle, I found continually, that after I had touched the yrons with the Stone, that presently the north point thereof would bend or Decline downwards under the Horizon in some quantitie: insomuch that to the Flie of the Compasse,[2] which before was made equall, I was still constrained to put some small peece of waxe in the South part thereof, to counterpoise this declining, and to make it equall againe."

"Which effect having many times passed my hands without any great regard thereunto, as ignorant of any such propertie in the Stone, and not before having heard nor read of any such matter. It chaunced at length that there came to my hands an Instrument to bee made with a Needle of sixe inches long, which needle after I had polished, cut off at just length, and made it to stand levell upon the pinne, so that nothing rested but onely the touching of it with the stone: when I had touched the same, presently the north part thereof Declined downe in such sort, that beeing constrayned to cut away

---

[1]The following is taken from the pamphlet *On the Correction and Use of Charts*, published by J. D. Potter, Minories, E.C., 1914. Magnetic laws do not permit of the supposition that it is the visible land which causes such disturbance (local magnetic), because the effect of a magnetic force diminishes in such rapid proportions as the distance from it increases that it would require a local centre of magnetic force of an amount absolutely unknown to affect a compass half a mile distant. Such deflections of the compass are due to magnetic minerals in the bed of the sea under the ship, and when the water is shallow, and the force strong, the compass may be temporarily deflected when passing over such a spot, but the area of disturbance will be small, unless there are many centres near together.

[2]Compass Card.

some of that part, to make it equall againe, in the end I cut it too short, and so spoyled the needle wherein I had taken so much paynes."

"Hereby being stroken in some choller, I applyed my self to seeke further into this effect, and making certayne learned and expert men (my friends) acquainted in this matter, they advised me to frame some Instrument, to make some exact tryal, how much the needle touched with the Stone would Decline, or what greatest Angle it would make with the plaine of the Horizon. Whereupon I made diligent proofs."

Correction for Variation.—From the works of Norman and Gilbert it appears that compass makers in different parts of Europe made their compasses in different ways and attached the needles to the cards in such a manner as to allow for the variation existing in their own particular regions.[1] On the Mediterranean seaboard the needle was placed directly under the north and south line of the card so that the compass always pointed to the magnetic north, but the instrument-makers in the Baltic and in the Belgian Provinces placed the needle one quarter of a point (2° 49′) to the eastward of the line; in Russia the difference was two-thirds of a point, and the makers in Seville, Lisbon, Rochelle, Bordeaux, Rouen, and throughout England placed the needle half a point to the eastward of the meridian line of the card. The result of these differences in the placing of the needle under the card was that in their particular localities the compass pointed to the pole star, but when a compass made in one part of Europe was taken to another it caused considerable errors in navigation. It is difficult to say how long this practice continued.

Towards the end of the seventeenth century great advances were, and had been, made in the systematic study of variation and in the seaman's knowledge of it. It is significant that, while reputable books on navigation, published at the end of the century, gave full instructions for the finding of variation, none of them warned the mariner of the differences in the placing of the needle under the card. A refinement of the process was, however, used by Dutch navigators at the end of the eighteenth century. Lieutenant Bligh, R.N., on his return from Timor to England in a Dutch ship in 1789, in describing the passage from the Straits of Sunda to the Cape of Good Hope, expressed surprise at the Dutch manner of navigating. He wrote, "They steer by line compass, or rather endeavour so to do, by means of a small, movable central card, which they set to the meridian: and whenever they discover the variation has altered $2\frac{1}{2}$° since the last adjustment, they again correct the central card. This is steering within a quarter of a point, without aiming at greater exactness."

---

[1] The *Newe Attractive and De Magnete*. See also *Jean Rotz, His neglected treatise on Nautical Science*, by E. G. R. Taylor, Geog. Journal, May, 1929.

This practice was persisted in by the Dutch, at any rate until iron ships became general, about the middle of the last century. Lieutenant Raper, in his *Practice of Navigation* (1852) in discussing the compass error, which is a combination of magnetic variation and deviation caused by the iron in a ship, said that part of the complexity and chance of mistake attendant upon the application of the two corrections would be obviated by correcting the compass itself for variation, the card being fitted to turn eastward or westward as necessary. He pointed out that this would be practicable in sailing ships making a passage with a fair wind (when constant tacking would not be necessary) and in steam vessels. Such a plan which he understood, was practised by the Dutch, would require, of course, constant vigilance, as the safety of the ship would depend on the proper correction being made. He thought, however, that, with care, especially where a second compass was employed no danger should attend it.

Later Improvements in the Compass.—We must now trace the evolution of the compass from the days of Cortes to the present century. Although it differed little in appearance from the modern dry card, it was very inferior to it in every respect, and lacked the refinements essential to make it an efficient instrument. Very little improvement was effected in the compass for about 200 years, from the middle of the sixteenth to the middle of the eighteenth centuries. John Robertson, F.R.S., who, in the eighteenth century was mathematical master at Christ's Hospital, in his exhaustive work on the *Elements of Navigation* (1754) gave the following description of the state of the compass in general use in his day. He said that before the introduction of the compass the navigating of ships was a very tedious and precarious operation, and that since its introduction it might be reasonably imagined that no necessary expense or care should ever be wanting in its construction. "But", said he, "it has so happened, that scarce one sea compass in ten is fit for the use for which it is made; and this has arose from their being fabricated by unskilful and ignorant workmen for the wholesale dealers in the shipping way; who generally pay no more regard to the construction of this instrument, whereupon the success of the voyage and the lives of the men in a great measure depend, than they do to any indifferent thing of the same price."

Robertson tells us that compasses in use in the Royal Navy, and some few merchant ships, were constituted with more care and on better principles, and were vastly superior to those in general use in the Merchant Service, whose compasses, from their construction seemed to be made purposely to vary from what was to be expected of them. The principal sources of error in the ordinary instrument were soft wire needles, which were fashioned into rhomboidal form in the expectation that the magnetic forces of the sides would strengthen the power of the needle; joining the sides of the compass box with iron nails; and making the pin and socket so badly that the card could not swing freely.

It was through the labours of a physician, Dr. Gowin Knight, F.R.S., a contemporary of Robertson, that the errors in the magnetic compass were brought to light, about the middle of the eighteenth century, when experiments were made to provide a better magnetic compass for general use. Dr. Knight became interested through seeing a magnetic compass, at the house of the Royal Society, that had been rendered useless by being struck by lightning. The effect of lightning on the compass was that the poles of the needle. which was lozenge shaped, were reversed. This, of itself, should not have rendered the compass useless, for the original poles of the needle had been completely reversed and the south point of the card pointed to the north magnetic pole. On certain headings, however, when the card was in the compass box the south point, instead of indicating magnetic north, came to rest in a position some two or three points to the eastward or westward of it. Upon examination it was found that the outward wooden case was joined with pieces of iron wire, all of which had become strongly magnetic through the lightning. This fact alone was not sufficient to cause an error of two or three points and a further investigation was made. It was then found that several iron nails or spikes had been driven into the bottom of the binnacle by the maker when it was made, presumably to hold the bottom to the sides. The captain of the ship informed Knight that he had given strict instructions to the compass-maker not to put so much as a single nail in it, so it appears that Robertson's strictures against the "wholesale dealers in the shipping way" were not without foundation. Dr. Knight ended his report on this compass as follows: "How, then, must anyone be shocked to hear that almost all the compasses made use of by our trading vessels are of the same sort, the boxes joined with iron wire. This, I am credibly informed is the case . . . one of this sort may be purchased for 5/- and it will cost about 2/6 more to buy a tolerable good one."[1]

Dr. Knight then procured many compass cards of both English and foreign manufacture and experimented upon them. It was found that, in nearly every case, the needles were made of two pieces of steel wire, each of which was bent in the middle so as to make an obtuse angle; and their ends were joined to form a composite needle of a lozenge shape. He touched the needles with magnets and, using the same cap and pin in every experiment, drew them 90° from the magnetic north and then observed upon what headings they came to rest. The result was illuminating, for every needle failed to

---

[1]*Philosophical Transactions*, Royal Society, Vol. 46, p. 113.

return to magnetic north. All varied more or less, either to the east or west of it, and some as much as 8°. Few of them returned to the same heading twice in succession, and when they did, it was not to magnetic north.

The next test was to draw the needles gently from their original heading to see how much they would stand from it without returning, and he frequently succeeded in making them come to rest a full point either to the east or west of it.

These tests led him to the conclusion that the irregularities were due to the indifferent method of hardening the needles. The wires were only hardened at the ends, and that was done by bringing them to a red heat and then dipping them in water. He condemned this haphazard method as too uncertain because the chances of making the ends of a needle of a uniform hardness were less than 1 in 100. He found that if the ends were not of equal hardness the needles would be unbalanced in their directive force, and the harder end would, upon magnetising, be much stronger than the softer end.

The lozenge shape of the needle, too, he found to detract from efficiency, for it was impossible for the whole of such a needle to be completely in the magnetic meridian at the same time.

Upon examining the better types of compasses, which were used in men-of-war and larger trading ships, he found that the needles were of one piece of better tempered steel, broad at the ends and tapering towards the middle, where a hole was made to receive the pivot cap. Though he found that the worst of these needles were preferable to those made of wire, the best of them were far from perfect. To test these needles he sprinkled them with fine magnetic dust, and upon examination through a magnifying glass, discovered that they had six magnetic poles instead of two. There was a pole at each end, two where the needle tapered, and two at the hole in the middle. Although such a circumstance did not prevent the needle from pointing to the magnetic north it weakened its directive force.

He also found that the broad ends of these needles terminating in an acute angle were likely to cause errors for, upon deflecting them, he observed that although their action was free and vigorous, they sometimes failed to return to their original heading. Upon sprinkling them with magnetic dust he found that the magnetic stream came out of the sides of the arrow-headed ends almost at right angles to those sides. From this he concluded that, when the needle was drawn a little from the true magnetic heading, the Earth's magnetic force acted stronger on one side of the needle head than the other, and prevented it from returning to the magnetic meridian.

The result of all his experiments was that he advocated the adoption of perfectly straight needles, properly tempered and, upon trial, he found that they always returned exactly to the same heading after vibrating for a

E

considerable time. This excessive vibration, however, was one disadvantage from which the broad-ended needle did not suffer for, by having its weight removed as far as possible from the point of suspension, its period of vibration was much slower.

In order to combine the advantage of both types of needles he departed from the usual practice of compass-making and produced an instrument which was superior to any of those which he had seen. He made a light circle of brass, of appropriate diameter, to weight the circumference of the card at the greatest distance from the centre. This circle also served to support the card, which, on account of the rigid frame, could be greatly reduced in weight and be made of thin paper. A further advantage of using the brass ring was that, being below the card and having the needle fixed above it, the centre of gravity of the whole was low enough to permit of the cap being put under the needle instead of through it as hithertofore. The placing of the needle above the card was a further improvement in those days, for it rendered it much more easily accessible for re-touching when its magnetism depreciated.

Knight then searched for an improvement to the cap and pivot where, in the ordinary compass, excessive friction was usually found. There were four kinds of caps in use in his day. Some were of brass and others were made of a mixed metal or crystal or agate. The first two precluded the use of other than brass pivots, and crystal or agate were too expensive for common use. He experimented with glass caps, finely polished, but found them unsatisfactory and decided that an ivory cap, into which was set a small piece of agate, gave all the advantages of an agate cap without its expense, and he adopted this type for his compass. For a pivot he chose a common sewing needle, which was strong enough for the purpose and yet not too brittle or soft. He would not trust the compass-makers to make these needles but preferred to use those made by needle-makers because they understood the manufacture of them and made a reliable article.

John Robertson wrote about this compass as follows: "It may be reasonably expected that such correct compasses will readily come into general use, as there have been several trials made of them both in men-of-war and merchantmen. But, like several other useful improvements, it must wait till time has removed old prejudices."[1] The dislike of the practical seaman for anything new, and his conservatism with regard to the old and well-tried instruments and methods was gradually overcome, and Knight's compass was adopted as the standard for the Royal Navy and by many large merchantmen. We learn from *Falconer's Marine Dictionary*, a book of repute, which passed through several editions, that in 1830 this compass was still generally

[1] *The Elements of Navigation*, 1754.

in use in the Navy, and it is probable that, with added improvements and refinements, it continued to hold pride of place until the epoch-making compass of Sir William Thomson (Lord Kelvin) was introduced during the latter half of the last century.

It is with some surprise, however, that, in the same book, we are told that in 1830 little care was taken of an instrument so vital to the safety of ships. In the Navy it was committed to the care of the boatswain who, generally, paid no more attention to it than he did to the other stores in his charge. Even when it was returned to the dockyard it was stowed away like the other stores without any regard for the preservation of its magnetism.[1]

The Investigation of Deviation.—The ever expanding field of trade, with its accompanying increase in shipping; the scientific expeditions which European nations undertook during the eighteenth century, and the improvement in instruments generally, produced a larger number of more critically-minded navigators than had hitherto been known. The striving after greater accuracy and the thirst for more detail in the lesser-known parts of the world caused the navigator and his friend, the scientist, to be more observant of everything that affected the way of a ship, and to take note of degrees where, previously, points had been sufficient.

It was due to the increasing refinement in the making of tne compass and the numerous careful observations for variation by an astronomer, William Wales, F.R.S., who accompanied Captain Cook on his Second Voyage (1772-1775), that certain peculiarities in the behaviour of the compass were first analysed. Wales remarked that, in the Channel, at the outset of the Voyage, and all the way to the Cape of Good Hope, the compass frequently showed differences of several degrees in the observations for variation. These irregularities continued after leaving the Cape and put him upon enquiry. Although he does not seem to have investigated the reasons for such irregularity with success, he was able to classify the results of his observations with some particularity.

In the Introduction to *Cook's Third and Last Voyage*, 1776-1780, Volume I., Wales gave the following details and results of his many observations for variation:—

1. It appears, from various instances, that the variations observed by the same compass would differ 3° to 6° and even 10°, from no other cause whatever, but putting the ship's head a contrary way.

2. That the same compass, in the same situation in every respect, within a few miles, but at two different times of the same day, would give variations differing from one another 3° to 7°.

---

[1]This is not mentioned in some of the earlier editions.

3. That the same compass on the same day with the same observer would give variations differing from one another by 5° on board the same ship when under sail and when at anchor in a roadstead.

4. That compasses made by the same maker, at the same time and place, on different ships, would differ 3° to 5°.

5. That the same compass in the same ship and within a few miles of the same place, but at different times, would give variations differing 4° to 5° or upwards.

6. That different compasses at the same time in the same ship would differ 3° to 6°.

He also noted, in the Southern Hemisphere, that the greatest westerly variation was observed when the ship's head was north and easterly, and least when south and westerly, and concluded that "variations observed with a ship's head in different positions and even in different parts of her will vary materially from one another."

It is a little surprising that the effect of iron in a ship did not occur to Wales or to other less scientific observers before him. Early in the seventeenth century, Captain John Smith, in his *Seaman's Grammar*, had warned the seaman against the danger of having iron nails in his compass box and, when editing the third edition of Wright's *Errors in Navigation*, in 1657, wrote, "other errors (of the compass) may be eschewed, as that there be no iron near the compass in the time of observation."

More specific warnings were given, later in the seventeenth century, by Captain Samuel Sturmy in *The Mariners' Magazine*, 1684, where he wrote, "The needle or wyers being Touched by the loadstone, are subject to be drawn aside by the guns in the steerage, or by any iron near it, and liable to variation and do not show the true north and south, which ought continually to be observed by a good azmuth compass."

Correction of Deviation.—It was left to Captain Matthew Flinders, R.N., to point to the solution of this problem during the beginning of the nineteenth century. In a letter to Sir Joseph Banks, F.R.S., who, in earlier years, had accompanied Captain Cook, he wrote that when he was surveying along the south coast of New Holland (Australia) in 1801-2, he observed considerable differences in the direction of the magnetic needle when there appeared to be no other cause than a difference in the heading of the ship.[1] That he quickly suspected the iron in the ship to be responsible for these differences is evident from the fact that he caused two guns, which stood near the compass to be put down into the hold, and then fixed the surveying compass exactly

---

[1] *Philosophical Transactions*, Vol. 95, 1805.

amidships upon the binnacle. This operation, however, produced no material effect in correcting the differences. By means of a table giving the dates, lines, positions and the supposed true variation and the variation observed he showed the results of his labours, and the inferences which he drew from them. He found:—

1. That there was a difference in the direction of the magnetic needle when the ship's head was on east and then on west.

2. That the difference was easterly when the ship's head was on west, and westerly when the head was on east.

3. That when the ship's head was on north or south the needle took the same or nearly the same deviation that it would on shore.

4. That the error in variation was nearly proportionate to the number of points which the ship's head was from the north or south.

From these facts he inferred that the attractive power of the different things in a ship which were capable of affecting a compass to be collected into something like a focal point, and that this point was nearly in the centre of the ship where the shot were stowed, for it was there that the greatest amount of iron was to be found. He further inferred that this point became endued with the same kind of attraction as the pole of the hemisphere in which the ship was situated. Consequently, in Australia the south end of the needle would be attracted by it and the north end repelled, and in the northern hemisphere the effect would be the opposite, while on the magnetic equator, the effect would be nil.

He was of the opinion that the attractive power of this point was sufficiently strong in ships of war to interfere with the action of the magnetic poles upon a compass placed upon or in the binnacle, which, of course, in those days, was in the after end of the ship.

The interesting account of Flinder's survey voyage to Australia was not published until 1814, but in it we find his considered opinion upon the whole question and an account of the corroborative tests made by the Admiralty. He tells us that similar errors had been noticed before, in other ships, but as they were not perceived to follow any regular laws, no correction had hitherto been applied. "There are", said he, "few experienced seamen who have not remarked occasional differences in the compass: but the most general opinion seems to have been that within some undefined and variable limits the instrument was radically imperfect.[1]

He then gave a true explanation of the causes of this error in the compass, which he found to have a close connection with the dip of the needle. It was his opinion that, north or south of the magnetic equator, stanchions

---

[1]*Voyage to Terra Australis*, Vol. II., Appendix 2.

and other upright pieces of iron became magnetised and exercised an attractive force on the compass, which could be neutralised if a position could be found near the taffrail, where the attraction of the iron at the stern would counteract, by its closer proximity, the more powerful attraction in the centre and forward parts of the ship. Should attraction in the after part prove too weak, it could be increased by fixing one or more upright stanchions or bars of iron in the stern. Thus, the name of Matthew Flinders will ever be associated with the compass error caused by vertical soft iron in a ship, in which magnetism is induced by the earth's vertical magnetic force, and with the correcting bar of vertical soft iron which bears his name.

It was during the first half of the nineteenth century that iron was being increasingly used in the construction and fitting of ships, especially in ships of war, and from the time of Flinders onwards many scientific seamen called for a thorough investigation of the errors caused by this iron and for some means to counteract them. Without such means it was felt that the compass would soon become useless as a nautical instrument. Much more iron was being used for ballast, water casks were being replaced by iron tanks, iron knees were being used for supports, cables of iron were rapidly taking the place of hemp, iron gun carriages were supplanting those made of wood, and the day of patent iron capstans and hollow iron masts was dawning.

In order to develop the mathematical principles of magnetism, and to apply them to the correction of the attraction from iron in wooden ships, Peter Barlow, mathematical master at Woolwich Academy, carried out an extended series of experiments. He experimented principally with a model ship, and invented a system of correction by means of an iron plate which was placed, after trial, in such a position in a ship that it would counteract the attraction from the other iron[1]. This plate seems to have given some satisfaction, though it was never generally adopted, because either a different plate had to be fitted after further experiment or, at least, another experiment had to be performed, and the original position of the plate, relative to the compass, altered with every large change of magnetic latitude. Such a system was undoubtedly better than no correction at all, although it failed to correct that part of the compass error caused by the attraction from hard iron in the ship, which was permanently magnetised and did not change with the latitude.

His contributions to the knowledge of magnetism were, however, most valuable, and he was one of the first to advocate the taking of reciprocal bearings from ship to shore and shore to ship in order to discover the compass error on any heading.

Within the next few years great changes took place in the architecture

---

[1] *Essay on Magnetic Attractions*, by Peter Barlow, 1823.

of ships, and iron began, by degrees, to oust oak from the shipyards, although England clung to it for her ships-of-the-line until about 1850. In order to meet this new menace to the magnetic compass, Sir George Airey, the Astronomer Royal, carried out a complete series of experiments in 1839 in two ships, the *Rainbow* and the appropriately named *Ironsides*.[1] In 1836, a naval officer, Commander Johnson, while experimenting on the best place for a compass in a ship, had found that the iron ship itself resembled a permanent magnet rather than a piece of soft iron in which magnetism was transiently induced by the earth's magnetism and that, as such, it possessed the power to attract the same end of the needle, irrespective of the geographical position of the ship.

Sir George Airey analysed the magnetic forces acting on a compass in an iron ship as:—

(1) The magnetism induced in soft iron by the vertical component of the Earth's magnetism, which attracted one or other end of the needle according to the magnetic latitude.

(2) The permanent and sub-permanent magnetism which has been hammered into the ship during her construction.

(3) The attraction of masses of soft iron turned into temporary magnets by induction of the horizontal component of the magnetic force of the earth.

In order to correct the error due to the permanent magnetism of the ship Airey applied permanent steel magnets, and to correct that part of the error due to the transient magnetism induced into horizontal soft iron he advocated the use of a mass of soft iron placed on each side or one side of the compass. It is now apparent that, with the addition of the vertical bar already proposed by Captain Flinders, the system of compass correction which is used in every ship to-day has been in existence for about 100 years.

The time had come when compasses were to receive the necessary attention and supervision. In order to insure a proper examination of the effects of local attraction in ships of the Royal Navy, the Lords Commissioners of the Admiralty, in 1842, appointed Captain E. J. Johnson, R.N., as superintendent of the Compass Department, whose duty it was to swing every ship when she was reported ready for sea. They also established a magnetic observatory at Woolwich, where all compasses used in the Navy were examined.[2] In 1847, Captain Johnson published a book entitled *Practical Illustrations of the necessity for ascertaining the Deviations of the Compass* in which, as a result of his experience in the Compass Department, he gave many good reasons

---

[1] *Results of experiments on the disturbance of the Compass in Iron built ships,* by Sir George Airey, published by John Weale, 1840. See also *Philosophical Transactions,* 1839.

[2] *Raper's Practice of Navigation,* 4th Edition, 1852, page 70.

for the systematic correction of the compass. He opened his argument with the following striking result of neglect in correcting the compasses of ships in a convoy, and wrote, "Officers in charge of convoys during the war will probably remember the care with which the general signal was displayed at sunset 'To steer a given course during the night,' with what alacrity that signal was repeated by the ships of war in their stations and answered by every merchant vessel in the fleet; and they may also remember with what surprise— nay, indignation—they observed, when daylight came, almost the entire convoy dispersed over the ocean as far as the eye could reach and mayhap a suspicious looking stranger or two escorting those farthest away, further astray, despite all the shots fired during a morning watch to recall them. That such dispersements were in part attributable to the difference of the compasses in each ship according to the position of the iron affecting them, there can be no doubt, but the greatest delinquents in this particular, in all probability, were not the merchant vessels but rather the ships of war; the attractive power of their guns upon the binnacle compasses being now a well-known and constantly proved fact."

Among the illustrations he gave, all of which are interesting and instructive, may be cited the loss of the *Reliance*. The *Reliance* was homeward bound with passengers and cargo from the East, and whilst in fog in the English Channel picked up the light at Dungeness. The course was then set for the Downs, and an hour or two later, when about to anchor, the ship struck heavily and eventually broke up with the loss of every person on board except one. Evidence was given that everyone on board thought they had stranded off the English coast when, in fact, they had struck the French coast, probably near Gris Nez. Upon a subsequent examination of the wreck a large iron tank was found 46 feet long, 8 feet wide, and 6 feet deep, which had been placed near the binnacle and about 18 feet below it, and that this had affected the compass with such disastrous consequences.

There is no doubt that the careless disregard and ignorance with which the compass was treated, less than a hundred years ago, were responsible for great losses in lives, property and time at sea. It was not surprising that even regular mail packets could not make a good landfall after crossing the Irish Sea when we learn that in some ships every principle of compass care was violated. Captain Johnson tells us that on inspecting a merchant steam vessel, which had been brought into Her Majesty's Navy, he found two compasses placed side by side in one binnacle, so closely together that they could not fail to produce serious errors by their reciprocal action upon each other. Upon cutting the binnacle in two it was found that it had been put together with iron nails and screws which weighed about $\frac{3}{4}$ of a lb.

From him we learn that the compasses used by other maritime nations were in no better state; and that one of the principal sources of error was that the needles were often rectangular in shape and consequently their poles did not always lie along the middle line but along the diagonal. In 1844, Edward J. Dent, Chronometer and Clock Maker to Her Majesty The Queen, presented a paper to the British Association for the Advancement of Science in which he remarked on the considerable error caused by the assumption that the Magnetic Axis of the needle coincided with what was called the maker's Axis. The maker's Axis was the line determined by the marks or zero points placed on the flat needle by the maker to indicate the two poles. In order to remove the error arising from the non-agreement of the marked and magnetic axis he suggested a simple contrivance to effect the inversion of the card whereby a mean of an equal number of observations in both positions would eliminate the error and give the correct magnetic bearing of the observed object. Some makers marked upon their compasses what they called their index errors, sometimes amounting to 3° or more, which had to be applied to the observed bearings in order to correct the difference between the two axes. It will be appreciated that Dent's method was only applicable to Azimuth compasses and was useless in steering compasses, and it is doubtful whether it ever attained any degree of popularity at sea.

Captain Johnson did not give much information about the results of applying Sir George Airey's system of correction although it appears that in some cases the results were not always satisfactory owing to a gradual decrease in the power of the correcting magnets. Lieutenant Raper in his work on navigation, however, wrote, in 1852, that the method had been adopted in several ships, and that the compass of the *Ironsides*, one of the ships in which Airey experimented, had been found perfectly correct in three voyages to South America.[1]

The growing interest in the care and correction of the compass was not for long confined to the Royal Navy, for, in 1855, a committee of prominent shipowners and scientific gentlemen was formed in Liverpool to investigate the magnetic conditions and the errors of compasses in Merchant ships. This energetic body, which was known as the Liverpool Compass Committee, made or caused to be made very searching investigations and carried out numerous experiments in various merchant ships, both iron and wooden. They considered the effect of iron cargoes on the compass heeling error, and the effect of the magnetic heading of an iron ship whilst being built upon the ship's permanent magnetism. By means of detailed questionaires and elaborate instructions to shipmasters they amassed a wealth of information about the magnetic conditions in all classes of merchantmen. By 1862 they had presented three comprehensive reports to the Board of Trade, which went far to make

---

[1]*Raper's Practice of Navigation*, 4th Edition.

a thorough working knowledge of magnetism and compass correction obligatory upon all who aspired to the command or navigation of a British merchant ship.[1] At their suggestion, and at the expense of the Dock Committee, marks, well remembered to this day, were painted on the dock walls at Liverpool, which when brought in line with Vauxhall chimney gave the correct magnetic heading, and facilitated the detection and measurement of compass errors. By swinging the ship the deviation on all points could be found and, as an example of the thoroughness of this praiseworthy body, if a steam-tug was employed in the swinging, the Committee recommended that it should be at least 60 feet from the ship, to avoid the possibility of its affecting the compass.

The Committee found that many errors were also caused by blunted and worn pivots, careless checking of courses and ignorant methods employed by some in the correction of the compass, and observed, doubtless with good reason, "while these causes of error are prevalent there will constantly be reports of deviation from the attraction of the land", of "compass disturbance from fog," of "unusual aberration" of "indraught", and other unfounded or imaginary pretexts which are now put forward when an iron ship gets stranded."

Captain Lecky, in his *Wrinkles in Navigation* wrote, in 1887, "One some-times hears wonderful stories of compasses suddenly jumping a point or two without actual alteration of the ship's head . . . some even go so far as to say that in the Red Sea, the sun beating fiercely on one side of the vessel in the morning and on the other side in the afternoon, will cause a change in deviation of several degrees". He concluded by saying that after making very careful experiments in that locality he had satisfied himself on the impossibility of this suggestion, and that the alterations were due to some cause within the ship herself, such as change of heel, errors of centering, bent shadow pins, loose iron, davits turned in that had previously been swung out and other similar causes.

Sir William Thomson, in his *Popular Lectures and Addresses*, 1891, remarked on the alleged effect of temperature on the compass and stated that early Arctic navigators imagined that the magnetic virtue was impaired by cold when they found their compasses becoming sluggish as they approached the north magnetic pole. This imagined effect was disproved by the dipping needle vibrating with greater energy, rather than with less, in polar regions.

The Modern Compass.—Although determined and successful efforts were made about the middle of the nineteenth century to detect the many external influences which caused grave errors in the magnetic heading of the compass, few efforts appear to have been made to inquire into the efficiency

---

[1]*Parliamentary Accounts and Papers*, 1857-58. Vol. LII., 1862, Vol. LIV.

of the compass itself since the introduction of Dr. Knight's compass about 100 years before. There must, of course, have been minor improvements and refinements effected in it by individual makers, but the general efficiency of the instrument had never been subjected to a rigorous investigation. In fact, many compass makers possessed little or no knowledge of magnetism and produced instruments of questionable worth. How long the navigator would have been content with his compass as it was is now only a matter of speculation, for by a fortunate chance, Sir William Thomson (Lord Kelvin), Professor of Natural Philosophy in the University of Glasgow, and a keen amateur yachtsman, undertook to write a series of articles on the mariner's compass for a periodical in 1873. He confessed that when he tried to write on it he had to learn his subject, and during the process he discovered so many deficiencies in the existing instruments that it was five years between the appearance of the first article and the second.[1] During those years he produced a magnetic compass whose principles of construction, apart from various slight improvements, remain unchallenged to this day. He tells us that the compass in general use at sea in all classes of ships of all nations were, in his time, substantially the same as the compass made by Robert Norman three hundred years before. The practice of placing the needle out of line with the north and south line of the card, to allow for the local variation, had been abandoned in favour of the Italian practice, already referred to, which placed the needle directly in line with the north and south axis of the card. The wooden compass bowl still held its place, not only in coasters and fishing boats, but in many old fashioned sailing ships of high dignity; but the bowls in H.M. ships and in merchant steamers were made of more durable material, such as copper or brass.

It is with some surprise that we learn that the pointed oval needle, and the pair of thin bent needles with their ends united, so roundly condemned by Dr. Knight, were still to be found in use at sea, though, generally, they had given way to the straight bar system advocated many years before. In the Admiralty standard compass there were two pairs of parallel straight bar needles, while the merchant service favoured just one pair.

With great thoroughness, Lord Kelvin, by which title he is so well known to seamen, investigated the problem of the unsteadiness of the compass in a seaway, the current remedy for which was, quite frequently, the blunting of the bearing point proposed by Cortes in the sixteenth century. It had generally been considered that the greater the magnetic movement of the needles the better the compass, but Lord Kelvin showed that the greater the strength of the needle the more unsteady would the compass be when the ship was

---

[1]*Popular Lectures and Addresses*, by Sir W. Thomson (1891), Vol. III. See chapter on Terrestrial Magnetism and The Mariner's Compass for a full description of his work on the compass.

rolling. After discussing the causes of the oscillations of the compass in a rolling ship, he said "When the free vibrational period of the compass card agrees with the period of the ship's rolling, a comparatively moderate degree of rolling may produce a great oscillation in the card. Now the longest period of actual rolling, to any considerable degree, in a seaway is from fourteen to seventeen or eighteen seconds. The vibrational period of the A card of the Admiralty standard compass is, in this part of the world, about nineteen seconds, and that of the larger compass (ten-inch) of the merchant steamers about twenty-six seconds; and it is certainly owing to the nearer agreement of the former than of the latter with the period of the ship's rolling, that in a heavy sea the Admiralty compass is more disturbed than the ten-inch compass in the merchant steamers. But to get satisfactory steadiness a much longer period still than the twenty-six seconds is necessary. Now, for the same weight and dimensions of compass card and needles, the smaller magnetic moment of the needle's magnetism the longer will be the vibrational period."

A further disadvantage in using large needles of great force was found to be their inductive influence upon the soft iron correctors, which Sir George Airey had recommended for the correction of that part of the compass error due to induction in the horizontal soft iron in a ship.

From his investigations, Lord Kelvin found that to produce an improved compass, which would be steadier at sea, and also be better adapted for the perfect correction of errors due to the iron of an iron ship or of cargo carried by it, the following requirements were necessary:—

(1) For steadiness a very long vibrational period with small frictional error.

(2) Short enough needles to allow the correction to be accurate on all courses of the ship for the place where the adjustment was made.

(3) Small enough magnetic moment of the needles to allow the correction of the error due to horizontal soft iron (*e.g.*, athwartship beams) to remain accurate to whatever part of the world the ship might go.

How well he succeeded in his labours is known to the entire maritime world. The description of the production of his masterpiece, which shows the care and attention which he lavished on every detail is best given in his own words.

"The accompanying diagram[1] represents the solution at which I have arrived. Eight small needles of thin steel wire, from 2 inches to $3\frac{1}{4}$ inches long, weighing in all 54 grains, are fixed (like the steps of a rope ladder) on two parallel silk threads, and slung from a light aluminium circular rim of

[1]On p. 297 *Popular Lectures and Addresses* Vol. III. , by Sir William Thomson.

10 inches diameter by four silk threads through eyes in the four ends of the outer pair of needles. The aluminium rim is connected by thirty-two stout silk threads, the spokes as it were of the wheel, with an aluminium disc about the size of a fourpenny-piece forming the nave. A small inverted cup, with sapphire crown and aluminium sides and projecting lip, fits through a hole in this disc and supports it by the lip; the cup is borne by its sapphire

Compass.

Reproduced by kind permission of the Executors of the late Lord Kelvin.

crown on a fine iridium point soldered to the top of a thin brass wire supported in a socket attached to the bottom of the compass bowl. The aluminium rim and thirty-two silk thread spokes form a circular platform which bears a light circle of paper constituting the compass card proper.

"Habitually, however, the whole movable piece which turns to the north consisting of magnets, supporting frame work, jewelled cap and, in the ordinary compass, pasteboard or mica with paper pasted on it, is called, for brevity, the card, or the compass card. In the new compass the outer edge of the paper circle is notched and folded down along the outside of the aluminium rim; pasted to tissue paper, with which the aluminium rim is firmly coated, so as to give a perfectly secure attachment; and bound all round with narrow silk ribbon to prevent the paper from cracking off in any climate. For the sake of lightness a circle of 6 inches diameter is cut away from the middle of the paper, leaving an annular band, 2 inches broad, on which are engraved the points of the compass, and a circle divided to degrees.

"The paper ring is cut across in thirty-two places, midway between the silk thread spokes, to prevent it from warping the aluminium rim by the shrinkage it experiences when heated by the sun. Compass cards of the new kind made before this simple piece of engineering was applied to the structure, used to be perfectly flat in cloudy weather at sea, and become warped into a saddle-shape surface when the sun had shone brightly on them for a few minutes. Now with the radial cuts in the paper the compass may be first thoroughly moistened by the steam of a kettle, and then toasted before a hot fire, without in any sensible degree warping the aluminium rim or disturbing the degree or point divisions printed on the paper; and in its proper place under glass in its bowl it remains quite undisturbed through all variations of temperature from coldest weather to hottest sun in actual sea service."

The result of this revolution in the making of the compass card was that its entire weight was about 170 grains instead of about 6 ounces, and that the frictional resistance upon the pivot was reduced to a minimum. The vibrational period of the new card was about double that of the ordinary card, and the whole magnetic moment of the eight short needles was only about one-thirteenth of that of the customary two needle compass used in the merchant service, and had an insensible effect on the soft iron correctors.

In order to give increased steadiness to the compass card in steamships, whose powerful engines caused much vibration, he slung the entire bowl and its gimbals in a brass grummet ring whose elasticity mitigated the effect of the vibration upon the bearings of the gimbals and upon the pivot of the card.

Although about forty years had elapsed since Sir George Airey had introduced his method of compass correction, it had been impossible to carry it out with completeness owing, as we have seen, to the large magnetic moment of the needles in use. In order to realise completely Airey's method, Kelvin made an improved type of binnacle in which the requisite changes in the adjustment of the permanent magnets could be carried out with ease whenever observation showed a change to be necessary. It contained an adjustable appliance for placing a steel magnet below the centre of the compass to correct the heeling error with every change of magnetic latitude, and also a means of placing and fixing a soft iron sphere on each side of the compass to correct the error due to induction in horizontal soft iron. Lastly, it had an appliance for fixing on the forward or after side of the binnacle a bar of soft iron, "to", as he said, "realise conveniently a most important but long strangely neglected correction, given so long ago as 1801 by Captain Flinders."

There have been no fundamental changes in the construction of the magnetic compass since Lord Kelvin's day. Slight instrumental improvements have of course, been effected, and the liquid compass has been adopted by the Admiralty, to ensure a minimum effect from engine vibration and heavy gunfire.[1] The liquid compass has also found favour in merchant ships as a steering compass, but the dry card of Lord Kelvin continues to hold its place in the standard compasses of the merchant ships of the world.

The Gyro Compass.—The early years of the present century saw the beginning of a new era in the ability of the navigator to set and maintain an accurate course without applying any corrections for variation and deviation. This has been attained by designing a compass whose power to remain in the true meridian is governed by mechanical laws which have no relationship with the laws of terrestrial magnetism.

The researches of scientists during the nineteenth century showed that if a gyroscope, i.e., a heavy disc or fly-wheel, through the centre of which passes a spindle, was placed in supporting rings so that it was free to move about its spinning axis and its horizontal and vertical axes, and then rapidly rotated, it would maintain its original direction in space. The same effect obtained with any freely balanced body, even when it was not spinning, though lack of spin caused it to be more responsive to disturbing forces.

It was also remarked that if an external force was applied to a spinning gyroscope, the resultant movement was not in the direction of the applied force but in the plane at right angles to that in which the force was applied. Thus, if a downward pull was exerted on it, it turned in azimuth about its vertical axis instead of tilting about its horizontal axis. This phenomenon is known as Precession, the law of which was expressed by the French scientist, Foucalt, as follows:— "Every free rotating body, when subjected to some other or new turning force, tends to set its axis of rotation parallel to the new axis of rotation, by the shortest path, so that the two rotations take place in the same direction."

By utilising these two properties and taking advantage of the modern application of electricity to mechanical devices to produce a fly-wheel capable of a high and regular speed of rotation over a lengthy period, an instrument has been evolved which will indicate true north, provided several small

---

[1]Preface to *Deviation and the Deviascope*, by Captain C. H. Brown, 1918.

corrections are made for latitude and the speed and course of the ship.

Neglecting the small corrections, which are outside the main argument, the effect of the above combination is as follows:—Suppose a spinning gyroscope to be placed with its axle horizontal to the earth in the east and west line. As the earth rotates from west to east the tangent plane to the earth's surface at that point, or the local horizontal, assumes an ever increasing angle with its original direction in space, until it has rotated through 360° from west to east in the course of 24 hours. The spinning axis or axle of the gyro, instead of following this ever-changing direction, as other terrestrial objects do, remains pointing in its original direction in space, and the eastern end of it tilts upwards from the horizontal.

If a weight is placed vertically below the centre of gravity of the gyroscope, so that the new centre of gravity of the whole is below the spinning axis, then as the axle remains in its original direction while the local horizontal changes, a vertical couple is applied about the horizontal axis. This causes the gyro to turn in azimuth or precess towards the meridian. At the same time the weight begins to act upon the gyro, gradually depressing the elevated end of the axle to the terrestrial horizontal.

When the original east end of the axle crosses the meridian the axle has not attained the horizontal, owing to the earth's continued rotation, and it continues to precess to the westward. Eventually the original west end of the axle, which is now to the eastward of the meridian, assumes an upward tilt causing precession in the opposite direction, with an oscillation to the eastward across the meridian. If matters were left at that the gyro axle would simply cross and recross the meridian in alternate directions. By incorporating certain damping devices into the instrument, however, the oscillations are gradually reduced until the axle assumes the horizontal on the meridian, in line with the axis of the earth. When this position is reached, the weight acts vertically downwards through the centre of rotation, thereby ceasing to exert a couple on the gyro and causing no further precession, with the result that the axle indicates and continues to indicate the true meridian.

CHAPTER III.

NAVIGATIONAL INSTRUMENTS.

THE introduction of the magnetic compass made it possible for seamen to traverse new seas and explore new lands. It increased the facility with which charts could be made to show the relative, if not the true, bearing of one point of land from another. There were, however, other instruments which helped the navigator in his voyagings and chartings, and these were the instruments evolved for the determination of the altitudes of celestial bodies. From these altitudes, even in the earliest days of deep sea navigation, the seaman was able to find his latitude with some approach to the truth and thereby improve his charts, and find his way with greater confidence.

The Astrolabe.—The principal instrument in use at sea for this purpose during the early voyages of discovery was the astrolabe, which had been used by astronomers on land since about 150 B.C. Before the evolution of the mariner's compass the need for such an instrument at sea was scarcely felt, but once the seaman could leave the land behind with some confidence, the astronomer's astrolabe, in a simplified form, became a useful addition to his equipment. It may be that Arab seamen used it in their voyages to India long before the European nations adopted it as a nautical instrument, and it may be that a few navigators of the Western nations used it in their coastal voyages, whereby their charts were improved, long before Columbus ventured across the Atlantic. Certain it is that the Portuguese navigators of the Fifteenth century used it in their explorations of the western coast of Africa, and that Columbus found his latitude by its aid in 1492.[1]

The adoption of the astronomer's astrolabe to the use of seamen in 1480 is credited to Martin Behaim, a native of Nuremberg, who saw sea service with the Portuguese.[2] Stripped of its astronomical complexities it was simply

---

[1]*Esmeraldo de Situ Orbis*, by Duarte Pacheco circ. 1500 A.D. (Hakluyt Society, 1937), and *The Journal of Columbus*, (Hakluyt Society, Vol. 86).

[2]"After that (the discovery of compass) Henry, sonne of John the First, King of Portugal, began to make voyages of discoverie up on the Coast of Africa, and John the Second seconded that enterprise and used the helpe of Mathematicians, Roderigo and Joseph, his Physicians, and Martin Bahamus by whom the Astrolabie was applyed to the Art of Navigation, and benefit of the Mariner, before used onely in Astronomie." *Purchas, his Pilgrimage*, 1613, Book I., Chapt. 9.

F

a flat ring of brass or other metal, graduated in degrees, at whose centre was pivoted an arm, upon which were fixed two pinhole sights. It was provided with a swivelled ring through which the thumb was slipped when holding it to take an observation. The celestial body was observed through the sights, and its altitude read off the graduated ring. Two holes instead of one were often pierced in each of the sight brackets, the one small and the other somewhat larger. When the sun was bright, the astrolabe was held towards it and the arm was moved until the beam through the small hole in the fore sight coincided with the small hole in the back sight. When the sun was dimmed by cloud, or when an observation of a star was taken, the sun or star was observed directly through the larger holes.

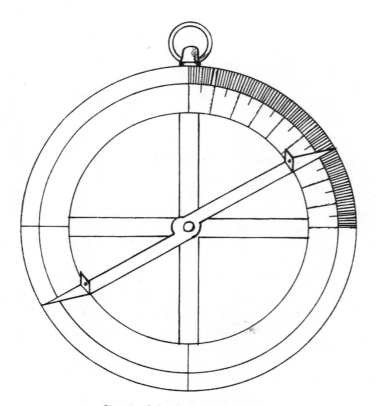

Sketch of simple form of astrolabe.

Most of the well-known writers on navigation from the time of Columbus until the end of the seventeenth century described the astrolabe as an instrument most necessary to navigation, and frequently gave instructions as to how it should be made. From them it appears that the simpler form of astrolabe was widely used at sea, and it is probable that few navigators made use of the more elaborate astronomical type, which predominates in the museums to-day. It is most unlikely that the astronomical astrolabes, many of which were either too large or too small for use in a rolling ship, were used at sea to any extent, though they may have been taken ashore by the navigators to find the latitude, when the ship touched land, to water or revictual, or have been used from the ship in a sheltered anchorage.

The astrolabe for use at sea had to be of such a size and weight to be of the greatest service in the varying conditions of wind and weather. This aspect was discussed by a writer early in the seventeenth century, who wrote, "But broad astrolabes though they bee thereby the truer, yet for that they are subject to the force of the wind and thereby ever moving and unstable, are nothing meete to take the altitude of anything, and especially upon the sea which thing to avoid, the Spaniards doe commonly make their astrolabes or rings narrow and weightie which for the most part are not much above 5 inches broad and yet doe weigh at the least 4 pound, and to that end the lower part is made a great deal thicker than the upper part towards the Ring or handle. Notwithstanding most of our English Pilots that be skilfull doe make their Sea Astrolabes or Rings sixe or seven inches broad and therewith verie massive and heavie, not easie to be moved with everie winde, in which the spaces of the degrees be the larger and thereby the truer."[1] Although the heavy astrolabe in use at sea tended to remain in the true vertical, when observing it was very difficult to obtain a satisfactory altitude with it in bad weather. In the *Journal of Columbus* the following remark appears for Sunday, 3rd February, 1493: "The North Star appeared very high as it does off Cape St. Vincent. The Admiral was unable to take the altitude either with the astrolabe or with the quadrant because the rolling caused by the waves prevented it."[2]

John Davis, writing about one hundred years later, in advocating the use of the Cross Staff at sea said, "But there can be no invention that can establish the certainty of the use of either Quadrant or Astrolabie at the Sea, for unless it be in very smoothe water, there can be no certainty of any observation by those instruments whereby the Seaman may rest assured of the latitude which he seeketh." It seems that during the seventeenth century the astrolabe went out of favour with English seamen, for Captain James in his description of his voyage to discover the North West Passage, in 1633, gives a list of the instruments he took with him, and there is no

---

[1]*Blundeville Exercises*, 1613 Edition.

[2]The quadrant was a quadrant of wood or metal, graduated in degrees, with sights fitted along one side and a small plumb line hung from the point of intersection of the two straight sides to indicate the vertical and, incidentally, the altitude or zenith distance when observing. It was really a land surveyor's instrument, but was usually carried at sea by the early discoverers.

mention of the astrolabe. Prints and books bear out this view, and John Seller in his book on navigation in 1694 does not even refer to it as an instrument for navigation.

The Cross Staff.—John Seller does, however, write at length upon the Cross Staff and tells us that, in 1694, it was an instrument of some antiquity. It was probably introduced to seamen about the same time as the astrolabe, and by the middle of the sixteenth century it was well-known among them. It was, by its very simplicity, most desirable for use on board ship, and as its principle depended upon being able to view the horizon at the moment of observation it was essentially a ship's instrument. It derived its name from its shape and consisted of a staff of wood from 30 to 36 inches long and from ½ to 1 inch in section. Upon this staff cross pieces were fitted, which could be moved along it at right angles. Three cross pieces, or crosses as they were called, were usually supplied the shortest for use up to angles of 30°, the longer for angles between 30° and 60°, and the longest for angles between 60° and 90°. Upon the flat sides of the staff scales of altitude were cut for use with the appropriate crosses.

The Cross Staff.

To observe an altitude with it the 30°, 60° or 90° cross was slid on to the staff, according to the angle to be measured, and the end of the staff was held to the eye and rested on the eye-bone. The cross was then moved along the staff until its upper end coincided with the observed body, and the lower end with the horizon, and the altitude was read on the appropriate scale where the cross intersected the staff.

The cross staff as well as the astrolabe was carried in ships in their ocean voyages, and it would appear that it was chiefly used for taking altitudes of the Pole star. It was not well suited for observing the sun when it was bright, for there was no protection to the eye from the glare. On these occasions the astrolabe, with its small pinhole sights, was to be preferred. When the sun was dimmed by cloud the cross staff would be better and more adaptable to quick observation. As Cortes wrote in the sixteenth century:— "It serveth not on the land nor for the sun, except the sun shall be under any thin cloud and the horizon clear." In the course of time, and before the end of the sixteenth century, the navigator sometimes used tinted glass to protect his eye when observing the sun with his cross staff. John Seller writes, in his *Practical Navigation*, "In observing forward by the cross staff 'tis usual to have a piece of red glass to defend the sight from the lustre of the sun in time of observation.[1] It would, in my opinion be better to have the glass fitted in a piece of brass, and so to be put upon the end of any of the crosses as occasion requires."

The personal equation entered more into the accuracy in observing with this instrument than in most. Edward Wright, in 1599, in his *Certain Errors in Navigation*, drew attention to the need for a correction due to, what he called, the eccentricities of the eye, *i.e.*, the distance wherewith the centre or point where the sight beams concurred within the eye were further backward than the end of the staff. He explained that if a correction for this was not allowed the observed altitude could be anything up to 1° in excess of what it should be.

Though the cross staff was much more satisfactory than the astrolabe it nevertheless suffered from a great drawback when large angles were observed. This drawback was inherent in the instrument and could not be overcome. As the spacing between the graduations for altitude marked along the staff depended upon the tangent of the angle observed the nearer the altitude approached to 90°, the closer together became the graduations and the less certain the accuracy of the reading. In a general way, therefore, the astrolabe was to be preferred in low latitudes where the weather was less boisterous and the sun's altitude higher at noon, and the cross staff was to be preferred in the higher latitudes where conditions were the reverse.

The Back Staff and Davis Quadrant.—At the end of the sixteenth century, John Davis, fully realising the limitations of the astrolabe and cross staff,

---

[1]Observing forward means facing the sun. The Dutch seamen, by fitting vanes to the cross staff, observed the sun with their backs to it.

invented a more complicated instrument which combined the good points of both. He wrote, in his *Seaman's Secrets*, "Finding by practise the excellencie of the Crosse staffe above all other instruments to satisfie the Seaman's expectation, and also knowing that those instruments whose degrees are of largest capacitie are instruments of most certaintie. I have very carefully laboured to search a good and demonstrable meane how a crosse staffe might be projected, not onely to containe large degrees, but also to avoide the uncertaintie of the sight, by disorderly placing of the staffe to the eye, which demonstration I have found, and have had the instrument in practise, as well under the sun as in other climates." This instrument was the backstaff, so named because an observation was taken with the observer's back towards the object. It was about 36 inches long, and upon it were placed two half crosses, the one forming an arc of a circle, and the other a straight bar which worked on the same principle as the cross staff.

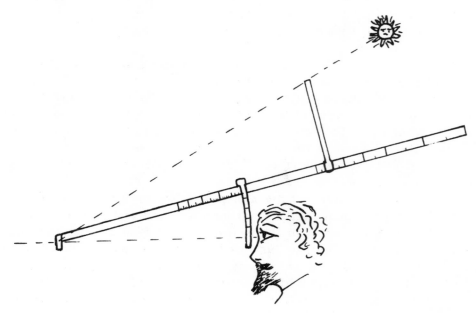

Sketch of Back Staff.

The observation was taken as shown in the sketch and the altitude was obtained by taking the sum of the angles shown by the two crosses.

During the seventeenth century the instrument was improved upon and made more compact and rigid, whereby altitudes could be taken with greater ease and accuracy. By the end of the century it had been so improved upon that Davis's **Quadrant**, as it was then called, became the principal instrument for observations at sea among English speaking navigators.

It consisted of two arcs, which together made 90°, from which it derived its name, quadrant. These two graduated arcs were fixed, the one above and the other below a straight wooden bar, whose length was equal to the radius of the lower arc, and was about three times the length of the radius of the upper arc. The upper arc contained about 65° graduated in degrees, and the lower arc about 25°, which, on account of its greater size could be subdivided into minutes of arc by means of a diagonal scale. Three vanes were fitted to the instrument, called respectively the horizon vane, the sight vane and the shade vane. The horizon vane was fitted on the end of the bar, opposite to the sighting end, and in it was a long slit through which the

Davis's Quadrant.

horizon could be seen. The sight vane was fitted to slide along the lower arc, and through it, when properly adjusted, and through the above-mentioned horizon vane the horizon was sighted at the time of observation. The shade vane was fitted to slide along the upper or 65° arc, and when observing the sun, was so placed that the shadow cast by its upper edge fell on the edge of the slit in the horizon vane. In the later models the shade vane was replaced by a convex lens or burning glass, which collected the rays of the sun into a bright spot upon the horizon vane.

To take an altitude, the navigator first placed the shade vane on an appropriate degree on the upper arc, and then turned his back to the sun, and moved the sight vane along the lower arc until the sun's rays or shadow were seen through the slit in the horizon vane. The sum of the readings on the two arcs was the observed altitude of the sun.

Though this instrument was superior to any that had yet been produced for deep sea navigation, it was far from perfect, especially in rough weather or in the Tropics. A gifted mathematician and keen observer, John Logan, Governor of Philadelphia, wrote in 1734, "Where the observer must bring the spot of light from the sun and the rays from the horizon to coincide exactly on the edge of the horizon vane—that though this can be done in moderate weather and seas with a clear sky, and when the sun is not too high, without any great difficulty—yet in other cases it required more accuracy than can in some junctures possibly be applied."[1] He stressed the importance of having some form of instrument with which altitudes could be observed quickly, especially in the lower latitudes where the sun, as it approached the meridian, had an apparent motion 80 times faster than in the higher latitudes. This very obvious difficulty when observing for latitude with the complicated Davis Quadrant had its repercussion upon the trade, and John Logan did not overstate the case when he wrote, "And yet, perhaps no parts of the world require more exactness in taking the latitude than is necessary in voyages to the West Indies, for it is owing to the difficulty of it that vessels have so frequently missed the island of Barbadoes and when they got to leeward of it have been obliged to run down a thousand miles further to Jamaica from whence they can scarce work up again in the space of many weeks, against the constant trade winds and therefore generally decline to try for or attempt it."

John Logan wrote the foregoing in a letter to the Royal Society in London when introducing to it an improved form of Quadrant, the invention of which was claimed by a fellow countryman, Thomas Godfrey. It was very like an ancient cross bow in appearance and was called the Mariner's Bow.[2] It had been tested by American shipmasters, in their voyages to lewor latitudes, and they had reported most favourably upon it, for it was possible to take an altitude by it in a quarter of the time required by the Davis Quadrant.

The day of these instruments was, however, drawing to its close, and

---

[1] *Philosophical Transactions*, 1734.

[2] Godfrey's improved Bow was fitted with a diagonal scale to ensure more accurate reading. He was not the inventor of this form of quadrant, though he was probably instrumental in getting it tried at sea by American seamen. There is a description of the Mariner's Cross Bow in Edward Weaver's *Description and use of the Sector*, published in London, 1624, and an illustration of it in that book, and also in the frontispiece of Moxon's edition 1657 of *Wright's Errors in Navigation*.

though they lived on until the latter half of the eighteenth century their period of usefulness was over when Hadley introduced his quadrant in 1731.

Hadley's Quadrant.—Hadley's Quadrant was the first instrument of double reflection to be used by navigators and, in principle, differed in no way from the modern sextant. According to Andrew Mackay, F.R.S., who was mathematical examiner to Trinity House, the East India Company and Christ's Hospital at the beginning of the nineteenth century, the first instrument for measuring angles by reflection appeared about the end of the seventeenth century.[1] Several eminent scientists, among whom were Sir Isaac Newton and Dr. Halley, invented instruments of a similar nature, but the first account of such an instrument was given by John Hadley to the Royal Society in May, 1731. There is some doubt as to whether Hadley actually invented it, he may have evolved it from the previous inventions of Newton, Halley and others, or he may have copied it from a similar instrument invented by Thomas Godfrey of Philadelphia, the inventor of the Mariner's Bow already referred to above. There is no doubt that Godfrey did produce a reflecting quadrant, and that a description of it was transmitted to the Royal Society before or about the time Hadley's account appeared in the Transactions of that Society.[2]

Whatever the truth, Hadley's Quadrant, as it is called, marked a stage in the accuracy of ocean navigation comparable with Lord Kelvin's magnetic compass and John Harrison's chronometer.

As Hadley said, the instrument was designed for use where the motion of objects or any circumstance occasioning an unsteadiness in the instruments commonly used, rendered observations difficult or uncertain. The principle of the quadrant is as follows:—

A ray of light coming from an object O, strikes the reflecting mirror I, (known as the index glass) from which, by movement of the mirror I, which is secured to a movable bar IC, it is reflected on to the silvered portion of the horizon glass G, and from thence along the line of sight GE to the eye of E.

Along the line of sight EG is also viewed the horizon H, through the unsilvered portion of the mirror G.

The ray of light from O follows the line OIGE, and $\angle$ between the first

---

[1] *The Theory and Practice of Finding the Longitude*, Vol. I., London, 1810.

[2] John Hamilton Moore, the Hydrographer, in 1800, wrote, "The inventor of this noble instrument is disputed; some say it was first invented by one Godfrey, in Philadelphia, and that Mr. Hadley, then an officer in the Royal Navy, pirated it from him, and brought it to England, who being the first that made it public, it still bears his name. How far this is true I cannot say, but certain it is, that two men in different parts of the world may hit upon one invention at the same time."

ray OI and the last ray GE = ∠OEH which is the altitude of O above the horizon.

By a well known rule of Optics, when a ray of light undergoes two reflections, the angle between the first and last rays is double the angle between the two reflecting mirrors.

Therefore ∠OEH = 2∠IKG

Because GK is parallel to IB, ∠IKG = ∠KIB

∴ when the Index Bar IC has moved from B to C through the arc BC it has moved half the angle of altitude, ∠OEH.

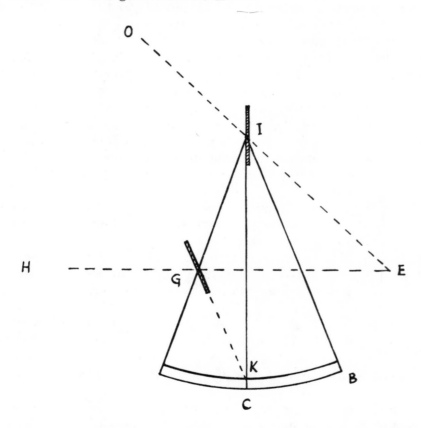

In order to avoid doubling the angle or the arc of the quadrant to obtain the observed altitude of a body the space of ½° of arc was marked 1° and so on.

The first quadrant made by Hadley was of wood, but the second one made by him, shortly afterwards, for Admiralty experimental purposes, was of brass. It was so heavy that it had to be supported on a pedestal when in use. In order to ensure lightness and handiness at sea the quadrants were usually made of wood and the graduations were cut upon an ivory arc. By means of a diagonal scale it was possible to read the altitude of an observed object to the nearest minute of arc, and in the course of time the diagonal scale was supplanted by a vernier, which had been invented about a hundred years before, to obtain a similar or closer degree of accuracy.

The principal advantages of this Quadrant over the Davis Quadrant may be summarised as follows:—

1. The instrument was lighter and its operation was much simpler, whereby speed and accuracy in the observation were obtained.

2. The object was viewed directly so that the observer was not obliged to search blindly to allign his instrument to an object behind his back—a difficult operation on a swaying deck.[1]

3. The instrument was capable of fine adjustment, by means of small screws, as in the modern sextant, whereas the Davis Quadrant was incapable of any adjustment and its approximate permanent error could only be found in a most unsatisfactory manner.

4. On account of the principle of double reflection less movement of the index was necessary to obtain the altitude.

Coloured glass shades were fitted to the instrument to protect the eye from the glare of the sun, and on the later instruments the index was fitted with a tangent screw to enable the observer to bring and keep the image of the observed body in contact with the horizon with greater ease and accuracy than had hitherto been possible.

The following advice was given to seamen in the choice of their quadrants by John Hamilton Moore, the author of *The New Practical Navigator*, a book which ran into many editions during the eighteenth and early nineteenth centuries. "The joints of the frame must be close, without the least opening or looseness, and the ivory on the arc and vernier inlaid and fixed, so as not to rise at the ends, nor above the plane of the instrument; all the divisions on the arc and vernier must be exceeding fine and straight, so that when the vernier is set to any division on the arc, the divisions on the arc, the divisions on the line that coincides may appear distinct . . . if the divisions are bad, the quadrant ought to be rejected. Again, look into the index glass slantways, holding it about ten or twelve inches from the eye, and observe the image of some distant object; if the image appears clear and distinct in every part of the glass, the index glass is good; but if it appears notched, or drawn with small lines, the glass is veiny, and must be rejected, if more images than one of the same object are seen, it shews that the two surfaces are not ground

---

[1] By means of an additional vane and mirror it was possible to take backward observations with Hadley's quadrant, but such an operation was only to be recommended when the horizon under the sun was obscured or rendered indistinct by fog or other impediment.

parallel. Observe the sun, or a candle, through the dark glasses severally, holding the glass about eight or ten inches from the eye; if they are veiny, the object will appear notched at the edges, but if clear and well defined, the glasses are good. Most people prefer black ebony, on account of its weight; but I have found by experience, that good mahogany takes the glue and stands the heat better. Quadrants, like watches, may appear well to the eye and yet be good for little; it is therefore much better to give two guineas and a half, or three guineas, for a good one, that will last a man for life, than purchase those wretched instruments, made up at a low price, which cannot be depended on.''

Two facts emerge from the above advice. The first is that the careful navigator of the latter half of the eighteenth century knew what to look for in purchasing his instrument, and was just as particular about its efficiency as any navigator of the present day. The second fact is that a wooden instrument was still preferred by seamen in general, although superior quadrants, for use on scientific expeditions were, by this time, made of brass.

The wooden instrument, whose vernier enabled altitudes to be read to the nearest 30'' of arc, was still a very popular instrument until the latter half of the nineteenth century, while the brass quadrant was not completely overshadowed by the more refined sextant until the beginning of the present century.

Those two eminent writers on navigation during the reign of Queen Victoria, Lieutenant Raper and Captain Lecky, both recommended the use of the quadrant for ordinary use at sea in preference to the sextant, not because the sextant was unfit for such use, but because of that almost loving care which the scientist bestows upon his instruments of precision. Captain Lecky, in his unique work, *Wrinkles in Practical Navigation*, which ran into several editions at the end of the last century, wrote, "The navigator who takes a proper pride in his work should possess a first class sextant . . . . and a good Octant.[1] The latter is fully equal to everyday work in the broad ocean, for example, during the winter months in the North Atlantic. The delicate exactness of the other instrument is quite thrown away when one can only get flying shots at the horizon, from the crest of a 60 feet wave. Showers of salt spray, with the chance of an occasional knock, certainly seem less suited to the sextant than to its hardier and more humble relative.

On the other hand, for fine weather use, for stars, lunars, observations on shore with artificial horizon, for fixing the ship's position in the neighbourhood of land by angles, the sextant is undoubtedly the proper and only reliable instrument.''

---

[1]The Quadrant was really an Octant and, here, Captain Lecky gives it its proper name although in popular speech it has always been called the Quadrant.

The Sextant.—About the middle of the eighteenth century, shortly after the introduction of Hadley's Quadrant, the need for a more accurate instrument, on the same principle of construction, was felt by scientists and the more scientific navigators, including Captain James Cook, to assist them in their surveying and, more especially, in finding the longitude of a place by lunar observations. This need was met by the sextant which, as its name implies, was the sixth part of a circle, whereas the Quadrant, or more properly, the Octant, was the eighth part of a circle. Because of the principle of double reflection, the arc of the sextant was divided into 120°, which gave a greater range of angles than the Quadrant, whose limit was 90°. It may be said that it was simply an extension of the earlier instrument and was, by means of closer marking on the arc, capable of recording angles with greater accuracy.

As the sextant was particularly devised to measure the distance of the moon from the sun or a star, in order to find the longitude by lunar observation, and great accuracy was essential, the arc and the vernier were so graduated as to enable an angle to be read to the nearest 10″ of arc. As the Quadrant was, in general, only capable of showing the nearest minute, or, at the best, the nearest 30″, the superiority of the one over the other in accuracy is at once apparent.

Differing from the Quadrant in other respects, the sextant was, from the first, usually made of metal and not wood. It was, almost from its inception, furnished with a tangent screw, by means of which the index could be moved slowly and regularly, to make the contact of the limbs of any two objects, such as the moon and a star, as perfect as the eye could distinguish, when assisted with one of the telescopes which was supplied with the instrument.

By the beginning of the nineteenth century, at the latest, a good sextant was supplied, as it is to-day, with two telescopes and a dark tube without lenses. The one telescope showed the objects in their natural position, and the other was of the usual astronomical type which inverted the objects viewed through it. By means of these the adjusting of the line of sight parallel to the plane of the instrument was performed and, in observing for a lunar, the all important accuracy of contact was rendered more certian.

The four well-known and necessary adjustments of the sextant were the same 150 years ago as they are at the present time, and they were carried out in the same way. Further adjustments were necessary in the Quadrant owing to the additional mirror and vane which were fitted to enable the observer to take backward observations.

The four adjustments of the sextant were:—

(1) To set the Index glass perpendicular to the plane of the sextant.

(2) To set the Horizon glass perpendicular to the plane of the sextant.

(3) To set the Horizon glass parallel to the Index glass when zero on the index (or vernier) was at zero on the arc.

(4) To make the line of collimation[1] parallel to the plane of the sextant.

Although the Quadrant remained a popular instrument for ordinary use at sea until the closing decades of the last century, the sextant was, in all its essentials, ready for the use of the navigator who desired it, before Nelson met his death at Trafalgar. The reason for the continued popularity of Hadley's Quadrant, in spite of the superior precision of the sextant, was probably that for observations for latitude it served the purpose well enough, and the tedious operation of observing lunars and resolving an approximate longitude from them at sea did not commend itself to the majority of seamen.

The Application of the Artificial Horizon to the Quadrant and Sextant.— Within recent years a means has been found of fitting an artificial horizon to the sextant, whereby fairly reliable altitudes may be taken at sea, or in the air, without recourse to the visible horizon, and it is therefore of interest to examine some of the earlier attempts to produce this result.

In 1732, about a year after Hadley presented his paper on the Quadrant to the Royal Society, the inventor of a "New Quadrant for taking altitudes without a horizon", John Elton by name, placed his proposals before the Society.[2]

In this instrument, the visible horizon was dispensed with by fitting two spirit levels at right angles to each other, which were designed, when properly levelled, to enable the observer to attain a line of sight parallel to the plane of the visible horizon. When this was accomplished it was only necessary to move the index bar until the reflection of the observed object was seen in the centre of the horizon glass.

Contemporary writers, however, paid no attention to this invention, and it may safely be assumed that it was never adopted for use at sea, probably because to obtain accuracy long levels had to be used which would be almost impossible to reconcile on board ship. The slightest movement of the ship and even a tremor of the hand would be sufficient to upset the reliability of the instrument.

About twenty years later, a most careful writer on navigation, John Robertson, F.R.S., in his *Elements of Navigation*, wrote in a most confident manner upon another type of artificial horizon, prefacing his description as follows: "One great inconvenience that mariners have to struggle with at sea is the frequent want of an horizon: for tho' the atmosphere may, at the height of 10 or 12 degrees and upwards, be clear enough to give a view of the

---

[1]The line of collimation is an imaginary straight line joining the centre of refractions of the object glass of a telescope and either the intersection of the cross wires, or the middle between the parallel wires of the telescope.

[2]*Philosophical Transactions*, 1732.

sun or other objects, yet all below that height is oft so hazy as to hinder a distinct sight of the horizon; and consequently an observation made at such a time cannot have the correctness wished for: But this defect is quite removed by a kind of horizontal speculum invented by Mr. Serson, who was lost with the *Victory*, man-of-war, wherein he was sent to make trial of his machine."

The principle of this machine was that a spinning top tended to remain steady in one position, and if a top, whose upper surface was a flat polished speculum, was to have a sufficient circular motion imparted to it, that speculum, when it was given a truly horizontal position would, so long as it maintained sufficient speed, retain its position irrespective of outside influences such as a rolling ship. It would then show all objects, which it reflected, as much below the horizon, as they were in fact above it, in the same way as in an ordinary mirror; consequently if the sun were reflected in this polished metal disc and the sun's image viewed in Hadley's Quadrant was made to coincide with it, the angle shown by the quadrant would be double the altitude. A great advantage of this method was that all undetermined instrumental and personal errors would be halved when the observed altitude of the sun's image was halved.

On the death of Mr. Serson, John Smeaton, F.R.S., improved the instrument and produced a well polished speculum of about $3\frac{1}{2}$ inches in diameter enclosed within a brass rim placed at right angles to the axis of the top. The centre of gravity of the top was placed near its spinning point to assist the axis of the instrument to assume the vertical when it was spun. The top was spun upon a cup of polished agate, flint or other hard substance, and the whole was contained in a box fitted with a pyramidal glass roof to protect the speculum from the effects of moist air or sea spray.

When the top was to be used for a meridian observation of the sun the observer was advised to start it spinning a few minutes before the sun reached the meridian, as the top would run for 12 to 15 minutes, but to safeguard against the result of it running down before the observation was complete, the tape had to be kept ready to give it a second spin without loss of time.

As soon as the top was spinning, and the glass roof put over it if necessary, the observer had to place himself in a convenient position and bring the image of the sun down to its reflection in the horizontal speculum, so that their centres coincided. From the quadrant was then read the double altitude of the sun, which, without any correction for height of eye or semi diameter of the sun, was halved to give the altitude.[1] Although a certain trembling in the images would be noticed, the observer was advised to pay no heed to it, provided the two centres coincided, for the observation would be as accurate as if there was no such trembling.

[1]Corrections for Refraction and Parallax had still to be applied to obtain the true altitude

Robertson evidently thought a great deal of this invention for he concluded his description with the following words, "As the great distresses to which ships are sometimes drove in several parts of the world for want of an horizon to observe by, are by this most ingenious contrivance quite removed, it is to be hoped that when the use of this instrument is more generally known, few ships will be without one, altho' the expense should amount to five guineas."

It is evident, however, that this instrument did not fulfil the great things expected of it, for the later writers on navigation did not even refer to it, except Raper, in 1852, who wrote, "It has also been attempted, but without success, to employ the principle upon which a top while spinning tends to preserve a vertical position, by balancing a horizontal mirror on a pivot, and causing it to revolve with great velocity." No reason is ascribed for its failure, but it is probable that the greatest difficulty was experienced in getting the top to assume a truly vertical position at the beginning, and even more difficult to correct its bearing in space once it had been spun and incorrectly placed out of the true vertical. The trembling of the images, too, referred to by Robertson, may not have enhanced its reputation in the eyes of critical observers.

The next serious attempts to provide the navigator with an artificial horizon at sea are referred to by Raper in his *Practice of Navigation*.[1] Two methods were tried, the one by means of the surface of a viscid fluid, and the other by a mirror attached to a pendulum, which by its weight, hung vertically.

As to the first method, Raper reports unfavourably, although oil had sometimes been used with success; he also says that treacle had been recommended and that it was said to be improved by a mixture of spirit.[2] His criticism of this method was not unfounded, for, as he said, "These viscid substances, from not being sensible to minute vibrations, may perhaps be serviceable in a uniform temperature; but when exposed to the strong heat of the sun, the fluidity varies, and the vessel itself may likewise, by unequal expansion, alter its form. Also the surface, after disturbance of whatever kind, recovers itself the more slowly as it tends to the true level; and this mechanical condition must, in cases where precision is aimed at, throw a doubt over all results obtained from any fluid whose constitution is not that of extreme fluidity."

The second method, too, was not free from error, for "With regard to the

---

[1] This outstanding work, which was first published in 1840 ran into four editions within 12 years of publication.

[2] The writer himself knows of one old sailing-ship master who, on more than one occasion, made use of a bucket of molasses to obtain the meridian altitude of the sun when fog had obscured the horizon for some days, and who described the results obtained as "far better than nothing."

motion of a pendulum", wrote Raper, "it is important to observe that when the ship comes to the end of her roll or lurch, it does not at once rest in the vertical position, but continues to move onwards, or to swing, with the velocity which it had before the ship's motion was destroyed; hence the pendulum moves through greater angles than the ship."

We learn, however, that Commander Becher, R.N., by combining the good points of both methods, produced a device, whereby altitudes at sea could be measured, without reference to the visible horizon, with sufficient accuracy for ordinary navigation, provided the motion of the ship was not excessive. Outside the horizon glass of the sextant he fitted a small pendulum, $1\frac{1}{2}$ inches long, which was suspended in oil. To this he attached a horizontal arm, carrying at the inner end a straight slip of metal, the upper edge of which represented the horizon, when the instrument was held in the true vertical.

Captain Beechey, another officer in the Royal Navy, also produced a variant of the last-mentioned method. Within the telescope of the sextant he fitted a balance, carrying a glass vane, one half of which was coloured blue, to represent the sea horizon, and to which the celestial object was brought down. The amount of oscillation above and below the level was indicated by divisions on the glass, the values of which were determined by the maker. The instructions issued for using this device were as follows:— "Bring down the object, as the sun's limb, to the edge of the blue and leave it there. As the ship rolls, catch with the eye the upper and lower divisions reached by the object and call them out to an assistant, who writes them down with the time against each. When two or more such readings have been taken, read off the altitude and write it down. Take the mean of the readings of the vane and turn it into arc according to the scale furnished. When the mean is above the edge, add it, when below, subtract it. Apply the maker's index error; the result is the apparent altitude, being clear of dip.

e.g.—Took an altitude, and readings as follows: the divisions 12′ each.

h.	m.	s.	Divisions				°	′	″
10	50	0	$(+1)$ above	⎫		Observed			
	50	30	$(-1\frac{1}{2})$ below	⎪ the blue		Altitude	20	25	20
	50	50	$(+1\frac{1}{2})$ above	⎬ edge.		Mean of			
	51	20	(-2) below	⎭		Divisions		−6	
							20	19	20
						Maker's Index			
						Error			−40
						Apparent			
						Altitude	20	18	40

Mean 10 50 40 $(-\frac{1}{2})$, $2\frac{1}{2}$ above, $3\frac{1}{2}$ below; diff. 1 below; the half is $\frac{1}{2}$ of 12′ or 6′ to be subtracted."

G

We are told that with practice the instrument afforded considerable accuracy; and in smooth water the mean of some altitudes was within 2'. It was recommended for use in fog (when, as a rule, there is no excessive movement of the ship) and also on moonlight nights when the horizon was uncertain.

It seems, however, that none of these devices was ever really taken up sea by the ordinary practical navigator, and Raper, himself concludes his description of them with the laconic sentence, "These instruments are very convenient on shore."

Some Uses of the Terrestrial Globe in Navigation.—The principal uses of the globes, both celestial and terrestrial, have always been instructional. The terrestrial globe was recommended to such uses during the first century A.D. by the great geographer Strabo (c. 60 B.C.—A.D. 24) who wrote, "whoever would represent the real earth as near as possible by artificial means, should make a globe . . . and upon this describe the quadrilateral within which his chart of geography is to be placed."[1]

On account of the relative smallness of a globe to the earth, which it was supposed to represent, he advised a globe of a diameter of not less than 10 feet.

The object of Strabo was to demonstrate the convergence of the meridians towards the Poles, and he was not concerned with the solution of the problems of the practical navigator. The celestial globe had been in existence for several centuries before Strabo, and had been used by astronomers for demonstration and experiment. It was not, however, until the fifteenth century A.D. that the terrestrial globe made a permanent appearance to assist the navigator at sea. In the same year that Columbus sailed to the west, Martin Behaim produced a terrestrial globe (a replica of which is in the home of the Royal Geographical Society in London) and he was followed by others during the sixteenth century. Towards the end of this century the terrestrial globe was well known in England, and several English writers wrote upon its instructional uses at some length.[2]

The first English seaman to advocate its adoption at sea as an instrument of practical navigation was John Davis, and it is not without interest that we find that his reasons for such adoption, at the end of the sixteenth century, were the same as those of Strabo when he recommended it for illustrative purposes. Each, in his sphere, appreciated the difficulties which beset the navigator or geographer in his work in high latitudes owing to the convergence of the meridians towards the Poles.

---

[1] *The Geography of Strabo*, Book II., Chapter V., Bohn Edition MDCCCLIV.

[2] The most comprehensive writer upon it was Robert Hues, whose *Tractatus de Globis* appeared in 1592. See Hues *Treatise on the Globe*, (Hakluyt Society 1889).

In presenting his case for the existence and exploration of the North West Passage, Davis raised the objections against it, and then answered them, giving his reasons why navigators should and could continue to search for it. One of the points he discussed was the difficulty of representing the higher latitudes, upon a plane surface, with sufficient accuracy to insure laying off and keeping a correct course. His own words upon this are well worth repeating. He said "Yet in that part of the world Navigation cannot be performed as ordinarily it is used, for no ordenarie sea chart can describe those regions either in the partes Geographicall or Hydrographicall, where the Meridians doe so spedily gather themselves togeather, the parallels beeing a verye small proportion to a great circle, where quicke and uncertayne variation of the Compasse may greatly hinder or utterly overthrow the attempt. So that for lack of Curious lyned globes to the right use of Navigation; with many other instruments either unknowne or out of use, and yet of necessitie for that voyage, it should with great difficultie be attayned."

His answer to this objection was as follows: "And now as touching the last objection that the want of skill in Navigation with curious instruments should be the hinderance or overthrow of this action, I holde that to bee so frivolous as not worth the answering, for it is well knowne that we have globes in the most excellent perfection of arte, and have the use of them in as exquisite sort as master Robert Hues in his book of the globes use, lately published, hath at large made knowne, and for Horizontal paradox and great circle sayling I am myselfe a witnesse in the behalfe of many that we are not ignorant of them, as lately I have made known in a briefe treates of Navigation naming it the Seamans Secrets. And therefore this, as the rest breadeth no hinderance to this most commodious discovery."[1]

The terrestrial globe of Davis did not differ in its essentials from the globes made to-day. Upon a sphere of convenient size was drawn the configuration of the lands and seas, as they were known, in their relative sizes, forms and situations. It was supported in its stand by the Brazen Meridian, a brass ring, graduated in degrees, which was attached to the sphere by two pins, one at each Pole, upon which it was free to revolve. At the North Pole was fixed a small brass circle, called the hour circle or wheel, graduated in hours, halves and quarters which, though not absolutely necessary, was a convenient way to measure time when the problem to be solved called for it.

The Rational Horizon, *i.e.*, the horizontal plane through the centre of the Earth, was represented by the upper surface of the wooden circular frame

---

[1]*The Voyages & Works of John Davis*, Hakluyt Society, 1880. Horizontal Paradox Sayling or Paradoxall Navigation is a term only used by Davis, to describe sailing on a rhumb line, which in ordinary language means the setting of a course upon a Mercator chart, which cuts every m eridian at the same angle.

Terrestial Globe.

By kind permission of the Royal Geographical Society.

which, when the north Pole of the globe was elevated to 90°, circumscribed the globe at the Equator. Upon this wooden frame were drawn several concentric circles, the number of which varied according to its size, and the ingenuity of the individual globe maker. Some of the later globes, used in the nineteenth century for instruction, had as many as eight concentric circles.

Measurement along these circles usually began at the two slots cut in the horizon frame through which the Brazen Meridian passed, and which represented the north and south points respectively of the horizon.

The eight concentric circles mentioned above were marked in the following way:—

The first circle was divided into four quadrants, marked in degrees, beginning at the east and west points of the Horizon, for the measurement of amplitude, which is begun at these points and not.at the north and south points.

The second circle was also divided in the same way, only the graduations were begun at the north and south points, for the measurement of azimuth.

The third circle was divided into the 32 points of the compass subdivided into half and quarter points.

The fourth was divided into the 12 signs of the Zodiac, and the fifth contained the degrees of each sign, i.e., 30° to each.

The sixth gave the days of the month answering to each degree of the place of the sun in the ecliptic.[1]

The seventh contained the equation of time, or difference of time shown by a clock keeping accurate mean time and the time shown by the sun upon a correct sun dial throughout the year.

The eighth contained the 12 calendar months, June being at the north point of the horizon and December at the south.

It will be seen that the eight circles contained several refinements which were unnecessary, but they have been given here to show the many uses to which the Horizon frame could be put.

The principal requirement of the Horizon of the globe was that it should be divided into quadrants showing every degree, and this is the only circle with which the navigator was really concerned when solving his problems at sea.

The globe was furnished with a Quadrant of Altitude, which was a curved metal strip whose inside curve was produced by a radius equal to the radius of the globe. It represented the quarter of a great circle and was

---

[1]The great circle of the ecliptic, i.e., the apparent annual path of the sun which cuts the celestial equator or equinoctial at an angle of 23° 28′, was marked upon all terrestrial globes. The equator of the globe could, of course, be made to represent the equinoctial when required.

graduated into 90°, equal to those on the Brazen Meridian. At one end of it was a screw and nut, by means of which it could be secured to the Brazen Meridian at any desired point. Its principal function was to represent a vertical circle passing through any given point. In the later globes this strip was lengthened to measure 18° below the horizon in order to solve twilight problems: astronomical twilight lasting until the sun is 18° below the horizon.

In the days of Davis, when the plane chart was universally used and the Mercator chart was yet in its infancy, a good globe was the only means whereby the navigator could sail in high latitudes and preserve any idea of the relative positions of the places at which he touched, or lay a course and find his distance with any accuracy.

It would be incorrect to say that through the globe he solved his difficulties entirely or that by its use he achieved great accuracy in his navigation, for the size of globe convenient for use on shipboard was too small to admit of great refinement. It was, however, simple to use and gave a clear picture of the surface of the earth over which he sailed. By constantly having before him the true form of the earth and the daily position of the sun in the celestial concave he acquired a full appreciation of the elements of nautical astronomy and the apparent motion of the celestial bodies which, except for the compass, were his only guides in uncharted waters. With ever-growing ingenuity and resource, and with a firm grasp of first principles, which might be envied by any navigator to-day, Davis and his scientifically-minded contemporaries tested the theories of the mathematicians and astronomers in the exacting school of experience upon the high seas, and laid the foundations of modern deep sea navigational practice. It must be remembered that Davis and other Elizabethan explorers were somewhat in advance of their time. The navigator as a rule was very conservative and cared little for principles. In fact we find in a letter written about 100 years later to the Earl of Northumberland by Mr. Graves, a contemporary of Pepys, that globes should be carried at sea, "The general omission of carrying which . . . has occasioned that so few understand the principles and ground of their profession."

Other writers contemporary with Davis did not urge the use of the globe at sea with the same strength. They were content to dwell more on the theory of it than its practical use to the navigator. Davis, however, who was one of the finest practical navigators of his time, whose repeated voyages to discover the North West Passage impressed upon him the advantages of the globe when navigating in high latitudes, where cloud and fog so often obscured the sun; where the variation of the compass altered so rapidly, and where the rapid convergence of the meridians made the plane chart useless, pointed out to the seaman the real benefits he could gain by its use.

It was through the globe, too, that the advantages of Great Circle sailing over Plane Sailing were thoroughly realised by the more enlightened Elizabethan navigator, though there is little convincing evidence that he used it much in practice. The idea was not new, for the mathematician had long ago discovered that a great circle was the shortest distance between two points on a sphere. Contrary winds, and, as will be seen later, the advantages to the earlier navigator of parallel sailing usually precluded him from taking advantage of great circle sailing. Nevertheless, it must not be forgotten that through the globe he well understood its principles and could find the initial course and distance with surprising ease and tolerable accuracy.

This he did in the following way. He extended his dividers between the two places and then applied them to the scale of degrees marked along the equator. By multiplying the resultant degrees and fractions of a degree by 60 he obtained the distance in nautical miles.

To find the initial course he elevated the pole of the globe equal to the latitude of the place of departure and brought that place to the Brazen Meridian by rotating the globe upon its north and south axis. This operation was known as rectifying the globe. The flexible Quadrant of Altitude was then screwed to the Brazen Meridian, over that place, and moved east or west until its edge passed over the other place. The number of degrees between the Brazen Meridian and the Quadrant of Altitude measured along the wooden horizon was the required course.

In order to keep to the Great Circle track, which necessitates constant alterations of course, Davis advised the navigator to repeat the above operation after sailing every 20 or 30 leagues until he reached his destination.

One of the most important problems in northern latitudes, where the variation altered quickly as a ship progressed easterly or westerly, was to find the true bearing of the sun in order to find the error of the compass. This could be done in the following way:—

The appropriate Pole of the globe was elevated equal to the latitude of the place of observation and the Quadrant of Altitude was screwed on to the Brazen Meridian over that latitude. The sun's position in the Ecliptic for the particular day was brought to the Brazen Meridian and the index of the Hour Circle set to XII hours. The globe was then turned on its axis and the Quadrant of Altitude moved about its pivot at the zenith until the sun's place in the Ecliptic coincided with its altitude which had been marked on the Quadrant of Altitude (the Quadrant was graduated from 0° at the horizon to 90° at the zenith).[1] The index of the Hour Circle then showed the number

---

[1] Before this problem could be solved the sun's altitude was observed by the astrolabe or cross staff, and at the same time its bearing by compass was taken. It will be appreciated that the above operation was nothing more than the graphical solution of the well-known Altitude Azimuth problem.

of hours and quarters before or after noon, and the azimuth was found by reading the number of degrees along the Horizon between the Brazen Meridian and the Quadrant of Altitude, which, in effect, was the vertical circle passing through the zenith and the observed sun.

In this way, as will be seen by reference to the diagram below, the terrestrial globe was used as the celestial sphere to form and solve the familiar spherical triangle *PZX*; where *P* is the elevated pole, *Z* the observer's zenith and *X* the position of the celestial body at the time of observation.

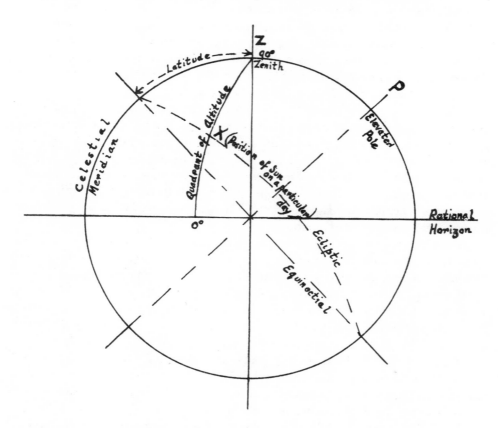

By similar ingenious uses of the globe the navigator could find his approximate latitude by other means than the meridian altitude of the sun. He observed the bearing of the sun at its rising or setting and corrected it for variation to find its true bearing. From his astronomical tables he found the sun's place in the Ecliptic at the date of observation, and by elevating or depressing the Pole and adjusting the globe he brought the sun's place, which he had marked on the ecliptic, to coincide with its true bearing (measured along the Horizon) at the Horizon. The resultant elevation of the Pole of the globe was equivalent to his latitude.

If the sun was above the Horizon he observed its altitude, and then with the assistance of the Quadrant of Altitude to indicate its height above the wooden Horizon of the globe and also its true bearing along the wooden Horizon (provided he knew the variation of his compass) he found his latitude by elevating or depressing the Pole until the position of the sun in the Ecliptic coincided with its altitude and bearing shown by the Quadrant of Altitude.

John Davis remarked, however, that because large errors might be committed in the above solutions unless the variation of the compass was accurately known, it was well to know how to find the latitude without relying upon a knowledge of the variation.

This was done by taking two observations of the sun for altitude, and at the same times taking the compass bearings, with an interval of an hour or two between them in order to give the sun time to alter its bearing by a point or two. The globe was then set to the approximate latitude and the sun's place in the Ecliptic made to coincide with its altitude above the Horizon, measured on the Quadrant of Altitude. When this was accomplished, the number of degrees between the Quadrant and the Brazen Meridian was noted along the Wooden Horizon.

The same operation was repeated for the second observation, and if the arc of the Horizon between the two observations agreed with the difference in the two compass bearings, the assumed latitude was correct. If they did not agree, then another latitude had to be assumed and the whole operation repeated until the differences in bearings did agree.

It was also possible to solve the same problem by measuring the interval of time between the two observations for latitude with a "good hower glasse, half hower glasse and minute glasse." The sun's place in the Ecliptic was brought to the Brazen Meridian and a piece of blacklead was held in that position while the globe was revolved. This traced upon the globe a small circle of declination of the sun for the material date. Upon this circle were marked two positions of the sun, one for each observation, the distance between them being measured along the Equator by turning time into degrees and minutes of arc in the proportion of 24 hours to 360°. As in the last problem the Pole was elevated to the approximate latitude, the Quadrant of Altitude was pivoted at the zenith and when the first position of the sun on the small circle coincided with its altitude on the Quadrant, and the second position of the sun with its second altitude, the resultant elevation of the Pole was the required latitude.

In another part of his *Seaman's Secrets* Davis explained why he searched for these means of finding latitude by day without relying solely upon the sun's meridian altitude "For," said he, "I have been constrayned in my north-west voyages, beying within the frozen zone, to search the latitude by the sun at such times as I could see the sun upon what point of the Compasse soever, by reason of the great fogges and mistes that those Northern partes are subject unto."

The foregoing solutions require no apology for their inaccuracies, which were to be expected when men worked with imperfect data and faulty instruments. That through the globe they realised the true principles of their art is the point to be remembered, and it may be with some regret that we realise that such instruments were relegated to the academies ashore by the general introduction of mathematical tables, during the latter half of the seventeenth century, which brought in their train long and complicated rule of thumb methods. Such methods, however accurate, reliable and necessary, resulted in a parrot-like repetition of rules which hid from many navigators the simple truths of Nautical Astronomy upon which the safe and speedy conduct of their ships depended.

PART II.

OCEAN NAVIGATION.

CHAPTER I.

INTRODUCTION.

THE principal implements of the navigator having been dealt with, it remains to enquire what use he made of them and how he found his way at sea when the land was left behind. It was not every seaman who took readily to the improvements and additions to the instruments and methods of navigation. Indeed, many resented the encroachment of the mathematician and scientist into the realm of the Ocean Sea which they regarded as peculiarly their own. It was, as already remarked in the previous chapter, the great discoverers who first enlisted the aid of the learned theorists ashore, and that is doubtless why so many of them succeeded in a work where narrower minds and poorer intellects would have failed. Such work which always called for the finest seamanship, a blend of daring and prudence, at the same time demanded a thorough knowledge of all that was best in navigation and nautical astronomy. Such knowledge helped the navigator to be daring with confidence and discretion.

Many of the less gifted navigators were slow to forsake the habits which their fathers had passed on to them and were suspicious of improvement and jealous of custom. The ritual at noon which is still observed in many ships to-day for the taking of the sun's meridian altitude is evidence that old customs suffer very slow changes at sea. Unlike many customs, however, this one at least has some reasons for its continued popularity. Its very simplicity probably makes it difficult for many to withstand carrying out that sound maxim of good seamanship which tells the mariner never to neglect an opportunity of verifying his position.

Yet there was a time when such an operation was scoffed at by many for being something new, and even the use of charts derided as a "new school trick." Although Columbus, Vasco da Gama and other navigators of the fifteenth century—chiefly Portuguese and Spanish, who are nameless— used charts and took observations of the sun for latitude with success, we find it recorded, over 100 years later, by William Bourne, that many seamen laughed at those who copied their illustrious predecessors. He wrote, "For this is general amongst seamen and also gunners how simple or without skill soever that they be, if that they have once taken charge to be master of a shippe he thinketh great scorne to learne at any man's hand, but will bragge of himself how long he hath beene a master and God knoweth utterly without skill, but that he is a coaster and doth know the markes for to carry a shippe over the landes ende . . . but good simple menne, if that they could not doe that, then there were nothing in them, for every man must needes be skillfull and know that place that a number of times he hath occupied and hath beene taught unto him.

"And who doubteth but a simple fisherman of Barking knoweth Barking Creeke better than the best navigator or master in this lande: so who doubteth but these simple men doth know their owne places at home. But if they should come out of the Ocean Sea to seek our Channell, to come unto the River of Thames, I am of that opinion that a number of them doeth but grope as a blinde man doth, and if that they doe hit well, that it is but by chance and not by any cunning that is in him.

"But I doe hope that in these daies that the knowledge of the masters of shippes is verie well mended, for I have knowen within this 20 yeeres that them that were ancient masters of shippes hath derided and mocked them that have occupied their cardes and plattes (charts) and also the observation of the altitude of the Pole saying that they care not for their sheepes skinnes (charts of parchment) for hee could keepe a better account upon a board.

"And when that they dyd take the latitude they would call them starre shooters and sunne shooters and would aske if they had striken it. Wherefore now judge of their skills considering that these two points is the principall matters in navigation. And yet these simple people will make no small bragges of themselves, saying that hee hath beene master this twenty yeeres and never had no misfortune and also if that they could heere of any that dyd use plats and instruments that had any misfortune then they would not a little brag of themselves what notable fellowes they themselves were.

"O what a notable folly was in these men, not considering what they themselves were. For this is most certaine, that it is not wisedome nor cunning, that can prevent nor alter God's providence, if that it pleaseth him to lay his scourge upon us . . ."[1]

Edward Wright, in his *Certain Errors in Navigation*, in 1599, referred to the same attitude of many seamen who said they had always performed their work successfully without charts and observations for latitude and were too old to change their ideas. Wright ended on a grim note, "But mark what cometh hereof: for one of these masters was he, as I take it, of whom an ancient seaman, yet living as I think, once told me, who having undertaken

[1] *A Regiment of the Sea*, by William Bourne, 1573.

the charge of conducting a ship from England to St. Michaels (in the Azores), and, after long seeking, not able to find it, for shame and sorrow cast himself overboard."

These words were written at the ending of the period which marked the change from haphazard and point to point navigation where the only guide was the compass, to the bold striking out across uncharted seas, where the mariner had need of some means of finding his position. Where the Portuguese and Spaniards had led the mariners of Holland, France and England followed, and Europe was in general becoming more and more enlightened as to the possibilities of searching beyond the horizon's rim. We must not blame the lesser gifted navigators too much for their attitude towards innovations which they could not understand. Though many books were written on navigation during the latter years of the sixteenth century they were inaccessible to most on account of their lack of learning. Various suggestions were put forward in England for the establishment of a college of navigation based on the lines of the school promoted by Prince Henry of Portugal over 100 years before. Nothing came of them and the British seamen in general were left to learn the rudiments of their art as best they could. Prejudice was strong against book learning, however, and the lack of proper communication between the bulk of practical seamen and the scholars led to a position of stalemate.

Sir William Monson (1569-1643) who fought against the Armada, and later became an admiral, was one of several who raised his voice at this time for the setting up of a lectureship of Navigation. He pointed out that as England was an island she should maintain her shipping and that ships without men to conduct them were useless. He complained that England had not respected the instruction of her mariners. He admitted that some help was to be derived from the writings of others, but the ordinary mariner was often ignorant of what he read and therefore it would be better to demonstrate it to him and have its meaning made plain. Urging the desirability for England to exceed others in navigation, he regretted the frequent controversies between the scholar and the seaman. "I confess," wrote he, "this is a great arrogancy in both to stand so obstinately upon themselves when they ought in reason one to assist the other, but especially the mariner is to receive comfort from the scholar, for he that has but bare experience receives what he hath by tradition, for learning is the original ground of all arts; but he that has his experience joined with learning, it makes that man excellent and the art he professes. What made Abraham Kendall and Mr. John Davies so famous in navigation but their learning which was confirmed by experience . . . Men of learning more able to give light for the finding out the longitude and for the discovery of new lands or passages which experience must beat out when they have their ground from learned men." With the over emphasis of the reformer he agreed with the mathematicians that there was no certainty in the Art of Navigation as practised by ordinary masters. There never can be absolute certainty in an art which has to contend with so many imperfectly known elements. No one, however, can disagree with him when he complained that it was common for several mariners in the same ship, after being any time at sea, between England and the Azores, to differ from each other as to their position up to 60 leagues.

In conclusion, he wrote, "Imagine by this what danger every ship is in that goes from England and comes home again, which to men of understanding is a wonder that more ships do not miscarry considering the danger of our coast. It is not Art but Fear and Care that preserves them . . . the masters having so provident a care and so great a mistrust in their own art, as though they observe the sun and stars never so exactly they will not presume to bear in with the land which they have not made, except the coast be clear and the wind large to claw it off again." In his zeal, Monson, did not refrain from criticising the prudence of the "star shooting" navigators, but as his purpose was to bring about a general improvement in the whole art of navigation his attitude is easy to understand. "If", said he, "the Art can be made perfect and the errors corrected . . . it will prove a happy thing to all seamen and by consequence to the whole Commonwealth."[1]

While the Elizabethan seamen were adapting themselves to deep sea navigation, a Scottish laird, John Napier, was quietly engaged in perfecting a system whereby large numbers of figures could be multiplied and divided with ease and certainty and without troublesome or tedious calculation. In 1614, after many years of labour, he published tables which every seaman was, in the course of time, to know as tables of logarithms. It was not, however, the tables of Napier that were adopted but those of Henry Briggs, who suggested to Napier, and finally published tables of logarithms having 10 for their base.

About the same time, Edmund Gunter, another mathematician, produced a table of logarithm sines and tangents which were destined to revolutionise the practice of navigation.

It will be remembered that Edward Wright, in 1599, expounded the true principles for the construction of the Mercator chart; so with truth it may be said that during the early decades of the seventeenth century navigation began to be considered as an art dependant to a great extent upon mathematical principles.

Little heed was taken of these principles by the ordinary navigator, and it was not until the beginning of the eighteenth century that there was

---

[1] Brit. Mus. ADD: MSS. 30221.

any general movement towards the new learning. The use of the plane chart and an observation for latitude at noon were the customary means by which ships were navigated during the seventeenth century.

Dr. Halley, who later became Astronomer Royal, was requested by Mr. Pepys to investigate the prevalent practice of navigation. In a letter dated 17th February, 1695, Halley, in reporting his conclusions to Pepys remarked: "Your Honour is not unacquainted with the methods used by masters of ships to find their ports and you will know how tenaciously or rather obstinately they resolve to make use of no other than the Common Plain Chart as if the earth were a flat, when at the same time they all know and allow that they sail on a Globe, and they content themselves that those that know no more have yet brought their ships home safe. Whence they conclude that any further Art, as they calle it, is superfluous."

In a letter from Mr. Flamsteed, the Astronomer Royal, to Mr. Pepys, dated 21st April, 1697, the state of ignorance of navigators in general was alluded to in terms similar to those used by Dr. Halley. We learn that the attitude of most mariners was that Drake, Cavendish, and other great navigators of the previous century, got on very well without all the new learning that the astronomers and mathematicians wished to teach them, and, continued Flamsteed, "They look upon Fortune as the sole disposer of wealth and honours and despise all that Knowledge and those Merits which contributed not to their wealth and advancement as useless."[1]

In spite of their apparent indifference described above, seamen were beginning to take more interest in the better methods of navigation and, as will be seen later, improved their laying of courses, by adopting Mercator's chart and practising the theory of middle latitude sailing. The seeds of scientific navigation which had been sown durng the seventeenth century chiefly by those whose works have already been referred to, and the keen interest shown in their development by Charles II., resulted in a general improvement in navigational practice during the early years of the eighteenth century. Even the most ill informed navigators forgot to deride their more scientific brethren, and observed the sun at noon with their Davis Quadrants. The search for a reliable method of finding longitude at sea occupied the minds of many scientists, but very few navigators at this time troubled about it. They kept a careful reckoning of their courses and, with the aid of noon observations for latitude, sailed into every sea.

During the eighteenth century numerous treatises on navigation were published. Where, before, book learning had been despised, an ever increasing demand for books obtained. Over 50 different authors produced treatises to improve the knowledge of the seaman, but few of them contributed anything

[1]Brit. Mus., ADD. MSS. 30221.

to clarify the principles or simplify their application. This spate of books, many of which passed into several editions, reduced a living art to an automatic adherence to rules of thumb which effectively obscured the underlying formulae from most seamen. Though nearly every problem depended either upon the simple solutions of plane triangles or the more difficult solutions of spherical triangles, few authors even attempted to explain these facts in simple language to the learner.

The result was that the majority of seamen either solved the more complicated problems by the aid of mathematical tables, without having the slightest idea what they were doing, or they gave up attempting any but the most elementary forms of navigation.

The following is an example of the type of rule given to the seaman without any explanation. It is one of the questions and answers contained in a navigation book "recommended to the perusal of young gentlemen belonging to the sea, in order to refresh their memories, previous to that examination which they must pass through, before they are appointed to a commission in the Royal Navy, or an officer in the East India Service; as it is probable similar ones may be asked by those appointed to examine them, at the Navy Office and the East India House."

Q. How do you find the true azimuth?

A. By adding the complement of the latitude, the complement of the altitude, and the sun or star's polar distance into one sum; from half this sum I subtract the polar distance, noting the half sum and the remainder. Then to the arithmetical complement of the cosine of the latitude, I add the arithmetical complement of the cosine of the altitude; the log sines of the half sum and the remainder; half the sum of these four logarithms will give the cosine of half the true azimuth, which being doubled is the true azimuth, reckoned from north in north latitude, and from south in south latitude.

There were of course exceptions to the usual manner of presenting the subject to the mariner, notable among which was *The Elements of Navigation*, by John Robertson, F.R.S. He was master of the Mathematical School, founded by Charles II., at Christ's Hospital, which school supplied many properly instructed masters to the Navy, during the eighteenth century. These masters, as the navigators of H.M. Ships were called, played a prominent part in the increasing accuracy of charts, and set a standard of professional ability which was unsurpassed elsewhere.

In the preface to his book, Robertson wrote, in 1753, "The maritime parts of this work . . . are delivered in a manner somewhat different from that of other writers on this subject, who, for the most part copying from one another, may be perhaps one reason why the art of navigation has been so little improved within the last 150 years: for excepting what Norwood and Halley have done, the art seems much in the same state in which Wright left it. However, I apprehend that the proper judges will from the method I have taken, find some few improvements, if not in the art itself, at least in the manner of communicating it to learners."

Later, he described the different types of readers he expected would use his treatise and went to some trouble to instruct them in what to read and what to omit. The treatise was made up of IX books, followed by a dissertation on fortification. He divided his probable readers into four groups and addressed each as follows:

"First. Those who having made a proficiency in the mathematics, will, it is likely, examine in what manner the subjects are here treated, and whether anything new is contained therein. It is conceived that such readers will find some things which may recompense them for their trouble, and in almost every one of the books.

"Secondly. Those learners who are desirous of being instructed in the art of navigation in a scientific manner, and would chuse to see the reason of the several steps they must take to acquire it: To such persons, it is recommended that they read the whole book in the order they find it. Or, if the learner is very young, he may omit the fourth book (on spherics) till after he is master of the fifth (Principles of Geography) and sixth (Plane Sailing). Adult persons, and those under the direction of a master, may, if they please read the VIIIth book (Astronomy) immediately after the Vth; and read the VIth, VIIth (Mercator and Great Circle Sailing) and IXth books (of the compass and a ship's reckoning) in succession.

"Thirdly. That class of readers, which, with too much truth may be said, comprehends most of our mariners, who want to learn both the Elements and the Art itself by rote, and never trouble themselves about the reasons of the rules they work by. As there ever will be many readers of this kind, they may be well accommodated in this work; thus, if they are not already acquainted with Arithmetic and Geometry, let them read the five first rules of Arithmetic . . . . thence proceed to the definitions and problems in geometry."

Such a reader was then recommended to read certain pages on Trigonometry which would give him sufficient knowledge to understand the mathematical tables, and then such parts of the remainder of the treatise as were necessary to him.

"Fourthly. That set of Readers who will not be at the pains of learning anything more than how to do the practice of a Day's Work. Such may herein meet with the practice almost independent of other knowledge . . . "

H

The introduction of the chronometer during the latter half of the eighteenth century, and its gradual adoption by all maritime nations during the early part of the next brought the finding of accurate longitudes at sea within measurable distance of attainment. Although many navigators then developed their art to a high degree of excellence, and took the fullest advantage of every benefit conferred by astronomy and mathematics, a great number of ships were navigated principally upon the Day's Work, Meridian altitude of the sun or observation of Polaris for latitude, and an observation of the sun to find the longitude by chronometer. The taking of lunars to find the correct Greenwich time at sea was also practised frequently with varying degrees of accuracy.

The following picture of the procedure in navigation in the Merchant Service, during the middle of the nineteenth century, is given by Dana, the author of *Two Years Before the Mast*.[1] "The master takes the bearing and distance of the last point of departure upon the land, and from that point the ship's reckoning begins and is regularly kept in the log book. The Chief Mate keeps the log book, but the master examines and corrects the reckoning every day. The master also attends to the chronometer, and takes all the observations with the assistance of his officers if necessary. Every day, a few minutes before noon, if there is any prospect of being able to get the sun, the master comes up on deck with his quadrant or sextant, and the chief mate also usually takes his. The second mate does not, except upon a Sunday, or when there is no work going forward. As soon as the sun crosses the meridian 8 strokes are struck on the bell and a new sea day begins. The reckoning is then corrected by the observation under the master's superintendence. The master also takes the lunar observation, usually with the assistance of both his officers: in which case the master takes the angle of the moon with star or sun, the chief mate takes the altitude of the sun or star and the second mate the altitude of the moon."

In spite of the great improvement in the observing instruments, during the nineteenth century, there seems to have been a curious reluctance on the part of many to make use of the stars in their navigation, or even to use the sun to its fullest extent. Admittedly the methods advised for the solution of most of the problems were cumbersome and lengthy, but they should not have accounted wholly for the apathy and suspicion which affected many mariners, traces of which, even in spite of improved tables and methods, existed until the present century.

Captain Lecky, in his *Wrinkles in Practical Navigation*, remarked on it towards the end of the last century in his inimitable way as follows. "There is, unfortunately, among sailors a very general and most erroneous notion

[1] Dana's *Seamen's Manual*, 1841.

that stellar observations and their calculation are something much too high and mighty to be tackled by ordinary mortals and that at least a University education is required to cope with them . . . There is no part of our entire subject which the author is more anxious to press upon the attention of the navigator than this matter of star observation. No reason exists why every man in command should not be thoroughly proficient at it. It is within the reach of all who choose to try: there are, however, men afloat who won't try, and who for downright, double-barrelled, copper-bottomed, bevel-edged bigotry are matchless in all other professions. For such as these this book is not written, as they are hopeless cases, whose pig-headed obstinacy is only equalled by their ignorance. Happily the class will soon become extinct."

He, with other writers of his time, deprecated cramming for examinations without any groundwork of education behind it, and looked forward to the days, which are now with us, "when fuller knowledge would serve to dispel such illusions and every man would be fitted to take advantage of the heavenly bodies which are available for his guidance at all times when visible."

CHAPTER II.

THE FINDING OF LATITUDE.

BEFORE the introduction of the chronometer, the navigator had to rely principally upon his observations for latitude, his true course, and the distance run as near as he could estimate, to take his ship with confidence from one place to another when out of sight of land.

The finding of latitude has never presented the same difficulties to the geographer or the navigator as the finding of longitude. Long before the Christian Era, ancient astronomers discovered the approximate maximum declination of the sun, at the solstices, and the pre-Christian geographers. by comparing the ratio of the shadow cast by the gnomon with its perpendicular height, at the solstices, were able to form fairly accurate ideas of the comparative latitudes of places in the then known habitable world.

By using a form of astrolabe the ancient astronomers were able to discover the latitude of a place, and the sun's declination on any day. Suppose a place where the altitude of the sun at the summer solstice was 74°, at the winter solstice 26° and at the equinox 50°; it followed that the declination

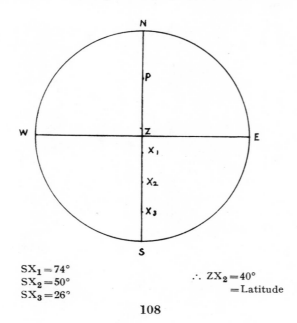

$$SX_1 = 74°$$
$$SX_2 = 50°$$
$$SX_3 = 26°$$

$$\therefore ZX_2 = 40°$$
$$= \text{Latitude}$$

108

of the sun at the solstices was 24° N. or S., and that the latitude of the place was 40° N.[1]

Once having found the latitude of the place, daily observations of the sun at noon enabled the astronomer to compile a table of declinations of the sun for every day of the year.

Such tables existed long before the mariner had need of them, and the Portuguese navigators of the fifteenth century were probably the first European seamen to put them to the test at sea.

The first real test of this new aid to navigation was provided on the first voyage of Columbus in 1492, and it may be said, with truth, that the closing years of the fifteenth century really marked the beginning of the use of observations for latitude in ocean-going ships. Though the tables of declination of the sun lacked the accuracy of those published in later years, and the absence of an efficient timepiece precluded them from accurately interpolating the declination at noon in any longitude; and though their astrolabes and cross staffs were far from being the instruments of precision which were evolved subsequently, the results obtained by those pioneers of deep sea navigation fully justified their use. Given moderate weather an experienced observer at sea was able to calculate his latitude to within 1° or 2° of the truth and on a calm day or on land, to within ½° or less.

Though such approximations would be of little use in modern navigation, it must be remembered that the earlier navigators were fully alive to the limitations of their methods and instruments, and navigated accordingly. In days when cumbersome ships made large leeway, compasses inclined to be erratic, and currents still awaited determination, a knowledge of latitude, even within a few degrees of the truth, was not despised but welcomed by those whose business it was to find new lands, open up new trades, and then return with their news and merchandise to those who had sent them forth.

During the sixteenth century most books on navigation, chiefly of Portuguese or Spanish origin, contained tables of declination of the sun and the following rules for finding the latitude upon observing the sun on the meridian.

If the observer's zenith was between the sun and the equinoctial (celestial equator), *i.e.*, where the declination and the latitude were of the same name and the declination was greater than the latitude, the zenith distance, obtained either directly by observation (for some instruments were so designed) or by subtracting the altitude from 90°, had to be subtracted from the declination to obtain the latitude.

---

[1]The declination of the sun at the solstices was found by some of the ancient astronomers to be 24°. See Strabo (Bohn Edition 1854) Vol. I., p. 173.

If the equinoctial was between the zenith and the sun, *i.e.*, where the declination and latitude were of different names, the declination had to be subtracted from the zenith distance to obtain the latitude.

If the sun was between the zenith and the equinoctial, *i.e.*, where the declination and latitude were of the same name and the latitude was greater than the declination, the zenith distance had to be added to the declination to obtain the latitude.[1]

A fourth proposition was impressed upon seamen by John Davis in his *Seaman's Secrets*: that of finding the latitude by meridian altitude of the sun below the Pole. By reason of his experience in high latitudes he was well qualified to advocate this method to be used when, in the Arctic, the sun bore north at midnight. This method was to subtract the sun's altitude from its declination in order to find how much the equinoctial was below the northern point of the horizon which, of course, was the same amount as the opposite point of the equinoctial was above the horizon. The complement of this was the required latitude.

We find an example of this method actually used by William Barents, in his northern voyage, at about the same time as Davis wrote his "Secrets". In *The Three Voyages of William Barents to the Arctic Regions* (Hakluyt Society, 1876) we read in the account given by Gerrit De Veer—"4th July, 1594, William Barents took the height of the sunne with his cross staff when it was at the lowest (altitude) *i.e.*, between **NNE** and **NE × N** (compass bearing) and found it to be elevated above the horizon 6° and ⅓, his declination being 22° 55′, from whence subtracting the aforesaid height there resteth (remains) 16° 35′ which being subtracted from 90° there resteth **73° 25′**."

A simpler way was to add the complement of the declination to the meridian altitude.

Where H P H_1 S represents the observer's Meridian,

Z	,,	the observer's zenith,
P	,,	the North Pole,
D_1	,,	the sun below the Pole,
Q Q_1	,,	the Equinoctial,
D D_1	,,	the Circle of Declination at the material time,
H H_1	,,	the Horizon

[1]The necessity for a thorough understanding of these rules was impressed upon seamen during the last century, by Raper, who gave the following examples of their wrong application. "A ship, on board which the declination had been applied the wrong way, made the Orkney Islands, in coming from the westward, instead of the Channel. A few years ago a ship bound homewards from Australia round Cape Horn got too far to the southward; a similar blunder was discovered to have been made, but the existence of an error in the latitude was suspected only from the circumstance of the ship being beset with ice."

Latitude = Elevation of the Pole
      $= P H_1$
      $= D_1 H_1 + P D_1$
      = Meridian Altitude + Complement of the Declination

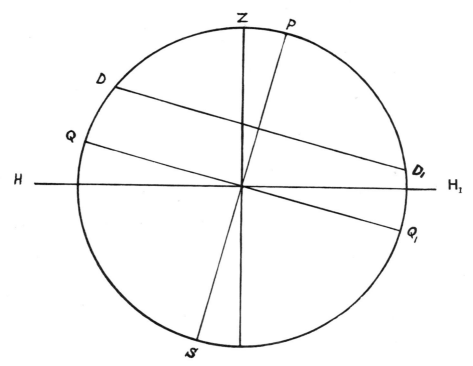

Cortes, a Spanish writer on navigation about the middle of the sixteenth century, described the sun as the mark, guide and governor in navigation, and enumerated the three things necessary to find the latitude by it, as an instrument to take its meridian altitude, a table of declination, and the rules given above.

Thus we find that the seamen discoverers of that century were fully equipped to find their latitude, within limits, in all the navigable oceans, on every day that the sun was visible at noon. It is interesting to note how well some of those seamen succeeded in assigning the latitude to the places at which they touched. We find that during Sir Humphrey Gilbert's voyage to Newfoundland, in 1583, the latitude of Cape Race was found to be 46° 25′ N., and of St. John's 47° 40′ N. Comparison with the correct figures of 46° 39′ N. and 47° 34′ N. shows how near they could approach the truth in spite of their inferior information and instruments.

More than one writer about the end of the sixteenth century pointed out the inaccuracies of some of the declination tables then in use, and advised the navigator always to use the latest tables.[1] During the next century it became the practice to include four separate tables of declination in the books on navigation. The first table gave the declination of the sun for several leap years in advance, the second table gave it for every first year after those leap years, and the third and fourth for every second and third year after the leap years respectively. In this way it was quite common to find one book containing tables of declination for twenty years.[2]

As a result of a more intimate knowledge of the Earth's orbit, and its effect upon the tables of declination, and the increasing accuracy of observing instruments, the navigator of the late eighteenth century was able to find his latitude by meridian altitude of the sun, at sea, with a precision equal to that which is sufficient to-day.

It was during the latter half of the eighteenth century that a variety of other methods were advocated for the finding of latitude without relying upon the meridian altitude of the sun or other celestial body. Just as John Davis had advised the method of finding it by a meridian altitude of the sun below the Pole, on those frequent occasions when cloud or fog made it impossible to observe it above the Pole, so the later writers, realising the importance to the navigator of knowing his latitude accurately, on all occasions, especially when approaching land, evolved other methods to gain this end.

The method, advocated by Davis, of obtaining the latitude by two observations of the sun, with a considerable interval between them, which he solved on the globe, was revived by mathematicians, to be solved with greater accuracy by spherical trigonometry. The calculation, however, was long and tedious, and there is little evidence that this method, or several of the others suggested, were used, except possibly by a few, when the weather prevented them from resorting to the simpler methods.

Latitude by Ex-Meridian Observation.—In spite of the complexity of the method mentioned above, it is probable that it would have achieved some measure of popularity among seamen had it not been for the general adoption of the chronometer during the early years of the nineteenth century. The chronometer opened up realms of nautical astronomy which had hitherto been closed to navigators and, amongst other things, provided another way for the determination of latitude which, in the course of time, was to be used by all seamen and known as the ex-meridian observation.

It so frequently happens during cloudy weather that the sun or other celestial body is visible shortly before it reaches the meridian but is totally

---

[1] Wright's *Errors in Navigation.* Hue's *Treatise on the Globes.*

[2] The greatest error, in accurate tables, would not amount to more than 3·6′ in twenty years. Vide earlier editions of Burdwood's *Azimuth Tables.*

obscured at its culmination. This circumstance was noted by seamen of past generations as well as by those to-day, and as soon as an easy and reliable method was evolved to overcome this aggravating occurrence, they quickly adopted it.

The principle of the Ex-Meridian observation is that as the change of altitude in a celestial body is small as it approaches the meridian it is possible to calculate with accuracy how much it will rise by the time it reaches the meridian. By applying this calculated amount to the altitude of such body at a time when it is near the meridian, its meridian altitude at that place may be known beforehand with sufficient precision without waiting for its meridian passage, and from this altitude the latitude can then be deduced in the way already described.

The above calculation, however, could only be made when the hour angle of the body from the meridian was known with accuracy and, as this could only be known when the longitude of the ship was known, it followed that such a method of finding the latitude was only possible when the reliability of the recently introduced chronometer was established. This, then, was the reason why little mention was made of the Ex-Meridian observation until the early decades of the nineteenth century.

Two solutions of this problem, were presented to the navigator, the one known as the Reduction to the Meridian, and the other the Direct Process. The solution by Reduction was the one already outlined above, and in order to compute the correction to be applied to the altitude it was necessary to use the dead reckoning latitude as one of the elements in the calculation. This necessity presented an objection to the adoption of this method, as a fairly large error in the dead reckoning latitude caused an appreciable error in the results. As an error of only a few miles in the assumed latitude, however, did not affect the calculation, this objection was easily overcome by using the first calculated latitude to obtain a more accurate latitude upon repeating the calculation.

The Direct Process was accomplished by an attractive trigonometrical solution which abolished the necessity for using the dead reckoning latitude. The introduction of Ex Meridian tables, during the latter half of the nineteenth century, which enabled the practical seaman to obtain the necessary correction to be applied to the altitude without recourse to trigonometry, however, relegated the Direct Process to the schoolroom from which it has never again emerged.

The general attitude towards the Ex Meridian problem about the middle of the last century was well described by Raper in his *Practice of Navigation*. He wrote in his preface: "The highly useful problem of determining the latitude at sea by the reduction of an altitude to the meridian, will be found greatly abridged; and a table is added for the purpose of shewing the limits within which the result may be depended upon when the time at ship is in error. This table will be found, it is presumed, of considerable utility, as it is perhaps from the want of some specific information as to the degree of confidence which it is safe to place in the result, no less than of a short and easy rule, that this excellent observation is almost entirely neglected; and, in consequence, the latitude, when the meridian altitude is not exactly obtained, is too often lost for the day.''

As a result of the increasing simplicity of the above-mentioned tables, and after the advent of steam, the comparative shortness of duration of ocean voyages, during which the chronometer had little opportunity to contract any serious error, the finding of latitude by Reduction to the Meridian was well established during the closing years of the nineteenth century.

Latitude by an observation of the Pole Star.—We have already seen in the chapter on Charts that pre-Christian seamen used the constellations of the Great and Little Bears to find the north point of the heavens in order to maintain a course. How soon they used a polar star to give them some idea of their latitude must remain a matter for conjecture. Certain it is, however, that by the time of Columbus the use of Polaris for finding the approximate latitude was appreciated by some seamen. It is probable that the first application of Polaris to the problem of latitude at sea was to use it to compare the latitude of one place with another. By means of such comparison the coasting mariner then knew whether to sail north or south to arrive at a given place.

On the voyage undertaken by Cadamosto, a Venetian seaman, who explored part of the west coast of Africa, at the instance of Prince Henry of Portugal, about the middle of the fifteenth century, we are told, with reference to the Gambia River, that during the days spent at its mouth (lat. 13° 23' N.) the Pole Star was only seen once, and that it appeared very low down over the sea, about one third of a lance length above the horizon. Other places, too, were distinguished by the lowness at which the North Star appeared in the sky.[1]

Columbus certainly used the Pole Star to gain some idea of his latitude, and such a method was recommended to seamen by a Portuguese writer about the beginning of the sixteenth century.[2] The Spaniard, Cortes, writing on the finding of latitude, about the middle of the sixteenth century, described the second method as finding the altitude of some fixed star, presumably when it was on the meridian, and recommended using the Pole Star for this purpose, as it was nearest to the pole. He laid down the two requirements for

[1] *The Voyages of Cadamosto*, translated and edited by G. R. Crone, (Hakluyt Society, 1937.)
[2] *Esmeraldo de Situ Orbis*, (Hakluyt Society, Series II., Vol. LXXIX.)

such method as an instrument, preferably the Cross Staff, to take the altitude, and a set of rules to enable the observer to make the necessary correction to it.

The instructions given in the English translation (1561) were as follows:—

"The altitude is taken of the Pole starre, which is a star in the extremitie of the tayle of the lesser bear, being a constellation commonly called the Horne. For this North Starre is nearest to the pole and shall therefore show a lesse circle than any of the other stars and so shall his altitude differ little from the altitude of the pole . . . This star hath a declination 85° 51′ and therefore 4° 9′ is his distance from the Pole . . . and although mariners hold opinion that it is not distant more than 3½° yet to my judgment more credit ought to be given to the Astronomers than to mariners."

From him we learn that the mariners had noted 8 positions from the two Guards of the Little Bear to the North Star which answered to the 8 principal winds, and when the Guards were in those positions the mariner knew what correction to apply to his observed altitude. In other words, when the Guards were on the 8 principal points of the compass from the Pole Star the following corrections had to be applied.[1]

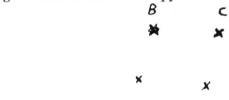

Ursa Minor. A — Polaris. B — Kochab.
B and C — The Guards

When the Guards bore				N. of the North Star				add 3°
,,	,,	,,	,,	N.E. ,,	,,	,,	,,	add 3½°
,,	,,	,,	,,	E. ,,	,,	,,	,,	add 1½°
,,	,,	,,	,,	S.E. ,,	,,	,,	,,	subtract 1½°
,,	,,	,,	,,	S. ,,	,,	,,	,,	subtract 3°
,,	,,	,,	,,	S.W. ,,	,,	,,	,,	subtract 3½°
,,	,,	,,	,,	W. ,,	,,	,,	,,	subtract 1½°
,,	,,	,,	,,	N.W. ,,	,,	,,	,,	add ½°

[1]When speaking of bearings from the Pole Star, the writers meant that when you looked at it, North represented the position when the Guards were directly above the Pole Star, i.e., at their highest altitude nearest the zenith, South directly below, East to the right and West to the left. Both Guards were usually mentioned, but the one that was really material was the brighter Kochab.

Cortes also instructed the mariner how to make an instrument which would automatically give the necessary correction to be applied on any bearing of the Guards from the Pole Star. This instrument was developed and improved upon in later years, and was in common use until the end of the eighteenth century, when accurate tables of correction took its place. As such tables could only be used when the longitude of the ship was known, again it is apparent how much the whole science of nautical astronomy was retarded until the reliable chronometer was introduced.

The above-mentioned instrument was called the Nocturnal, and in its simplest form was a circular piece of wood with a small hole in the centre. Pivoted about this hole was a moveable index which projected over the edge of the circle. Upon the circle was cut the appropriate Pole Star correction for every point of the compass. To find the correction the Nocturnal was held to the eye, and the Pole Star was observed through the hole, the index was then moved about the centre until its projection cut the Guards; where the edge of the index cut the graduated edge of the circle was found the approximate Pole Star correction.

Nocturnals were generally adapted so that the hour of the night could also be found by the help of the Pole Star and the Guards, and the later instruments were also graduated for use with the Pointers of the Great Bear as well as with the Guards of the Little Bear.

Various books on navigation during the seventeenth century repeated the rules given by Cortes,[1] and there is no doubt that this method was used at sea, for we find that Henry Hudson frequently had recourse to it during his voyages. The following extract is taken from the account of his voyage in 1607—"At midnight I observed the north starre upon N.W. × N. guarde— a good observation, 49° 30'." The rules were introduced into the 1657 edition of Wright's *Certain Errors in Navigation* and explained therein at considerable length. The following warning to seamen was, however, given at the end: "The above was the account that had always been made of the North Star from the time that it had 3½° from the Pole unto this present. But because at this time the fixed stars have notably varied their places the Pole Star hath also approached nearer the Pole, being now distant 3° 8'.

The above use has caused errors and ∠17 now propose

The Guards being	E.	Add to	1° 20'
in the	N.E.	Altitude	3° 8'
	N.		2° 41'
	N.W.		0° 27'

In the contrary rhumbs you must deduct.

---

[1] *Henry Hudson the Navigator*, (Hakluyt Society, 1860.)

THE NOCTURNAL.

Reproduced by kind permission of the Royal Geographical Society.

John Seller, in his *Practical Navigation*, 1694, after describing the Nocturnal and its uses, gave a complete table of corrections to be applied to the altitude of the Pole Star for every point of bearing of both the Great and Little Bear. Part of the table is given hereunder to show the substantial differences of opinion, as to the proper correction, that existed between writers of the seventeenth century, for Blundeville in his "Exercises" differed again from both Seller and the editor of Wright's *Errors in Navigation*.

Points of the Compass	Guard of little Bear.		Pointers of Great Bear.	
N.	2° 09′	N. Star above the Pole.	2° 20′	N. Star above Pole.
N. × E.	1° 52′	do.	2° 30′	do.
N.N.E.	1° 29′	do.	2° 35′	do.
N.E. × N.	1° 04′	do.	2° 33′	do.
N.E.	0° 35′	do.	2° 26′	do.
N.E. × E.	0° 06′	do.	2° 13′	do.
E.N.E.	0° 20′	N. Star under the Pole.	1° 55′	do.
E. × N.	0° 50′	do.	1° 33′	do.
E.	1° 18′	do.	1° 07′	do.
E. × S.	1° 41′	do.	0° 38′	do.
E.S.E.	2° 01′	do.	0° 08′	N. Star under the Pole.
*	*	*	*	*
S.	2° 09′	N. Star under the Pole.	2° 20′	N. Star under the Pole.
*	*	*	*	*
W.	1° 18′	Above Pole.	1° 07′	N. Star under the Pole.

N.B.—It will be noted that Seller used the N. S. points of the compass in their direct sense, *e.g.*, when the Guards lie further along the N. line (at their lowest altitude, on the meridian below the Pole) they were said to lie N. This was opposite to the method used by the earlier writers, but both resulted in the corrections being applied in the correct way provided the user understood them. In other words, in either method, when the altitude of the Guards above the Northern Horizon exceeded that of Polaris the correction was additive and when less, subtractive.

The following are two examples given in some Rules of Navigation about the beginning of the eighteenth century, in which Seller's method of application was used.[1] "Suppose that being at sea I find the altitude of the N. Star to be 16° 25′, and suppose also at the same time I find by my nocturnal that the foremost of the Guards of the little bear is found to be on the N.W. × N. of the compass on the Nocturnal in respect of the N. Star. I demand the height of the pole or latitude of the ship."

[1]British Museum. Sloane MSS. 3143.

From the altitude of Pole Star   ..   ..   16° 25'
Subtract the distance of Star above the
     Pole for a N.W. × N. Guard   ..   2° 30'

                                          13° 55'   Latitude

To the altitude of Pole Star   ..   ..   20° 20'
Add the distance of the star under the Pole
     for SS.E. Pointer   ..   ..   ..   1° 44'

                                          22° 04'   Latitude

For some unexplained reason the navigation books of the eighteenth and early nineteenth centuries seldom made any reference to finding the latitude by an observation of the Pole Star. Whether it was on account of differences of opinion as to what was the proper correction to be applied, or because even at its best the Nocturnal could only give an approximation of it, it is remarkable that few writers touched upon this particular star. That the Nocturnal was popular there is no doubt, for it is one of the most numerous of the instruments of nautical science in our museums to-day; it even appeared upon a card in a pack of Instructive Playing Cards of the late seventeenth century, where it was described as "An instrument used at sea to find the altitude or depression of the North Star in respect of the Pole itself in order to find the latitude and nearly the hour of the night."[1]

On the other hand, these later writers told the mariner how to find when a given star would be on the meridian, and how to find the latitude from an observation of a star taken at that time. It is noteworthy that in the list of stars, whose declinations and right ascensions were given, which was usually included in books of navigation during the eighteenth century, the Pole Star is always one of them. It is possible, therefore, that writers of that period rightly considered that better results would be obtained by observing it on the meridian than trusting to some often questionable correction derived from a Nocturnal.

As we have already remarked, the adoption of the chronometer enabled the navigator, if he so desired, to employ methods other than that of a meridian altitude to find his latitude, and in the course of the nineteenth century the Pole Star returned, with greater importance than ever, to its ancient place as a guide in ocean navigation.

---

[1]British Museum.

CHAPTER III.

THE VARIATION OF THE COMPASS.

JOHN DAVIS placed a knowledge of the variation of the compass as next in importance, in ocean navigation, to the finding of latitude, and urged the navigator to make "A very diligent examination of the truth of the compasse that it be without variation or other impediments." He did not indicate what other impediments the navigator should guard against, but it is possible that he was referring to bad workmanship, and a faulty placing of the needle under the card.

There is evidence that the existence of variation was known to landsmen in very early times. A passage in the Chinese Annals indicates that the Chinese were aware of it many centuries before Columbus, for in them it is stated, "When an iron point is rubbed with the loadstone, it acquires the property of showing the direction of the south; nevertheless it always declines to the west and is not due south."[1] Alexander von Humboldt, whose researches into magnetism have already been mentioned in the chapter on the compass, was of the opinion that the knowledge of the existence of magnetic variation was diffused over the Mediterranean by reports from China through the medium of Indian, Malayan and Arabian mariners.

There had been communication and trade between the East and the Mediterranean for centuries before the Christian Era. It was old at the time of Alexander the Great, though his conquests in the fourth century B.C. quickened the process. The spices, the precious stones and other treasures of Arabia, India and countries farther East arrived in Alexandria, Tyre, Sidon and other ports, principally by camel caravan. Some of the merchandise came overland from India through Afghanistan, Persia and Mesopotamia; some by sea to the Persian Gulf and thence by caravan; and some in Indian and Arabian vessels to the Red Sea, the navigation of which was chiefly, if not exclusively, in the hands of Arab seamen. Strabo, in Book XV, makes a brief reference to merchants who sailed from Egypt and the Arabian Gulf (Red Sea) to India.

The first appreciation of the variation of the magnetic compass from true north at sea is often credited to Columbus, though many have doubted the truth of this statement. William Gilbert in his *De Magnete Magneticisque*, 1600, boldly affirmed that "Sebastian Cabot first discovered that the magnet-

---

[1] *The National Encyclopaedia*, 1882 (Wm. Mackenzie).

[2] *A Treatise on Magnetism,* by Tiberius Carallo, F.R.S. (3rd Edition, London 1800).

ised iron (needle) varied." Samuel Purchas in his "Pilgrimes", 1625, expressed a doubt as to whether Columbus or Cabot was the first to detect it. There is evidence that Sebastian Cabot spent some time investigating the question, but this was after the famous voyage of Columbus in 1492.

Another claimant to the honour has been put forward, one Andrea Bianco, who is said to have published an atlas, in 1436, in which the variation of the needle from the geographic meridian was shown for different parts of the sea.[1]

It seems difficult to believe that variation was not discovered at sea by some one very shortly after the compass was introduced into ships that traversed substantial distances. There must have been considerable differences in the compass between Alexandria and Gibraltar, which would have been apparent in calm weather in spite of the faulty workmanship which existed in most of them.[2]

The Portuguese navigators of the fifteenth century, who spent much time exploring the west coast of Africa, were silent on the question, and in all probability never suspected the existence of variation. Any discrepancies between the compass and true north were probably accounted for by them as due to the movements of the ships, the oscillations of the compass, and the movements of the Pole Star about the Pole, which latter had been known of for centuries. Another reason why no great changes in the compass were noted by them may have been that their southerly courses ran approximately along the lines of variation, in that part of the world, and not across them, and consequently no sudden changes would be experienced. Once they crossed the Equator the Pole Star would no longer be visible to indicate the existence of a phenomenon which they did not suspect.

Whatever the truth, there can be little doubt that Columbus was the first to discover the existence of westerly deviation. The European seaboard at that time was affected by a moderate easterly variation, and therefore it is not surprising that on the first voyage of Columbus it was recorded on the 13th September, 1492, when over 200 leagues west of the Canaries, "On this day, at the commencement of the night, the needles turned a half point to North West and in the morning they turned somewhat more North West."

On Monday, 17th September, 1492, a further remark was made upon the compass: "The pilots observed the North point and found that the needles turned a full point to the West of North. So the mariners were alarmed and dejected . . . but the Admiral knew, and ordered that the North should be again observed at dawn. They then found that the needles were true.

---

[1]A. M. Mayer, *The Earth a Great Magnet*, 1872, p. 253.

[2]At the present time there is over 10° difference in the variation between the eastern and western ends of the Mediterranean.

The cause was that the star makes the movement and not the needles."[1]

By what means Columbus arranged for the needles to point true at dawn is a matter for speculation, but we do know that he had to resort to many subterfuges to allay the fears of his men during the voyage. That the Pole Star did not always indicate true north must have been well known to Columbus, but many of his crew would possibly be ignorant of the fact and be only too glad to receive any reason to allay their fears. The reason given, then, was probably effective in its result, but the movement of the Pole Star about the Pole was not sufficient to account for a variation of one point to the west of north, Moreover, if its movement was responsible for the variation it should have been also responsible for an equal amount of error to the east as it circled round the Pole.

The westerly course maintained by Columbus cut the lines of variation at about right angles and, at some time, passed across the line of no variation, which we know, one hundred years later, passed through the Azores in a north and south direction. After this, as he progressed to the westward the variation manifested itself in the opposite direction to that which had hitherto been experienced. It is little to be wondered at that the seamen were perturbed, but with some confidence it can be said that Columbus was the first to note the existence of variation in a westerly direction.

Portuguese and Spanish writers about the middle of the sixteenth century were by no means in agreement as to the existence of variation. Pedro Nunez and Pedro de Medina took no account of it in their writings, and the latter did not even admit its existence. He attributed any error in the compass to the faulty placing of the wires on the compass card.

On the other hand, Cortes spoke of the North Easting and North Westing of the compass, by which he meant its variation to one side or the other from true north. He also said what most writers of the latter half of the century said, that, "It is the opinion of some mariners that the meridian where the compass sheweth directly the pole passeth by the island of Santa Maria (Azores) and others by the Isle of Casservo in the Azores."[2]

The existence of variation was acknowledged on all sides before the end of the sixteenth century, and from Dr. Gilbert's treatise upon the magnet, 1600, and other works of the early seventeenth century, we learn that observations were taken, by seamen, to obtain its amount in every sea in which ships sailed. There was no unanimity, in those days, as to its value in the parts of the world where it was obtained, chiefly on account of the inaccuracy of the observations themselves, and also as a result of the practice

---

[1] *The Journal of Christopher Columbus* (During his first voyage, 1492-93). (Hakluyt Society, 1893.)

[2] Eden's Translation, 1561.

of different nations to construct their compasses in such a way as to allow for the variation found in their own localities. This, as we have already seen, when dealing with compasses, was effected by placing the needle out of the line of the north and south points of the card.

Gilbert's comment on the accuracy of the observations taken at sea was as follows: "From the time when first the variation of the needle was discovered, many alert navigators have in sundry ways striven to investigate the difference in the direction of the mariners compass: but this has not been done with the exactness that was requisite, much to the disadvantage of the art of navigation. For either being unlearned, they knew of no sure method, or they used ill-constructed and unsuitable instruments, or they adopted some conjecture based merely on the false hypothesis of some prime meridian or magnetic pole: while many copy others' writings and pass off for their own the observations of early writers: and these early authors, however stupid the writings in which they entered their observations, are held in high respect just because of their antiquity: and their posterity hold it to be not safe to differ from them."

He remarked that on long voyages, particularly to the East Indies, the early and inexact records of variation made by the Portuguese were prized, although it was obvious from the writings of the Portuguese that they understood little about variation, and that they neglected to say whether their observations were taken by a magnetic compass or by one corrected for the variation which existed in Portugal.

Continuing, he wrote: "Even expert navigators find it very difficult to observe the variation at sea on account of the ship's motions and her tossing in every direction, though they may employ the best instruments yet devised and in use. Hence have arisen various opinions about magnetic deviation (*i.e.*, variation). For example, the Portuguese navigator Roderigues de Lagos takes it to be $\frac{1}{2}$ point off the island of St. Helena; the Dutch in their nautical journal make it 1 point there; Kendall, an expert English navigator, makes it only $\frac{1}{6}$ of a point, using a true meridional compass."

Other similar examples were quoted, which showed the same uncertainty and confusion, and the only reliable conclusion that can be drawn from them is that navigators of every maritime nation were at pains to discover, in their own ways, the measure of variation in the seas they traversed.

The usual method of observing for variation, in those days, was by, what John Davis called, an instrument magnetical. It was an azimuth compass whose use was to take a bearing of any celestial object either when it was at or above the horizon. Such a compass differed from the ordinary sea compass in that the circumference of the card was often divided into degrees, and sometimes was so constructed as to indicate the magnetic meridian instead of the true meridian of the country of origin. This latter distinction, of course, only applied to the period during which makers indulged in the practice of so allowing for the local variation, and is not recorded after the end of the seventeenth century.

Fitted to the azimuth compass was an index upon which were secured two upright pieces of brass with slits down their centre lines, and through which the sun or a star was viewed at the time of observation. String or wire was often stretched down the centres of the slits to ensure greater accuracy in taking the bearing. The idea of using sights in this way was probably borrowed from the land surveyors, who used a similar method in their surveying by plane table.[1] This bearing instrument, fitted to the compass, was, in all respects, very similar to the present day Cross Bar Sight, and was used in the same way.

The compass was contained in a portable wooden box which was placed in a convenient part of the ship to take any particular bearing. It was by no means a fixture, but was carried about and placed at will as circumstances directed. The sights were then moved until they were directed towards the object to be observed, and in the case of a bright sun, were manipulated until the shadow of the string fell directly along the middle line of the index which, of course, then indicated the compass bearing. When the sun was not strong enough to cast a distinct shadow of the string, or when the bearing of a star was required, the sights were moved until the object came into the line of the two strings, when its bearing was read from the compass.

In rough weather when the ship was unsteady it was usual for two persons to take the observation, one to keep the object in the sights as the ship yawed, and the other to read the limits of the apparent swing of the compass. The mean of the bearings was then taken to be the approximate compass bearing as it is to-day by a single observer through an azimuth mirror.

During the eighteenth century the azimuth compass underwent several refinements and improvements, though the more elaborate instruments were confined to the ships engaged in scientific investigation and discovery. There were, however, many such voyages during that century, which resulted in a general raising of the level of all instruments of navigation. A special compass, now in the National Maritime Museum at Greenwich, was fashioned for the taking of observations for variation for Captain Cook, during the latter half of the eighteenth century, which in accuracy might be favourably compared with the ordinary instruments in use to-day. By the end of that century there were many good instruments available for those who cared to use them, though they were probably too delicate and expensive for rough work at sea, where the mariner had little need for extreme accuracy, and an observation to the nearest degree was sufficient for his purposes.

---

[1]Wright's *Certain Errors in Navigation*, Chapter XIII.

For surveyors and others who had need of great accuracy an admirable instrument was available at the beginning of the nineteenth century, which, apart from its obvious refinements, represented the type of instrument which had been used at sea for over 200 years.

Description of McCullock's Patent Azimuth Compass.[1] "The above illustration is a perspective view of the azimuth compass ready for observation

[1]Taken from *The Theory & Practice of Finding the Longitude*, 3rd Edition, 1810, Andrew Mackay, F.R.S.

The needle and card of this compass are similar to those of the steering compass, with this difference only, that a circular ring of silvered brass, divided into 360°, or rather four times 90°, circumscribes the card; b represents the compass box (bowl) which is of brass, and has a hollow conical bottom, e is the prop, or support of the compass box, which stands in a brass socket screwed to the bottom of the wooden box, and may be turned round at pleasure; h is one of the guards, the other, being directly opposite, is hid by the box. Each guard has a slit in which a pin, projecting from the side of the box, may move freely in a vertical direction. 1 is a brass bar, upon which, at right angles, the side vanes are fixed; a line is drawn along the middle of this bar; which line, the lines in the vanes, and the thread joining their tops, are in the same plane. 2 is a coloured glass moveable in the vane 3; 4 is a magnifying glass moveable in the other vane, whose focal distance is nearly equal to the distance between the vanes; 5 is the vernier, which contains six divisions, and as the limb of the card is divided into half degrees, each division of the vernier is, therefore, five minutes. The interior surface of the vernier is ground to a sphere, whose radius is equal to that of the card. 6 is a slide or stopper, connected with the vernier; which serves to push the vernier close to the card, and thereby prevent it from vibrating, as soon as the observation of the amplitude or azimuth is completed; and hence the degrees and parts of a degree may be read off at leisure, with certainty. 7 is a convex glass to assist the eye in reading off the observed amplitude or azimuth."

All instruments for the taking of bearings were constructed on the pattern of the Cross Bar Sight until the latter half of the last century, when it was found that the soft iron spherical correctors, referred to in the chapter on the compass, interfered with the line of vision for objects of low altitude which bore on the beam. In order to overcome this difficulty, Sir William Thomson invented his azimuth mirror, which is familiar to every modern navigator. Its use, even for taking bearings of objects on the horizon, was not interfered with by the globes introduced for the correction of quadrantal deviation, even if their highest points rose 5 inches above the glass of the compass bowl. Sir William Thomson described his instrument as follows: "A tube, so placed that an observer looking down centrally through it sees the divisions on the compass-card beneath, is supported on a frame resting on the cover of the bowl, and moveable round a vertical axis. In the tube is fixed a lens at such a distance from the compass-card that the degree divisions of its rim are in the principal focus. At the top of the tube a prismatic mirror is mounted on a horizontal axis, round which it can be turned into different positions when in use.[1]" By turning the instrument towards the object whose bearing was required, and turning the prismatic mirror until the object was reflected

---

[1] *Popular Lectures and Addresses,* by Sir William Thomson, 1891.

down the tube on to the magnified division of the compass card, its compass bearing was readily obtained.

Such is the instrument still in use to-day at sea, where extreme accuracy is unnecessary, and where a rapid and reliable method is of primary importance when a ship is moving in a seaway, and the sun and stars are frequently seen only for a moment through a fast closing gap in the clouds.

Methods of finding the variation.—Having the means at his disposal to find the compass bearing of a celestial object, the sixteenth century navigator only required some means for finding the true bearing of that object in order to deduce his variation in any part of the world. No doubt the earliest observers at sea relied upon the bearing of the sun at noon, when it was on the meridian, for this purpose, or, in the northern hemisphere, an observation of the Pole Star when it was on or near the meridian to gain some idea of the truth of the compass. Both these methods were uncertain, as in high latitudes the bearing of the Pole Star was difficult and almost impossible to obtain with any accuracy, and in low latitudes the quick passage of the sun across the meridian and its high altitude at that time rendered the observation anything but reliable. Thus either of these methods was only useful for obtaining an approximate error in the middle latitudes; approximate only, because with their imperfect astrolabes and cross-staves there was always some doubt as to when the sun actually reached its maximum altitude.

We have already seen how by taking the altitude of the sun at any time it was possible to discover its bearing by a graphical solution upon the terrestrial globe. This ingenious method, however, was open to objection, in that as the data available to the navigator were only approximate, the result, generally, could only approach within a few degrees of the truth.

In order to overcome the errors inherent in the above methods, another way was devised by taking equal altitudes of the sun, which became exceedingly popular at sea and on land, and which remained one of the principal means by which the variation was found, from the late sixteenth century until the end of the nineteenth century.

It is recorded by William Borough, one of the many scientific navigators of the Elizabethan era, in his *Discourse of the variation of the Cumpas*, 1581, that in order to find the variation at Limehouse he used a method of, what he called, Double Altitudes. The commonplace way in which he refers to this method indicates that it was by no means new then.

The broad principle of this method was that if the sun was observed twice on the same day at the same altitude, once before it reached the meridian and again after it had passed it, the sun would bear on the meridian at the mean time between the two observations. If at these two times the compass bearings of the sun were taken, then the difference between the mean of these bearings and the meridian would represent the error of the compass.

William Borough put this principle into effect in October, 1588, in the following way.

Altitude.	FORENOON Variation of the shadow from the North of the needle to the West.	AFTERNOON Variation of the shadow to the eastwards.	Variation of the needle from the Pole.
17°	52° 35'	30° 00'	11° 17½'
18°	50° 08'	27° 45'	11° 11½'
19°	47° 30'	24° 30'	11° 30'
20°	45° 00'	22° 15'	11° 22½'
21°	42° 15'	19° 30'	11° 22½'
22°	38° 00'	15° 30'	11° 15'
23°	34° 40'	12° 00'	11° 20'
24°	29° 35'	7° 00'	11° 17'

By taking the mean of the variations recorded in the right hand column he found the variation with some nearness to the truth, and his error probably did not exceed a few minutes. Such exactitude was possible when the observation was taken on firm earth, but at sea where such accuracy was unnecessary in practical navigation, the observer usually contented himself with one observation on each side of the meridian. With the observing instruments at his disposal it was not easy to take a series of altitudes at each degree, such as Borough did, ashore, so he took an altitude and bearing at some convenient time before noon and left his astrolabe or cross staff untouched until it was used to take the same altitude in the afternoon. The mean of the two bearings was then applied to the meridian to discover the variation.

There is no doubt that this method was used at sea by the end of the sixteenth century, for it is reported that William Barents, in his northern voyages, resorted to it frequently.[1] The following extract is taken from the contemporary record of his voyage in 1594. "On Sunday in the morning the 3rd July it was very faire and cleare weather, the wind blowing S.W.. at which time William Barents found out the right meridian, taking the high (height) of the sunne with his cross staff, when it was S.E. and found it to be elevated in the S.E. 28°½' and when it had passed over West and by North, it was but (again) 28½° above the horizon, so that it differed 5 points and a half which being divided, there rested (remained) 2¾ points: so that their compasse was altered 2¾ points" (from the meridian).

It will be appreciated that this method did not take into account the change in declination of the sun between the times of the two observations nor, if the ship was moving the difference between the two positions of observation. As neither of these two sources of error would cause any serious error in a result which was only required to be to the nearest degree, they were not taken into account by these earlier navigators.

---

[1] *The Three Voyages of William Barents to the Arctic Regions,* 1594-1595-1596, by Gerrit De Veer (Hakluyt Society, 1876).

Another method which came into some prominence during the first half of the seventeenth century was that of finding the variaton by the amplitude of the sun. It was advocated by Henry Gellibrand, who at that time was professor of astronomy at Gresham College.[1] The advantages of this method were that only one observation was necessary; opportunities for taking it offered themselves twice every day in any latitude where the sun rose and set and, as the bearing was taken at the rising and setting the sun was in the best position for accurate observation. The finding of the sun's true bearing at these two times depended upon a simple trigonometrical calculation, which had recently been made possible to any intelligent navigator by the publication of logarithmic tables.

How soon this method, which is in common use to-day, was generally adopted is not clear, but there is no doubt that it had become deservedly popular by the end of the seventeenth century. In the meantime a most useful little book had been published, which, *inter alia*, contained corrected tables of the sun's declination, and a table of amplitudes in points of the compass, for use between the Equator and the latitude of 60°. These tables of amplitude gave the true bearing of the sun for those declinations which caused the sun to rise or set upon a full point of the true compass, and a second table which gave the amplitude for every degree of declination, which differed little from the arrangement of modern tables of azimuths and amplitudes. That they were extensively used is indicated by the fact that the book passed into many editions during the following century. This book was first compiled by a mathematician, Andrew Wakely, who, in his preface to the reader, expressed himself as follows:—

"Courteous Reader,

When I first entered upon these my Labours, and after I had begin the Calculation, I found that, tho' the Book be small, yet my Labour was so great, that I almost fainted. Yet at length, when I considered the ordinary necessary, and frequent Use that might be made of these my Labours, I was thereby encouraged to go on and prosecute my Work; and how ready and easy I have made it for actual Performance, will plainly appear, by immediate Inspection to the meanest Capacity.

"Here follows a Brief Explanation of the method and order of the Book. First you will find Tables of the Sun's Declination, newly Calculated from the best Hypothesis yet discovered, and applied to the Meridian of London, whose Latitude is 51° 32′ North, and Longitude according to my Table 00° 00′. Next you will find Tables shewing the True Hour and Minute of the Day, the Sun being upon any Point of the Compass, which Tables are as

---

[1]*A Discourse Mathematical on the Variation of the Magnetic Needle*, by Henry Gellibrand, 1635.

Dials, fitting all Places in the World, whose Pole is elevated not above 60 deg. either North or South. Likewise by these Tables you may know the true Hour and Minute of the Night by the bearing of any of the known Fixed Stars between the Tropicks. Then you will find Tables shewing the true Time of the Sun's Rising and Setting with the Length of the Day and Night. Also by these Tables you may find the true Time of Rising and Setting of all the eminent Fixed Stars between the Tropicks. Next you will find Tables shewing the Points of the Compass that the Sun and all the above-said Stars Rise and Set with; which Tables are of excellent Use for the ready Finding of the Variation of the Compass, and may be performed by a Meridian Compass that is about Ten Inches in Diameter, whose Points being divided into Halfs and Quarters; such a Compass I suppose to be convenient for the Mariners Use, where he hath not an Azimuth Compass. Next you will find Tables of Amplitudes to every degree of the Sun's Declination: All these Tables are calculated from the Equinoctial to Sixty Degrees of Latitude, either North or South; and they will last with Exactness as long as God upholdeth the Order and Course of Nature.

"In the Appendix you will find the Use of all those Instruments that are most in Use in the Art of Navigation, either for Operation, or Observation. Likewise a Table containing the most and chiefest Harbour, Headlands, and Islands in the World; shewing the Latitude, and Longitude of each of them; beginning the longitude at the Meridian of London, newly Composed in a new successive Order.

"This Method I own, but how I have acquitted myself therein, I shall leave to the Judgment and Experiments of the Skilfullest Mariners that the World affords, which are my native Countrymen of England.

Fare ever well, so wishes he;
who is more yours, than he can seem to be."[1]

ANDREW WAKELY.

There is strong evidence that this useful book was first published in 1664, and that it was well received by navigators. The first corrected edition appeared in 1693, when the editor, James Atkinson, an old pupil of the author, was requested by the bookseller concerned to revise the original. This he did out of the respect he bore to the memory of his deceased master, and because the treatise "hath obtained good esteem with our Navigators."

By means of inspection and interpolation the user was able to find the true bearing of the sun at its rising or setting, with rapidity and accuracy.

The following example is taken from the book to show how, by means of the most minute explanation, this method of finding variation was open to the unlettered seaman.

---

[1] *The Mariner's Compass Rectified.*

A Table of Amplitudes, fitting all Places from the Equinoctial to 60 degrees of Latitude, either North or South.[1]

THE DEGREES OF LATITUDE.

Sun's Declination. (Degrees of Declination)	40 D	40 M	41 D	41 M	42 D	42 M	43 D	43 M	44 D	44 M	45 D	45 M
0	0	00	00	00	00	00	00	00	00	00	00	00
1	01	18	01	20	01	21	01	22	01	23	01	25
2	02	36	02	39	02	41	02	44	02	47	02	50
3	03	54	03	58	04	02	04	06	04	10	04	15
4	05	13	05	18	05	23	05	28	05	34	05	40
5	06	32	06	38	06	44	06	51	06	58	07	05
6	07	50	07	57	08	05	08	13	08	21	08	39
7	09	09	09	17	09	26	09	35	09	45	09	56
8	10	28	10	37	10	47	10	58	11	09	11	21
9	11	47	11	58	12	09	12	21	12	34	12	47
10	13	06	13	18	13	31	13	44	13	58	14	13
11	14	26	14	39	14	53	15	07	15	22	15	38
12	15	45	16	00	16	15	16	31	16	48	17	06
13	17	04	17	20	17	37	17	55	18	13	18	33
14	18	24	18	42	19	00	19	18	19	39	20	00
15	19	45	20	04	20	23	20	43	21	05	21	28
16	21	05	21	25	21	46	22	08	22	32	22	56
17	22	26	22	48	23	10	23	34	23	59	24	25
18	23	47	24	10	24	34	24	59	25	26	25	54
19	25	09	25	33	25	58	26	25	26	54	27	25
20	26	30	26	56	27	24	27	53	28	23	28	56
21	27	53	28	21	28	50	29	20	29	53	30	27
22	29	16	29	45	30	16	30	48	31	22	31	58
23	30	40	31	11	31	43	32	16	32	51	33	36
23·30	31	22	31	54	32	28	33	03	33	40	34	20[1]

"The use of these Tables of Amplitudes.

Example. In the Latitude of 42° 30′, the Sun's declination being 12° 15′ I demand the Amplitude.

Answer. The Amplitude is 16° 43′, found as follows:—

Look the Latitude in the Head of the Table, the declination in the first column on the left-hand, and in the common angle of meeting, is the amplitude desired. According to these directions, for the Latitude of 42°, and Declination being {12° / 13°} the amplitude is 16° 15′ / 17° 37′

Subtract and their difference is 1° 22′

Then say as 1° or 60′ is to 1° 22′ or 82′, so is 15′ to 20′ found as hereunder:—

If 60′ give 82′ what shall 15′

```
       15
      410
       82
60) 1230 (20 Proportional Part
     1200
       30 Remainder
```

[1]Upon comparison with the most recent tables the above true bearings are found to be correct.

Latitude 42° and Declination 12° the Amplitude is   16° 15′
To it add Proportional Part above   0° 20′

Gives Amplitude for Declination 12° 15′ to be   16° 35′

Again for Latitude 43° and Dec: $\begin{cases} 12° \\ 13° \end{cases}$ Amplitude is $\begin{cases} 16° 31′ \\ 17° 55′ \end{cases}$

Subtracted makes Difference to be   1° 24′

Then say: As 60′ is to 1° 24′ or 84′ so is 15′ to 21′ found as hereunder:—
         If 60′ give 84′ what shall 15′

$$15$$
$$\overline{}$$
$$420$$
$$84$$
$$\overline{}$$
$$60)\ 1260\ (21'\ \text{Proportional Parts}$$
$$1260$$
$$\overline{}$$
$$00\ \text{Remainder}$$

Latitude 43° and Declination 12° Amplitude   16° 31′
To it add Proportional Part above   0° 21′

Gives for Declination 12° 15′ the Amplitude   16° 52′

Now because the given Latitude 42° 30′ is in the middle, between 42° and 43°, therefore the medium of the Amplitudes before found is the Amplitude required, and is thus:—

Latitude $\begin{cases} 42° \\ 43° \end{cases}$ Declination 12° 15′, the Amplitude is $\begin{matrix} 16° 35′ \\ 16° 52′ \end{matrix}$

        Added together is—   33° 27′
        The half is the Amplitude required   16° 43′

Thus may the amplitude be found for any odd minutes of Latitude or Declination, though the Table is calculated for whole degrees only.

By this Table the Variation of the Compass is most readily found; for by the Azimuth Compass find the Sun's magnetical amplitude, at their Rising or Setting; and the true amplitude (according to the Latitude of the Place, and the Declination) by this Table, the Difference of these Amplitudes (when both are North or both South) but their Sum (if one North the other South) is the Variation of the Compass."

With these detailed instructions as a guide to such a simple table it is easy to imagine why, after its publication, the method of amplitudes was adopted by all and sundry.

A further aid to the accuracy of this method was given by the celebrated astronomer, Dr. Halley, who spent much time in experiment and investigation to improve the art of navigation. In an address to the Royal Society, in 1692, he drew attention to an error which arose in the observation from the effects of refraction, and the height of eye of the observer above the sea. Owing to these two causes the image of the sun is in fact seen after the true time of its setting and before its rising, so that if the bearing is taken when the centre of the sun cuts the visible horizon, it will be somewhat in excess of the correct amplitude by compass. This excess is not material in low latitudes, where the path of the sun cuts the horizon steeply, but it is appreciable in the higher latitudes, where the angle is more oblique.

The criticisms of Dr. Halley were always constructive and he showed how this error could be overcome by observing the sun when its lower limb was elevated above the horizon about ⅔ of its diameter, or 20', above the rim of the horizon.[1]

Altitude Azimuth.—The general adoption of tables of logarithms began to bear fruit during the eighteenth century, when some writers introduced a further method for the finding of the sun's true bearing at any time. The latitude of the place of observation being known, and the declination of the sun (or star) being readily obtainable from the nautical tables, it only remained to observe the altitude of the sun (or star) in order to have the three elements necessary for the solution of a spherical triangle. By solving this triangle by trigonometry it was possible to obtain the true bearing of a celestial body from the meridian.

Some writers contented themselves by simply mentioning that this method did exist, but made no attempt at explanation or example. For instance, one writer dismissed it by saying: "There is also a way to find the variation by a single azimuth, but very troublesome to calculate".[2] The solution of this problem was certainly less simple than the calculation of the amplitude and, as yet, no tables had been produced to enable the observer to take out the true bearing, at any altitude, by inspection. Nevertheless, this method was used by some, for in a poem entitled "The Shipwreck", by William Falconer (who compiled the well-known *Falconer's Marine Dictionary*) which was written in 1762, we find the following description in verse of the taking of an altitude azimuth:—

---

[1] *Philosophical Transactions*, 1692.
[2] *Navigation; or the Art of Sailing upon the Sea.* Printed for J. Nourse, 1764.

"The dim horizon low'ring vapors shroud,
And blot the sun yet struggling in the cloud:
Thro' the wide atmosphere, condens'd with haze,
His glaring orb emits a sanguine blaze,
The pilots now their rules of art apply,
The mystic needle's devious aim to try.
The compass plac'd to catch the rising ray,
The quadrant's shadows studious they survey,
Along the arch the gradual index slides,
While Phoebus down the vertic-circle glides.
Now, seen on ocean's utmost verge to swim,
He sweeps it vibrant with his nether limb.
Their sage experience thus explores the height,
And polar distance of the source of light:
Then thro' the chiliad's[1] triple maze they trace
Th' analogy that proves the magnet's place,
The wayward steel, to truth thus reconcil'd
No more th' attentive pilot's eye beguiled."

This accurate description by a seaman of taking the altitude of the sun with Hadley's quadrant leaves no doubt that such a method was in use at the time the poem was written to find the true bearing of the sun. It is probable that such a means was only used then by those fairly well acquainted with mathematics, or whose earlier years had been spent in gaining the mathematical background to their art ,whom Falconer described in another poem, in 1760, "The Midshipman".[2]

"In canvassed berth, profoundly deep in thought,
His busy mind with Sines and Tangents fraught,
A Mid reclines! in calculation lost!
His efforts still by some intruder crost:
     *   *   *   *   *
But think not meanly of this humble seat
Whence sprung the Guardians of the British Fleet:
Revere the sacred spot, however low,
Which formed to martial acts—an Hawke! an Howe!"

The difficulties of calculation were gradually overcome, and this method, by which the true bearing of the sun or star could be obtained at any time, became generally popular at sea. The increasing use of iron in the construction of ships prompted every careful navigator to have a greater regard for the truth of his compass, and induced him to take advantage of every reliable method of finding his error upon every change of course, whether by day or by night. In the earlier years of the nineteenth century, therefore, a set of Altitude—Azimuth tables was published for the use of seamen, whereby the true bearing of the sun could readily be found from its altitude, without

---

[1]Chiliad—literally a group of 1000 but often used during the eighteenth century to denote a logarithmic table.

[2]*Falconer's Marine Dictionary*, 1830, edited by Dr. Burney.

resort to tedious calculation. Such tables were first compiled, in 1829, by Thomas Lynn, a commander in the East India Company's Service.[1]

Azimuth by the Hour Angle.—Another advantage which accrued to seamen through the introduction of the chronometer was still a further method of finding the true bearing of a celestial body. This was the azimuth by Hour Angle method, which, when once established, thrust all other methods into positions of secondary importance, and is more widely used at sea to-day than any other.

As we have already seen, in dealing with the Pole Star and ex-meridian observations for latitude, a knowledge of accurate longitude made such methods possible, because through this knowledge the navigator was able to find the hour angle of the observed object from his meridian, so by applying the same knowledge he was able to find its true bearing.

The solution of all problems in nautical astronomy depends simply upon the solution of the spherical triangle in the celestial concave whose three angles are at the elevated pole (P), the observer's zenith (Z), and the observed object (X) respectively.

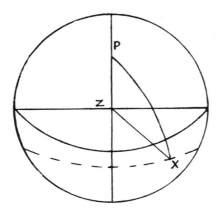 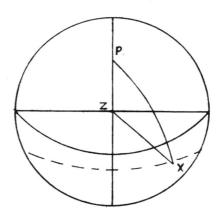

ALTITUDE AZIMUTH
Known Elements PZ, ZX, PX

AZIMUTH BY HOUR ANGLE
Known Elements PZ, PX, ∠ZPX

Whereas in the Altitude Azimuth problem the three known elements, from which the true bearing **PZX** was obtained, were derived from the Latitude of the place of observation, the altitude and the declination of the sun or other celestial body, in this later method the altitude could be dispensed with and the Hour Angle of the body be used in its place.

Thus it was no longer necessary to observe the altitude of the celestial body when its true bearing was required, and even when low lying fog

---

[1]Advertisement to *Burdwood's Azimuth Tables*, Edition of 1888.

obscured the horizon, the navigator was able to calculate his compass error provided the sun pierced it or any recognisable heavenly body showed above it.

The advantages of this method were quickly realised by those whose concern was for the improvement of navigation and the safety of lives and ships at sea, and in order to make the use of this new method more certain and easy Time Azimuth Tables were published in 1866 by order of the Lords Commissioners of the Admiralty. In this way came into being the tables of the Sun's True Bearing, by Burdwood and Davis, and the whole art of finding the error of the compass was reduced to the simplest possible form and became but the labour of a few minutes.

The Investigation of Variation and its uses.—We have already remarked that the existence of variation was not generally admitted by nautical writers during the sixteenth century and that both Pedro Nunez and Pedro de Medina took no account of it in their writings. Of them, William Gilbert wrote, in 1600, "But Pedro Nunez seeks the meridian by the mariner's compass or versorium (which the Spanish call the needle) without taking account of the variation: and he adduces many geometrical demonstrations which (because of his slight use and experience in matters magnetical) rest on utterly vicious foundations. In the same manner Pedro de Medina, since he did not admit variation has disfigured his *Arte de Navegar* with many errors."

William Gilbert spent much time on the investigation of magnetic phenomena and the results of his researches were collected and published by him in 1600. It would be safe to say by this time no doubts lingered in the minds of seamen as to the existence of variation and that more than one philosopher was trying to discover the reason for it.

Many theories were advanced in Gilbert's day, chief among which were the existence of magnetic mountains or certain magnetic rocks, while others favoured the existence of a distant phantom pole of the world which controlled the movement of the compass. Some spoke of a motive force beyond the furthest heavens, some to the heavens themselves and some to the effect of a star in the tail of the Great Bear.

But Gilbert would have none of these. "Every turn and dip", wrote he, "and their standing still (of the needles) are effects of the magnetic bodies themselves and of the earth, mother of all, which is the fount and source and producer of all these forces and properties. Thus, then, the earth is the cause of this variation and tendence to a different point in the horizon."

His opinion was that if there was a distant phantom pole or a magnetic rock, the variation at any point on the Earth's surface would change in geometrical ratio to the east or west, but as experience taught that such was not the case, and that variation changed in different ways in a most erratic manner, some other cause must be found. He argued that variation was due to the inequality of the surface of the Earth and that continents and mountains exercised a greater effect than the oceans in keeping the compass needle in the magnetic meridian. His conclusion was that the force that produced all magnetic movements came from the constant magnetic earth-substance, which was strongest in the most massive continent and weakest over the oceans. It followed, therefore, that a compass at sea would be drawn from the true meridian towards the land mass which was capable of exerting an influence upon it in excess of some other opposite mass or elevated continent.

This theory is easily understood when the information at Gilbert's disposal is considered. In his day the variation along the European seaboard was easterly, and on the American seaboard westerly, while near the Azores most seamen were agreed that the needle showed the true meridian. The fact that the variation was not nil along the whole meridian of the Azores in no way conflicted with this theory but rather strengthened it for, generally speaking ,the variation on this meridian was found to be less near the Equator and greater in high latitudes owing, as Gilbert said, to the masses of land in the Arctic regions exerting a superior force.

One further deduction was put forward by Gilbert, as a result of his experiments and observations, and that was that the variation of the compass remained constant at any given place. Though this and the other findings of Gilbert with regard to variation were later proved to be wrong. little blame can be attached to him who so truly laid the foundations of the broader principles of terrestrial magnetism. That he failed to appreciate the causes of variation was not so much from lack of experiment as from lack of accurate information and time to find the truth by trial and error over a considerable number of years.

Some years after Gilbert's death several enquiring scientists applied themselves to further research into the problem of variation, chief among whom was Henry Gellibrand, sometime professor of astronomy at Gresham College. In 1635 he published *A Discours Mathematical on the Variation of the Magneticall Needle*, in which he referred to Gilbert's work as follows: "Neither will these few lines permit me to speake of all magnetical qualities, they that list may have recourse for their Satisfaction herein, to that most learned worke (admired by all Foreiners) long agoe penned by Mr. Dr. Gilbert, our countryman, Sometimes Physitian to that Renowned Lady, our Queene."

He agreed with Gilbert's theory that midway between continents the variation should be nil, and that the needle should be drawn to one side or the other as the ship approached one of the continents. Thus far his enquiries added nothing new to the existing knowledge of variation.

K

His observations, however, led to a most important discovery, the existence of the variation of the variation. This discovery he announced in the following words, from which it will be seen that it is difficult to decide to whom the credit for it should be given. "Thus hitherto (according to the tenets of all our Magneticall Philosophers) we have supposed the variations of all particular places to continue one and the same. So that when a seaman shall happly returne to a place where formerly he found the same variation he may hence conclude he is in the same former longitude. For it is the assertion of Dr. Gilbert that the same place always retaines the same variation. Neither hath this assertion (for ought I ever heard) been questioned by any man. But most diligent magneticall observations have plainely offered violence to the same, and proved the contrary namely that the variation is accompanied with a variation. For whereas in the yeare 1580 Mr. Burrows (a man of unquestionable abilities in the mathematics) found the variation at Limehouse neere London to be 11° 15′ or neere 1 point of the compasse. In the yeare 1622, Mr. Gunter, sometime professor of Astronomie at Gresham College, found the variation in the same place to be but 6° 13′. And my selfe this present yeare, 1634, with some friends had recourse to Deptford (where Mr. Gunter had heretofore made the same observation with those at Limehouse) and found it not much to exceed 4°."

Gellibrand tells us that when he and his friends first found such a difference in the variation between the observations of Burrows and Gunter they were "overhasty in casting an aspersion of error upon Mr. Burrows observation" until a friend of theirs told them that after a recent experiment he found he could not make the variation as much as that found by Gunter in 1622. He then carried out careful observations which showed a further reduction in the variation to 4° 10′; still not satisfied he conducted further experiments which showed the variation then to be about 4° 0′, or a difference in the variation at London of over 7° in 54 years.

Observations carried out with accuracy and system during the years which followed proved the correctness of Gellibrand's observations, and showed that while in some parts of the world the variation remained almost stationary, in others there was a marked alteration, which in the course of a few years made a substantial difference in the direction indicated by the magnetic compass.

It was during these earlier years of the seventeenth century that men of science tried to use the ever-growing knowledge of variation in different parts of the world to find the longitude. The idea was by no means new, and there is reason to suppose that seamen had used their knowledge of variation to give warning of their approach to previously visited localities, during the preceding century. William Bourne, in his *Regiment of the Sea*, in 1574, impressed upon navigators the advantage to be gained from making notes of the variation when falling in with land so that they could have some guidance when they wished to find the particular place again[1]. It is evident that such a proceeding had already proved of use or Bourne would not have gone out of his way to bring it more generally to the notice of seamen. In the last voyage of John Davis to the East Indies, 1604, during which he was killed, we find it reported that observations for variation gave warning of their approach to land in the vicinity of which observations had previously been obtained. The report reads: "The first of Aprill, toward night, wee descried Land from the maine top, which bare of us South South-East, when, according to our reckoning and accounts, wee were not neere by fortie leagues, but yet the variation of the Compasse did tell us that wee were on Land thirtie leagues before we saw Land."

The growth of this idea as a means of solving the navigator's greatest problem, that of finding longitude at sea, resulted in more searching enquiry into the phenomena of magnetic variation, dip, and the annual variations of both. Prominent among the searchers was an English mathematician, Henry Bond, who first attracted attention, about the year 1648, as editor of the popular *Seaman's Kalendar*.[2] In this book he affirmed the existence of the magnetic poles of the earth and claimed to have calculated their geographical positions, though he did not divulge what they were. He accounted for the variation of variation by a theory of a slow revolution of these poles about the true poles of the earth which, over a course of years, affected first one place and then another. He wrote: "There are some places within a certain longitude whose variations continue constant for hundreds of years, and yet afterwards doe vary as ours here at London doth now—but at London it is never constant although in former time the variation of it was not sensible, it is now in its swiftest motion." At the time of writing he obviously felt the need for testing his theories by further practice and observation, and this may have been the reason why he did not divulge more of his secrets until later, for he expressed the wish "that (as many noble-minded men have been at charge often-times to adventure toward the seeking out of a passage Northwest into the South Sea) some nobly-minded would take this into consideration, so that some able men, furnished with convenient and exact instruments might make observation to the westwards, it would make much for their lasting fame and for the honour of this kingdome."

---

[1]Bourne, however, did not advocate it as a means of finding the longitude at sea because of the comparatively large distance that had to be sailed before there was any appreciable change in the variation. See *Regiment of the Sea*, 1574 and 1596.

[2]This book contained an Ephemerides of the Sun, Moon and certain of the brightest fixed stars, sailing directions for the coasts of Europe, tables of declination for the sun and stars, corrections to be applied to the Pole Star for latitude, and a general discourse upon the art of navigation. It passed through many impressions during the first half of the seventeenth century.

He mentioned one thing more, which in later years greatly increased his reputation, and that was that those who lived until the year 1657 would not find any variation at all in London and, that afterwards, it would increase in the opposite direction (westerly) and continue so for at least 30 years.

Bond continued his researches, and meanwhile the variation in London, in 1657, was found to be nil, as he had predicted. Some years later he communicated to the Royal Society some further results of his work which was a table of predicted variation at London for the next 49 years. His theories, however, were not then complete and he forebore to say more until later.[1] It must be remembered that Bond was not conducting his researches with the idea of finding the true causes of variation, he was concerned with the more important problem of discovering a reliable and easy method for the finding of longitude at sea. As already remarked, the principle of using a knowledge of the variation to find position was no novelty. William Bourne, in 1574, had advocated it as a means of detecting the proximity to a previously visited place, and about the end of the same century, a Netherlander, named Stevin, had treated of the practice in a short treatise entitled *The Haven Finding Art*.[2] *The Haven Finding Art*, or the way to find any haven or place at sea by latitude and variation was published in Dutch, French and Latin by the command of Count Maurice of Nassau, Lord High Admiral of the United Provinces of the Low Countries, wherein all seamen who took charge of ships under his jurisdiction were enjoyned to make diligent observations in all their voyages according to the directions prescribed in the book. This treatise was translated into English by Edward Wright and incorporated by him into his *Certain Errors in Navigation*, 1599, "for the common benefite of the Seamen of England."

Stevin probably did little more than put into print a practice which had been followed by a number of navigators for some years. This practice was to use the variation of the compass in conjunction with the observed latitude to give an approximation of the longitude. In *The Haven Finding Art* a table of positions of all the principal parts and places of importance in navigation was given, similar to that found in some books of nautical tables to-day. The longitudes of those positions were doubtless obtained by using the age-old method of taking the mean of the longitudes assigned to them by reliable shipmasters, who kept as careful account as they could of the courses and distances sailed in reaching them. The longitudes of some parts had been instrumentally determined by infrequent observations of eclipses by astronomers, but these were imperfect and unreliable.

To each of these places was assigned its observed variation, the amounts

---

[1] *Philosophical Transactions*, October 19th, 1668.

[2] "The Haven Finding Art" by E. G. R. Taylor published by Hollis and Carter is a publication of The Royal Institute of Navigation.

of which had been compiled chiefly through the labours and care of Peter Plancius, a Dutch geographer. He extracted most of his information from the log books and journals of the Dutch East India ships which, at that time, maintained a service to the Far East by way of the Cape of Good Hope.

By analysing the table it was found that from the prime meridian of Corvo, in the Azores, where the variation was nil, to the Cape of Good Hope, which was then assumed to lie about 60° east of it, the variation of the compass was easterly. From Corvo to about 30° E. it increased to about 13° in the latitude of Plymouth, and 19° in the South Atlantic at the island of Tristan da Cunha, after which it decreased to zero at the Cape of Good Hope. From the Cape of Good Hope eastwards the compass needle was then drawn to the west of the true meridian, reaching a maximum of 33° between the 110th and 120th meridians east of Corvo, from whence it gradually decreased to zero again at the 160th meridian. Although observations were lacking beyond

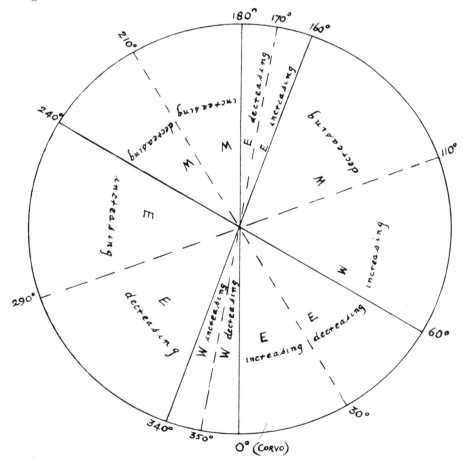

there, the assumption was that the variation would be easterly again until 180° east, on the opposite side of the world from Corvo, reaching a maximum in 170° E. A further assumption was made, that as the variation was in the hemisphere east of Corvo so in the western hemisphere it must be of an opposite character, as appears from the diagram opposite.

An unknown writer on the use of the compass commented during the eighteenth century on the use of the table and diagram as follows: "Now these observations and suppositions . . . do fall out accordingly in the first and second parts of the circle (*i.e.*, 0° to 60° and 60° to 160°) and are of great use to seamen in their voyages to the East Indies, and for the instruction of seamen according to the variation Captain John Davis did long since publish a journal of his voyage to Bantam in the East Indies. I could wish other men would do likewise . . . so this famous Art of Navigation might in a short time come to greater perfection."[1]

The following extract from John Davis's log, kept on the voyage referred to above, is given to show with what care he noted his variation, whenever he could observe for it.

Day	Leagues	Course	Latitude	Longitude		Wind	Variation
June 3	32	S. × W.	16° 30′ S.	15° 24′ W.		E.S.E.	12° 15′ E.
				off Lizard			
,, 4	26	S.	18° 18′ S.	15° 34′	do.	E.S.E.	13° 30′ E.
,, 5	24	S.	19° 30′ S.	15° 24′	do.	E.S.E.	14° 15′ E.
,, 6	12	S.S.W.¼W.	20° 03′ S.	15° 33′	do.	E.S.E.	14° 51′ E.
,, 7	13	E. × S.	20° 11′ S.	14° 57′	do.	South	14° 27′ E.
	x	x	x	x			x
Nov. 7	15	E.	06° 26′ S.	71° 30′ E. of Cape		S.	6° 40′ W.
				Good Hope			
,, 8	40	E.	06° 24′ S.	73° 30′	do.	W.N.W.	
,, 10	50	E.	06° 03′ S.	76° 00′	do.	N.W.	
		northerly					
,, 12	59	E. × S.	05° 30′ S.	79° 08′		W.N.W.	4° 13′ N.
,, 14	52	E.S.E.	06° 29′ S.	81° 27′		W.N.W.	Land seen (Java)

There is no doubt that this knowledge of the variation was used as a check upon the easting and westing made by ships, especially by experienced traders in the Indian Ocean, but apart from that the Haven Finding Art was, in truth, little more than a haven finding art, by which a navigator sailing upon the parallel of the desired haven could, by observing periodically for variation, obtain some warning of his approach to it as his variation changed to that of his objective. It told him when his own longitude was becoming near to that which he desired.

The discoveries of the investigators of the first half of the seventeenth century did not pass unnoticed by Moxon, the editor of the third edition of "Wright's Errors" (1657), who wrote, " . . . then may it not be very difficult

---

[1]British Museum—Sloane MMS. 1440.

by the latitude and variation of the compass observed to find the longitude. I confess it may be thought that that opinion may be refuted by the variation of variation, but Time who hath lately revealed the variation of variation, hath also discovered the Regularity of the motion of this variation, by which the variation of any place being already known may be calculated what the variation shall be for any year to come."

Shortly before the publication of the results of Bond's labours, a contemporary, Dr. Hook, communicated to the Royal Society, in 1675, a theory of the variation, the substance of which was that the north magnetic pole of the earth was distant about 10° from the geographical pole, about which it made one complete revolution in 370 years. This slow revolution caused the variation to alter in London about 10' every year and such annual alteration would continue for some time, after which it would diminish, until at length it became stationary, and then proceed to cause an opposite effect.[1]

At last, in 1676, William Bond published his long expected treatise upon the finding of longitude by utilising the knowledge acquired of terrestrial magnetism. The book was published by the special command of King Charles II., and was entitled *The Longitude Found*. After reviewing the results of former experiments by William Burrough, Gunter, Gellibrand and others, and taking into account his own researches to show the gradual decrease in the easterly variation, he affirmed that there were two magnetic poles and that they had a circular motion about the geographical poles. Their period of complete revolution he calculated to be 600 years or an annual change of position of $\frac{6}{10}°$, and this, said he, was the cause of the variation of the compass and the variation of the variation. He concluded, too, that the magnetic poles were situate near the earth's surface, because the closer they were approached the greater was their strength. The book included a long table of positions of practically every port and headland of primary importance in navigation, and to each place was assigned the inclination or dip of the magnetic needle. His method of finding longitude was by using the latitude as found by observation in conjunction with the dip as found at the same time by the inclinatory needle, and referring it to the prime meridian of London. It should be noted here that a similar method had been advocated in Blundevilles *Exercises*, in 1602, for the finding of latitude, which failed because information upon dip in any latitude was so scant, and still less was accurately known of its cause.

Bond concluded his treatise as follows: "Whereas we ought to give all Praise and Glory to Almighty God for his infinite wisdom and mercy in these latter days of the world, to make known the motion of the Magnetic Sphere round about the Earth, and its admirable use: yet there are some that

---

[1] *Falconer's Marine Dictionary.*

snarle against it, but let such have a care how they snarle against the Almighty Jehovah."

From the above words it may be concluded that Bond's theories were not accepted wholeheartedly, as indeed they were not, and two years later, in 1678, Peter Blackborrow published a reply to him entitled *The Longitude Not Found.* Blackborrow's arguments are involved and extremely difficult to follow, and contributed little to the knowledge of magnetism or the finding of longitude. On the other hand, while Bond's method of finding longitude never developed into a practical solution of that problem and was never adopted at sea, chiefly because of his reliance upon insufficient and inaccurate data and the impossibility of great refinement in observation which was so essential to his hypothesis, his systematic collection of information enabled him to enunciate the theory of variation and its annual changes, which has never been displaced.

The glorious failure of Bond and the destructive criticism of Blackborrow exercised an influence upon the minds of contemporary scientists, and aroused the interest of Dr. Halley, who later became Astronomer Royal, to investigate the theories of magnetism.

After some years of research and the compilation of information, Halley produced his *Theory of the Variation of the Magnetical Compass* in the year 1683.[1] After giving a table of observed variations for many parts of the world, and analysing it, he discounted Gilbert's theory of the effect of continents, by showing that off the coast of Brazil the compass needle was deflected away from the land instead of towards it. He exploded the other theories, still current, that variation was due to iron and loadstone hidden in the bowels of the earth and under the sea, though he admitted the existence of areas of local abnormal attraction. He concluded that the whole earth was one great magnet, having four magnetic poles or points of attraction, two in either hemisphere, and that the one nearest the compass always exercised a predominant influence upon it.

Though he had insufficient data to determine accurately the position of these four poles, he placed the first one on or about the meridian of Land's End in Latitude 83° N. This pole, he said, chiefly governed the variation in Europe. The other northern pole, which influenced the compass in North America he placed on the meridian of the middle of California in an approximate latitude of 75° N. The two southern poles were placed by him as follows: One along the meridian of 20° W. of Magellan Straits in latitude 74° S. whose influence was felt primarily in South America and the Pacific, and the other, which dominated the Indian Ocean, in latitude 70° S. upon the meridian of about 120° E. from London.

---

[1]*Philosophical Transactions,* 1683.

He explained that lack of observations was the chief difficulty in finding out more of the magnetic theory of the earth and, said he, "It will require some hundreds of years to establish a compleat doctrine of the magnetical system." He was convinced, like Bond before him, that the poles had motions, but lack of information made it impossible for him to say whether such were circular or libratory; if circular about what centres, if libratory after what manner. These problems, he felt, could only be properly investigated after years of accurate observation, and their final solution was "reserved for the industry of future ages."

Dr. Halley did not rest upon his theory but continued to investigate it with the thoroughness which made him so renowned in the world of astronomy. It is not surprising, therefore, that we find a further account of his labours, a few years after he had presented his theories to the Royal Society. In 1692, he alluded to his former theory and said that two things had troubled him about it.[1] Firstly, he had never heard of any other magnet that had more than two poles, whereas he envisaged the earth to have four, and possibly more. Secondly, the poles of the earth shifted from place to place, but so far as he knew the positions of the poles of a loadstone remained constant.

He overcame the first objection by supposing that the earth was a hollow shell in which was placed another solid globe, with a fluid medium between them. Each of the two globes had two poles, and the periods of their movements were different, which accounted for the slow changes in variation.

With obvious regret he had to leave his theory as it was until much more investigation had been undertaken, and he ended with the following urgent recommendation: "I take leave to recommend to all masters of ships and all others, Lovers of material Truths, that they use their utmost diligence to make or procure to be made observations of these variations in all parts of the world, as well in the north as the south latitude (after the laudable custom of our East India Commanders) and that they please to communicate them to the Royal Society in order to leave as compleat a history as may be to those that are hereafter to compare all together and to compleat and perfect this abstruse theory."

Investigations into the theory of variation, the cause and amount of its annual changes, and the possibility of using accurate observations for variation to find the longitude (for the latter was not practical without a knowledge of the former) continued to occupy the attention of most European maritime nations until the general acceptance of the chronometer, about a century later.

It must not be assumed, however, that every seaman was diligently

---

[1]*Philosophical Transactions*, 1692.

searching for improvement in his art through a knowledge of variation, for we have it on good authority that many did not even trouble to allow for it in their steering, and some were incapable of finding it.   It was always the striving discoverer and explorer or the interested scientist who advanced the art of navigation, while the majority of seamen were suspicious or ignorant of any improvement.   Edward Harrison, an officer in the Royal Navy, expressed his opinion on the state of affairs, in 1696, in his *Idea Longitudinis,* one of the many treatises on the finding of longitude which appeared during the late seventeenth and early eighteenth centuries.   He observed that many ships had missed their objectives, and more had been totally lost for lack of knowing the variation than had been lost for want of knowing their longitudes.   He asked the question, "How many ships in sailing from the South Foreland to the Maese (Maas) hath been put to Northward of the Maese for want of minding the variation?" and added "For the like cause some ships have missed the island (of) Barbadoes and met with other dismal accidents." He impressed upon his readers the necessity of a true knowledge of the variation in the keeping of a sea reckoning, and regretted the ignorance of masters of ships upon this most important matter.   After relating a further instance of the result of such ignorance, whereby certain of His Majesty's ships had approached too near the Burlings, off the coast of Portugal, on a fine night with a fair wind, he added "I have belonged this war (English Succession War) to six several rates in the Navy and never saw an azimuth compass aboard any of them."   It was his opinion that every ship of war should carry at least three such instruments whereby the variation could be observed even though the ships just rode at anchor at the Nore or in the Downs.   In this matter he did not blame the Commissioners of the Navy, for they had taken care to provide azimuth compasses, and masters of men-of-war could have them for the asking, provided the boatswains indented for them.   He believed that many masters were ashamed to ask for them for they did not know what to do with them, and added, "the instruments if well used may be a means to help to save a ship and ship's companies lives, they are good to be used for the instruction of ship's company and youth, there is education in the Navy (little enough) that is good.   Navigation seems to decay or decline: I wish it be not a crime for some gentlemen in the Navy to understand it."

Even the masters of the East India Company's ships did not escape his criticism, and he suggested that more ships had been lost for want of a better knowledge of the variation than they were aware of. How far these strictures were warranted it is not easy to say, for Harrison made no mention of the imperfect knowledge in his day of ocean winds and currents, nor of the effects of storms and fogs. There were doubtless some good reasons for his contentions, which he exaggerated somewhat in order to bring about an improvement in the general state of the art of navigation.

From him, too, we learn of the use made by some of their observations for variation to find their longitude. He tells us of one, Captain William Wildey who had a good understanding of the variation, and to whom it was almost as good as the longitude between St. Helena and any part of the East Indies. Harrison himself claimed to have a deep knowledge of the variation in the East Indies, and told his readers that he understood it so well in that region, that he had offered, in discourse, in company, to go in a ship that sailed from any part of the Indian coast, bound any way two, three or four hundred leagues, and without keeping any reckoning for a week or ten days would, on any day when he could observe for variation, tell them the position of the ship as well as any who kept the most exact account. He qualified this, however, by adding, "almost as well, if you please, provided they had not seen the land since I saw it, and this I must have done by the latitude and variation observed."

He then gave the following example of the use to which an experienced observer could put his knowledge of the variation. On 30th October, 1688, with the Cape of Good Hope bearing north six or seven leagues, the mean variation by three azimuth compasses and nine observations was 10° west. On 16th November of the same year, the variation at St. Helena was 1° 4' west, giving a difference of variation between the two places of 8° 56'. The difference of longitude was 21° 54'. During this part of the voyage he found the variation to alter gradually and therefore from this and observations for latitude, the approximate longitude could be found in the future by working a simple proportion sum. It was his opinion that in most places in the world, not more than 20° or 30° apart, the variation of the variation was the same, and therefore by working on the differences in variation between them, as found by any reliable observer, the approximate longitudes could be found, by simple proportion, by anyone possessed of this information.

There were, however, certain regions where the variation did not change gradually as the ship made easting or westing, and there were places, fairly near to each other, where the annual change in it was not the same. To overcome these difficulties he suggested, "If the variation of the compass were better known and tables of variation for all the most noted parts in the world, as headlands, capes, islands—the tables calculated to a certain year, because of the increase or decrease of the variation—then the knowledge thereof would be almost as good as the longitude known."

Meanwhile, Dr. Halley's interest in the causes of variation had by no means faded and, in 1698, he received welcome encouragement to continue his researches at the public expense. The discovery of the laws by which the variation of the magnetic needle was governed had, as a result of England's increasing maritime importance, become an object of great public interest, and thus we find one of the King's ships placed at his disposal for the furtherance of this object. Sponsored by the Royal Society, he received from King William III. his commission as commander of the pink *Paramour*, with express orders to seek by observation the discovery of the rule of the variation and "to call at His Majesty's settlements in America, and make such further observations as are necessary for the better laying down of the longitude and latitude of those places, and to attempt the discovery of what land lies to the South of the western ocean."[1]

He left England in the November of 1698, and reached Madeira during the following month under the convoy of Admiral Benbow's squadron, after which he continued his voyaging alone. His subsequent experiences were, however, unenviable for upon arrival at St. Jago in the Cape Verde Islands, although flying British colours, he was fired upon by another British ship who believed him to be a pirate. He then sailed southwards to continue his observations, but with the approach of winter he decided to return northwards, after reaching a position 100 leagues south of the Equator, deeming it to be more satisfactory to adjust the longitudes of some of the West Indian islands. The voyage proving far from satisfactory, he returned home in the June of 1699, owing to the impossibility of doing useful work during the winter in the South Atlantic, and the insubordination of his first lieutenant and the crew. The reason for this insubordination appeared in his letter to Mr. Burchett, Secretary to the Admiralty, upon his arrival in England, part of which was as follows:—[2]

Plimouth,
June 23rd, 1699.

Honoured Sir,

I this day arrived home . . . . a further motive to hasten my return was the unreasonable carriage of my mate and Lieutenant who because perhaps I have not the whole Sea Dictionary so perfect as he has for a long time made it his business to represent me to the whole ship's company as a person wholly unqualified for the command their Lordships have given me and declaring that he was sent on board because their Lordships know my insufficiency . . . . "

I am,

Your Honours most obedient servant,
EDM. HALLEY.

---

[1]Vide *Biographia Britannica*, 1757; and *A Chronological History of the Voyages and Discoveries in the South Sea or Pacific Ocean*, Vol. IV., 1816, by Captain James Burney, R.N.

[2]Public Record Office, Captains' Letters. A.D. 1/1871.

In spite of these misfortunes, Halley accomplished some of the work he set out to do and, with the aid of a large map which he had constructed, gave an account of his voyage to the Royal Society, before setting out again to complete his observations.[1] His lieutenant having been tried by court martial and another appointed in his place, he left England in September, 1699, and continued his quest into the South Atlantic. On this voyage his ship's company apparently gave entire satisfaction and he recorded that, while outward bound, being unable to fetch Madeira by reason of the wind shifting he was obliged to put into Rio Janeiro in Brazil to get some rum for his ship's company. In several letters to the Secretary of the Admiralty he expressed gratification at the results of his observations for variation which, said he, "left no doubt of an exact conformity in the variation of the compass to a generall theory, which I am in great hope to settle effectively." He reached the latitude of 52° 30' S., where he encountered the southern ice, and being unable to penetrate further or to obtain useful observations on account of the cold and fogs he sailed northward, touching at Tristan da Cunha, St. Helena, the coast of Brazil, and finally reached the West Indies in the summer of 1700. From there he continued his observations in the North Atlantic, calling at Bermuda, and after reaching Newfoundland he returned to England at the end of August, 1700.

Although he does not appear to have made any formal report upon the results of his investigations, he published a chart shortly after his return showing the variation of the compass in the North and South Atlantic Oceans.[2] At about the same time, he also published a general chart of the world showing the variation in all those seas "where the English navigators were acquainted."[3] Both these charts were upon Mercator's Projection, and for the first time in the history of navigation, the distribution of terrestrial magnetism was accurately illustrated by means of lines of equal variation.[4] As a tribute to their illustrious originator these isogonic lines were, for a long time, referred to as "Halleyan lines". The general chart of the world was compiled from his own observations, and from those taken by reliable navigators in other seas unvisited by him. As his information of the variation in some parts, notably the northern Pacific Ocean, was very scanty, he had to rely upon his theories and the general trend of the isogonic lines indicated by such recorded observations as were obtainable.

Remarkable proof of the correctness of Halley's suppositions as to the

---

[1]Brit. Museum, Sloane MSS., 747, 17th August, 1699.

[2]"Halley's Equal Variation Chart", L. A. Bauer in the *Magazine of Terrestrial Magnetism*, 1896.

[3]*Biographia Britannica*, 1757.

[4]"In 1530, Alonso de Santa Cruz drew the first general variation map, founded, it must be admitted, on very imperfect materials." Humboldt's *Cosmos* (Sabine's Translation, 1858).

variations in the North Pacific was forthcoming in a most unexpected manner, some years later, when Anson captured the Spanish treasure ship which yearly voyaged from Manila to Mexico.[1]   In this ship were found charts and recorded observations, which had been compiled through 150 years of sailing on that route, which were confirmed by all the prisoners taken in her. Richard Walter, who recorded Anson's Voyage round the World, wrote, in 1748, as follows:— "I must add too (what in my opinion is far from being the least recommendation of these materials) that the observations of the variation of the compass in that Ocean, which are inserted in the chart from these Spanish journals, tend greatly to compleat the general system of the magnetic variation, of infinite import to the commercial and seafaring part of mankind. These observations were, though in vain, often publickly called for by our learned countryman the late Dr. Halley, and to his immortal reputation they confirm, as far as they extend, the wonderful hypothesis he had entertained on this head, and very nearly correspond in their quantity, to the predictions he published above fifty years since, long before he was acquainted with any one observation made in those seas."

The publication of Halley's chart of lines of equal variation added fresh vigour to the practice of finding the approximate longitude at sea by observing for latitude and variation. Falconer, in his *Marine Dictionary*, later in the eighteenth century, treated of the subject at considerable length. It must be noted that Halley, during his two voyages, had made substantial corrections in the longitudes of many places, by using his outstanding knowledge of astronomy and, as a result, his general chart of the world was probably one of the most accurate of the time. Falconer suggested that by using a chart of equal variation, the navigator could find his longitude by drawing upon it the parallel of his observed latitude. Where this line cut the line of variation which represented the observed variation would be the ship's position. The navigator was warned of the deficiencies of this method in certain circumstances, the first of which was that wherever the line of variation ran east and west, or within about 30° of that direction, the point of intersection between it and the parallel of latitude would be indefinite and might lead to grave error. At that time those conditions obtained chiefly on the west coast of Europe between the parallels of 45° N. and 53° N., and on the eastern coast of North America, but for many other parts of the world the variation chart could be used with considerable advantage. The ingenious Falconer, however, pointed out that the above drawback could be turned to profitable use for the correcting of the latitude, when conditions were such

[1]Manila had been taken by a Spanish fleet which sailed westwards from Mexico across the Pacific, in 1571. Shortly after this the Spaniards instituted an annual trading voyage between the two places, but took the greatest care to keep all accounts and information of the route secret from other nations.

that the meridian observation of the sun could not be taken. If the variation could be found with accuracy, then the east and west curve on the chart, which answered to that variation, would indicate the latitude of the ship.

The second source of error which had to be guarded against was the variation of the variation. To overcome this it was suggested that new charts should be published every seven or eight years, or whenever the changes in the variation made it expedient.

How long Halley's chart remained of great assistance would be difficult to say. It is possible that some navigators kept their copies up to date so far as it was possible for them to do from their own observations. Though Halley's system of showing the variation has remained to this day, his original chart quickly passed out of date, with respect to some parts of the world, owing to the constant changes in the amount of variation. Nothing was done to improve matters for over forty years, when the nautical publishers, William Mountaine and James Dodson, published a new variation chart adapted for the year 1744.[1]

For the compilation of this chart the proprietors were given access to the logs and journals of His Majesty's ships, together with those of most of the chartered companies, chief among which were the East India Company and the Royal Africa Company, and also to such other journals of privately owned ships which were of use. At the same time they urgently requested all navigators to keep records of variation so that better charts might be published more frequently.

Falconer tells us that this chart was well received and, as several instances of its great utility to navigators were communicated to the publishers, a corrected edition was published in 1756. Over 50,000 observations had been collected by this time, and it is safe to assume that the variations shown on this chart were substantially accurate for the more frequented parts of the oceans.

The introduction of the chronometer, during the latter half of the eighteenth century, whereby the longitude could be found with greater certainty than was ever possible by using the variation chart, probably had an injurious effect upon the popular demand for such charts. It became the general practice then to insert the variation at intervals upon all charts in the same manner as upon large scale charts to-day, and from the beginning of the nineteenth century little was said in the text books of finding the ship's position through the variation.

The establishment of the Hydrographic Department of the Admiralty, in 1795, ensured for the future a systematic collection and publication of all information regarding the variation of the compass in every part of the

---

[1]Vide *An Account of the Methods used to describe lines on Dr. Halley's Chart of the Terraqueus Globe,* by William Mountaine and James Dodson, 1746.

navigable world. Navigators placed reliance upon the information given in their charts and, in addition, most ships were, by then, equipped with azimuth compasses, and their officers were able to observe for changes in the variation as their ships progressed. For these reasons the theory of variation and its predicted amounts ceased to be of such vital interest to practical navigators, who were ensured of a regular supply of up-to-date charts, and were better equipped to rely upon themselves.

The causes of variation, nevertheless, continued to interest the scientist, and during the nineteenth century much research was undertaken by men of many nations to gain a fuller understanding of them. As the matter was then, as now, of purely academic interest to the practical navigator, it is no part of this book to follow it in detail.[1] It is of interest, however, to note that Dr. Halley's theory was not disproved by the labours of those who followed him in the investigation of terrestrial magnetism. A.G. Findlay, whose well-known and detailed work on the North Atlantic Ocean ran into many editions during the last century, informed the seaman in that work, in 1873, that Halley's theory of magnetism was supported by the results of the labours of Professor Hansteen, one of the chief promoters of the science. Findlay continued as follows:— "From his most valuable work (*Magnetismus der Erde*, Christiania, 1817) his views may be learned. Having collected all the observations of value that have been made on the variation of the needle, he proved that there were four points of convergence among the lines of variation; viz., a weaker and a stronger point, in the vicinity of each pole of the globe . . . Professor Hansteen considers that the strongest poles, N.S., lie almost diametrically opposite to each other, and the same is true of the weaker poles n.s. These four poles he found to have a regular motion obliquely; the two northern ones N.n., from West to East, and the two Southern ones S.s. from East to West. The following he found to be their periods of revolution, and their periods of revolution, and their positions in 1830:—

				Longitude from Greenwich.	Time of revolution round each pole of the earth.
Pole N.	69° 30′ N.	..	..	..	87° 19′ W.	1,740 years.
Pole S.	68° 40′ S.	..	..	..	131° 47′ E.	4,609 years.
Pole n.	85° 6′ N.	..	..	..	141° 17′ E.	860 years.
Pole s.	78° 29′ S.	..	..	..	137° 45′ W.	1,304 years.

From calculations based upon subsequent observations he slightly varied these positions and periods; but he has shown very clearly that the changes in the variation and dip of the needle, in both hemispheres, may be well explained by their motion."

---

[1]For useful references to the investigations conducted during the nineteenth century see *Memoir, descriptive and explanatory of the Northern Atlantic Ocean*, 1873 (13th Edition), by Alexander George Findlay, published for Richard Holmes Laurie.

Another writer of great eminence, Lord Kelvin, gave his opinion on the causes of variation towards the close of the last century as follows:— "In virtue of the irregularities of the distribution of terrestrial magnetism, rightly noticed by Gilbert, but wrongly attributed to magnetic continents, and mountains, and headlands, the lines of direction indicated by the compass are not great circles on the earth's surface, but somewhat irregular curves joining the north and south magnetic poles; and the magnetic equator is not a circle, but a sinuous line round the earth."

From the information available, Lord Kelvin constructed two diagrams to show the lines of direction of the mariner's compass in all parts of the world. One diagram showed the lines of direction in the northern hemisphere, and the other those in the southern.

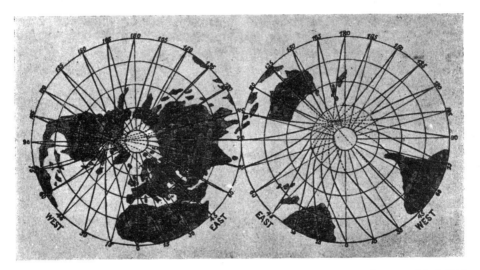

Reproduced by kind permission of the Executors of Lord Kelvin.

These lines of direction indicated the existence of two magnetic poles, one in about 70° N. and 100° W., and the other in about 73° S. and 146° E. If, said Lord Kelvin, these were the only poles, then Halley's celebrated hypothesis was disproved for the present time. He remarked, however, that some of the lines indicated a somewhat determined tendency to converge towards a point in the unexplored sea north of Siberia, in about 80° N. and 105° E., and it seemed not improbable that there was another north magnetic pole in that region. In the above diagrams it will be seen that in the high latitudes the lines of direction are not drawn with the boldness that exists elsewhere and that, from lack of observations, their directions have been decided in a somewhat arbitrary manner.

L

Lord Kelvin concluded his observations as follows:— "Even should it turn out that there is only one north and one south magnetic pole now, it by no means follows that there may not have been at other times of the history of terrestrial magnetism more than two magnetic poles. Indeed, Halley had seemingly strong reason for inferring two north poles from observations of early navigators, showing large westerly variation of the compass in Hudson's Bay and in Smith's Sound (longitude 80° W., latitude 78° N.), and at sea in the north-west Atlantic; at different times, from 1616 to 1682, when the compass in England was pointing due north (in the earlier part of the period a few degrees to the east of north, in the latter a few degrees to the west). It may be that the present tendency to converge to a point in the unexplored Siberian Arctic Sea may be a relic of a north magnetic pole which existed in Halley's time and has since ceased to exist; but the amount of trustworthy information available scarcely suffices to justify such a conclusion. One thing is certain, the distribution of terrestrial magnetism has been changing ever since accurate observations were made upon it, and it is now enormously different from what it was in the year 1600."

It must be left to the future to discover all the causes of variation and its variations, and to divine the intricacies of their effects upon each other. Over 200 years after Halley first expressed the need for fuller and more accurate observation to establish a complete doctrine of the magnetical system, Captain Scott, R.N., the British Antarctic explorer, wrote in 1907: "The general reader may well wonder why so much trouble should be taken to ascertain small differences in the earth's magnetism, and he could scarcely be answered in a few words. Broadly speaking, the earth is a magnet, and its magnetism is constantly changing; but why it is a magnet, or why it changes, or indeed what magnetism may be, is unknown, and obviously the most helpful road to the explanation of a phenomenon is to study it. For many reasons the phenomenon of magnetism could be recorded in few more useful places than our winter station in the Antarctic."[1]

By means of methods already described, the navigator has, for many years, been able to find his compass error in every part of the navigable world, and to overcome the difficulties imposed upon the steering of a true course by the ever-changing variation and the magnetic field of the ship itself. That there are two primary magnetic poles, one north and the other south, is undoubted and that, in addition to these, there are also other areas of abnormal magnetic intensity must be conceded. That these poles move is certain, for variation and dip vary year by year, but our knowledge of their exact movements must await further experiment and observation.[2]

---

[1] *The Voyage of the Discovery*, by Captain Robert F. Scott, R.N., Vol. I.
[2] See *Dictionary of Applied Physics*, MacMillan & Co., 1922.

CHAPTER IV.

LOG LINE AND LOG BOOK.

BEFORE a satisfactory method was evolved for the finding of longitude at sea, navigators had to rely principally upon three things in order to find their positions during ocean passages. These three things were:—

1. Their ability to find their latitude.
2. Their knowledge of the variation of the compass and the resultant true course steered by their magnetic compasses.
3. Their estimation or observation of the distances run upon those courses.

We have already seen how, as the years progressed, the navigator was able to find his latitude with increasing accuracy and how, with the compass he was able to keep a course with ever-growing precision.

Before proceeding to examine the methods which he adopted to make the fullest use of those abilities, some consideration must be given to the means whereby he measured his distance sailed from day to day when out of sight of land. There are two ways of measuring distance, one by actual measurement of the route traversed, and the other by calculation based upon two known factors, speed and time interval. The first way had been used by land surveyors for many centuries before the navigator was seriously concerned with his distance sailed. It was not until he attempted ocean navigation, with his compass and astrolabe, that speed, time and distance began to assume any great importance in his eyes. He was unable to use the land surveyor's method upon the unstable sea, and was compelled to resort to the alternative and adapt his means and knowledge to its solution. Happily, both means and knowledge were at his disposal, for he could measure time within a near approach to the truth by means of the sand glass, and could estimate his speed, either by guesswork or, as will be seen later, calculation.

Estimation of speed by guesswork was not so haphazard as it sounds, for it was really an estimation based upon experience. Every observant man, and the seaman by the very nature of his calling had to be observant, could form some idea of the speed of his ship at sea by comparison with his own walking pace. Ships in the fifteenth and even later centuries were not speedy, and walking or running pace would approach very closely to their ordinary or extraordinary speeds respectively. Again, the time taken to sail from one headland to another when compared with the distance between them, which could be measured on their charts, would help seamen to judge their rates of progress, under similar wind and weather conditions, when out of sight of land.

Greater accuracy than this, however, was called for on long ocean voyages, when the accumulation of errors in the judgment of speed would be considerable. It is not surprising, therefore, to find that during the early decades of the sixteenth century an effort was made to calculate the speed of a ship with greater accuracy than was possible by experienced guesswork. This effort took the form of the log ship, with which every seaman to-day is acquainted. The first certain evidence of its employment is, according to Alexander Humboldt, to be found in Antonio Pigafetta's ship's journal of Magellan's voyage in an entry for the month of January, 1521. Neither Columbus nor Vasco da Gama, nor any other navigators prior to that date, mentioned its use, and it is assumed that they estimated their ships' rates by eye alone and judged of the distance run by time measured by hour glasses.[1]

The use of the log ship and line was to find how far the ship ran in a given time. Then by simple proportion it could be calculated how far the ship sailed, under the same conditions, in one hour, in other words the speed in nautical miles per hour. Probably the earliest account of this type of log was given by an Englishman, William Bourne, in 1574, when he wrote:— "And to knowe the shippes way some doo use this which (as I take) is very good: they have a pece of wood, and a line to vere out over borde, with a final line of a great lengthe, which they make fast at one ende, and at the other ende, and middle they have a peece of a lyne, which they make fast with a small thred to stande lyke unto a crowfoote: for this purpose that it should drive asterne as fast as the shippe doth go away from it, always having the line so ready that it goeth out as fast as the shippe goeth. In like manner they have either a minute or an houre glasse, or else a knowne parte of an houre, by some number of wordes, or such other lyke, so that the line being vered out and stopt juste with that tyme that the glasse is out or the number of wordes spoken, which done, they hale in the logge or peece of wood again, and looke howe many fadome the shippe hath gone in that time: that being knowne, what parte of a league soever it be, they multiplie the number of fadome the shippe hath gone in that time: that being knowne, what parte of a league soever it be, they multiplie the number of fadomes by the portion of time or parte of an houre. Whereby you maye knowe justly howe many legues and parts of a league the ship goeth in an houre, *i.e.*, for an Englishe league doth containe 2500 fadome. And a Spanish or Portugale league doth contayne 2857 fadome."[2]

The piece of wood, referred to above, was the log chip or ship. It was

---

[1]*Cosmos*, by Alexander von Humboldt (Sabine's Translation, 1858).
[2]*Regiment of the Sea*, by William Bourne, First Edition, 1574.

flat, and cut in quadrantal form, with its circular side weighted with sufficient lead to make it float upright. The log line, usually of about 150 fathoms in length, was attached to the wood by means of a small bridle, so that when the log was hove overboard it would assume a position of maximum resistance, at right angles to the course of the vessel. Then as the vessel progressed the log remained in situ, provided the line was allowed to run out freely. At the end of the time interval allowed, usually about 30 seconds, the line was stopped, hauled in, and measured. When the log was first used it is probable that the line was measured in fathoms, as it was hauled in, by stretching the arms to full extent in the way common to all seamen of all periods.

Bourne referred to the difference in length between the English and Spanish leagues. The English league contained 2500 fathoms, and the Spanish 2857, but whereas the English navigators allowed 20 leagues to one degree of a great circle, the Spaniards and Portuguese reckoned 17½ of their leagues to one degree. From this it followed that according to English ideas there were 300,000 feet to one degree, and to Spanish and Portuguese ideas 299,985 English feet to the same unit. The difference between them was negligible, and it can therefore be taken that the principal navigators of the late sixteenth century were agreed upon the measurement of 300,000 feet to one degree of a great circle. Unfortunately this figure was in error by about one fifth short of the true measurement. Until the beginning of ocean navigation the true dimensions of the earth mattered little to anybody. Those who thought about the matter at all seem to have been content to accept the figures given by Ptolemy in his "Geographia" during the second century A.D., who in his turn had accepted the calculations of Posidonius (135 B.C.-50 B.C.).

The first serious attempt to determine the circumference of the earth had been made by Eratosthenes (c.276-196 B.C.), whose measurement of an arc of the meridian of Alexandria had shown it to be about 252,000 stadia. Taking the length of a stadium as 600 feet means that his measure of one degree was equal to about 420,000 feet, which was later found to be considerably in excess of the true amount. A further measure was made by Posidonius of 180,000 stadia for the circumference, or 300,000 feet to one degree. This later figure was adopted by succeeding geographers, including Ptolemy, and became that upon which navigators based their calculations of distance run by reference to their log lines.

Although, as we have seen, English and Continental navigators were agreed upon Ptolemy's measure for one degree, one fruitful source of error existed for English seamen, in that their length of a league varied from the others. This would have been of little account had England at that time produced her own charts. As she did not, and relied upon those of other nations, William Bourne issued a warning on this account in the following words, "But heere is one thing to be noted (as I suppose) in the most part of cardes they allow for every degree but 17 leagues and a halfe: your cardes be most commonly made in Lishborne in Portugal, in Spayne or else in Fraunce. But as I take it, we in England should allowe 60 myles to one degree, that is, after three myles to one of our Englishe leagues, wherefore twenty of our Englishe leagues should answeare to one degree, for that three of our myles will not make one of their leagues. And because they make their accountes by their leagues in the cardes, and not by ours, therefore I will shewe you by our Englishe myles. An Englishe myle conteyneth a thousande pases and every pase five foote and every foote twelve inches. Now some think that a pase cannot be fyve foote: but a pase geometricall is two reasonable steppes, for it can not be a pase untyll the hynder foote be removed forwardes and those two steppes wyll containe five foote."

There is some difficulty in reconciling the different accounts of the units of linear measurement in England during the latter half of the sixteenth century. William Cuningham, a doctor of physic, who published a book on cosmography, in 1559, gave the following table of measurement. His book was not primarily a treatise on navigation, but took the form of a dialogue between a philosopher and a student of cosmographical science.[1] In this he said the chief measures were a pace, a furlong, a league and a mile and a degree.

| A barley corne is the least measure, yet from it do all other measures procede, as | A finger breadth
An inche
A hand breadth
A spanne
A fote
A geometricall pase
An Englishe pearche
A furlonge
An Englishe furlonge
A legue
An Italian mile
A common German mile
An Englishe mile | Conteyninge in it | 4 barley cornes
3 fingers
4 fingers
3 hand breadth
4 hand breadth
5 fine fote
16 feet and a ¼
125 pace
660 fote or 132 pase
1500 pace
1000 pace or 8 furlongs
32 furlongs
8 furlongs |

In the above table it will be seen that two kinds of furlongs are mentioned, one of 125 paces and the English furlong of 132 paces.

By the first measure an English mile is equal to 8 × 125 × 5 feet or 5000 feet, and by the second 8 × 132 × 5 feet, 5280 feet. Cuningham went on to say that Pliny had determined the length of a furlong to be 125 paces, and that 8 of them made an Italian or English mile. He may have meant to imply by this that the geographical mile in England was equal to 5000 feet, in which case he agreed with the navigators, but the mention of English furlongs of 132 paces, which made one mile equal to 5280 feet (an English Statute mile) leaves the matter in some doubt. Again, his account of a league

---

[1]*The Cosmographical Glasse.*

containing 1500 paces is not clear, for it would allow only 2500 feet to a mile, a measure accepted by nobody. It may be, of course, that this figure was a misprint. He ended his account of such measures by saying there were 253,440 barley corns in an English mile, which for 5280 feet meant that there were 48 in an English foot, or 4 to the inch.

John Davis, in his *Seaman's Secrets*, 1594, allowed 20 leagues to 60 miles or one degree, and said that "a mile is limited to be 1000 paces, every pace five foote, every foote 10 inches, and every inch 3 barley cornes dry and round, after our English accompt, which for the use of Navigation is the only test of all other." He obviously made a mistake in ascribing only 10 inches to a foot, but seems to have been satisfied that for navigational purposes one mile was to be reckoned as 5000 feet.

Whatever the true units of measurement were in England, it seems fairly certain, as we have already remarked, that navigators in general accepted the equivalent of 300,000 English feet to one degree of a great circle, and calculated their speed by log upon that assumption. There is good reason to believe, however, that the log was not generally adopted by seamen during the sixteenth century. Apart from William Bourne, no writers on navigation seem to have deemed it worthy of mention. Davis's advice to the seaman, in 1594, for the keeping of the account of distance at sea was, "a careful consideration of the number of leagues that the ship sayleth in every houre or watch, to the neerest estimation that possibly he can give," from which it would appear that he who based his entire book upon his own wide experience at sea, favoured the method of estimating a ship's speed by careful judgment, and took little notice of the log line.

The early years of the seventeenth century witnessed an increasing interest in the use of the log, and further attempts were made to ascertain the dimensions of the earth with greater accuracy in order that the navigator might be able to place greater reliance upon it. Frequent mention was made of its use by navigators during those years, and their journals often referred to it in terms similar to the extracts given below.

Extracts from the journal of Captain Anthony Hippon, kept during a voyage to the East Indies, 1612.[1]

"From the foure and twentieth at noon till the five and twentieth at noon (March, 1612) we had the wind betweene N.N.W. and S.S.W. and we steered away S.S.E. We ran by the logge one and twentie leagues, and then we were in the latitude of fiftie seven minutes to the southward of the Line."

"From the five and twentieth at noon till the six and twentieth at noon we had the wind variable between N.N.W. and W.S.W. We steered S.S.E.

---

[1] *Purchas, His Pilgrimes*, 1625.

We ran fifteen leagues by the logge and then we were in the latitude of one degree thirtie minutes."

Many writers, both English and foreign, described the log in their works during the first half of the seventeenth century, and their references, coupled with the records of their contemporaries at sea, indicate the fairly general adoption of the log as an aid to navigation during that time.

In 1615, Willebrord Snellius, a Dutch astronomer and mathematician, took upon himself the task of determining the length of a degree of the meridian. His figure of 352,347 feet showed the great error in the popular figure of 300,000 feet, which up to then was used by navigators. One navigator, at all events, was quick to see the advantage in using the lately calculated and more accurate figure, and used it upon his voyage to discover the North West Passage, in 1633. This was Captain Thomas James, after whom the bay to the south east of Hudson's Bay was named. In the account of his "strange and dangerous" voyage, as he described it, he related how, before leaving Bristol, he caused many small glasses to be made, whose part of time he knew with accuracy, and marked off the log line in accordance with Snellius's measure of feet to one degree.[1]

By this time it had become the general practice to mark the log line so as to facilitate the calculation of speed. This was done in the following way. If a half minute glass was used then the length of line necessary to indicate a speed of one mile (of 5000 feet) per hour was $\dfrac{30 \times 5{,}000 \text{ ft.}}{60 \times 60}$ or $41\frac{2}{3}$ feet. In other words, at one mile per hour the ship would advance, and the line would run out $41\frac{2}{3}$ feet in 30 seconds. The line was then divided as follows:— From 10 to 20 fathoms, depending on the size of ship, were allowed as "stray line" next to the log ship, to ensure it being clear of the effect of the wake. The end of this stray line was marked either by a knot or a piece of red or white rag, and then from there the line was divided into sections of $41\frac{2}{3}$ feet or 42 feet, each section being marked by a knot in the line. Thus came into being the term of knot as the measure of a ship's speed in nautical miles per hour.

Edmund Gunter, an English mathematician, approved of the measurements given by Snellius, and in a mathematical work, in 1623, hinted that English seamen would be well advised to adopt the new figures, instead of persisting in the old erroneous markings adopted from Ptolemy.[2]

Another method of estimating the speed of the ship was mentioned by Gunter, which had for some time been used by navigators, especially the

---

[1] *The Strange and Dangerous Voyage of Captaine Thomas James in his intended Discovery of the N.W. Passage into the South Sea*, 1633.

[2] *Use of the Sector*, Edmund Gunter, 1623.

Dutch in their numerous voyages to the East Indies. Indeed its popularity with them had earned for it the title of the Dutchman's log. This method was simply a variant of the ordinary log, and called for two marks on the ship's side at a known distance apart, with an observer stationed abreast of each of them. The foremost observer threw a floating object overboard and counted or measured the seconds from the time it was abreast of his mark until it was abreast of the observer further aft. The speed was then calculated by simple proportion, as it had been in the early days of the log line. There were several objections to this method, which some writers were quick to condemn, the chief of which was the shortness of time of the observation (for the marks were seldom spaced more than 40 feet apart) when a very small error in the performance of the operation would be magnified excessively in the multiplication afterwards. Other objections were the difficulties of accurately sighting the object abreast of the two marks, and the effect on it of the disturbed water near the ship's side caused by the ship's forward motion. A further source of inaccuracy in this method was that, whereas with the log line the time interval was always constant whatever the speed and could therefore be measured by a sand glass specially prepared for the purpose, the time interval was not constant and was usually measured by repeating a number of words. This system of time measurement, already referred to by William Bourne, consisted of repeating a word or phrase, the speaking of which was known to occur a certain number of times during a given number of seconds. Thus, for example, one writer suggested that the time a man took to count sixty, pronouncing every number as fast as he conveniently and distinctly could, would take about 30 seconds:[1] while another suggested using the beatings of the pulse to time the interval.

In spite of the above objections, however, it is interesting to remark that the Dutchman's log was still popular in Dutch ships at the end of the eighteenth century. Captain Bligh, on his return to England in a Dutch ship, in 1789, after completing his memorable boat journey across the Pacific, remarked that the navigators in the ship hove no log. He added, "I was told that the company do not allow it. Their manner of computing their run, is by means of a measured distance of 40 feet, along the ship's side: they take notice of any remarkable patch of froth, when it is abreast the foremost end of the measured distance, and count half seconds till the mark of froth is abreast the after end. With the number of half seconds thus obtained, they divide the number 48, taking the product for the rate of sailing in geographical miles in one hour, or the number of Dutch miles in four hours."[2] From the measured distance of 40 feet, and the constant divisor of 48, it can readily be shown that

---

[1]Richard Norwood, *The Seaman's Practice*, 1637.
[2]*Bligh and the Bounty*, edited by Laurence Irving, 1936.

the measure of a geographical or nautical mile adopted by seamen in the eighteenth century was 6000 feet. In order to show how this new figure was arrived at, it is necessary to give some account of the experiments which followed closely upon those conducted by Snellius, in 1615.

In 1635, Richard Norwood, an English mathematician, applied himself to the task of measuring an arc of a terrestrial meridian in order to improve the practice of navigation. While he was of the opinion that the art of navigation had reached a greater perfection in his day than it had in any former age, yet, as he said, it still remained imperfect in some points. The practice in his day relied upon the knowledge of latitudes, courses and distances, and actuated by the conviction that the way of finding distances at sea by the log line was "opinionative and conjectural rather than certain", he resolved to remedy this defect. In order to find the true measure of a degree of a great circle, he proceeded, as the ancient geographers had done before and as Edward Wright had recommended as the most perfect way, on the principle that as a measured distance on a terrestrial meridian was to its arc on a celestial great circle; so was the circumference of the earth (spherical) to 360°.

His first task was to find the difference in latitude between two parallels, in other words, to measure an arc of a celestial great circle. For this purpose he chose two places, York and London. In 1633, he had observed the apparent meridian altitude of the sun, at the time of the summer solstice, near the Tower of London. Two years later, in June 1635, he took a similar observation of the sun, in York, upon a day when its declination was the same as it had been at the time of the observation in London. By so doing he was able to calculate the difference in latitude between the two places, without having to make any allowance in his observations for declination, refraction or parallax. This difference he found to be 2° 28'. He then began the complicated task of finding the actual distance between these two places by land measurement, in other words to measure an arc of a terrestrial meridian. This measurement between the two parallels was arrived at by keeping a record of all distances measured in every direction in which he travelled along the winding roads between York to London. At the end of every day he resolved these courses and distances, as we may call them, by traverse table, to find the difference in latitude and departure made good every day, until finally he was in possession of the actually measured differences between York and London.

The result of his labours was that he found the difference in latitude by mensuration to be 9149 chains of 99 feet, from which he calculated that one degree of 60 miles was equal to 3709 chains or 367,196 feet, which, for the sake of convenience, he called 367,200 feet. This figure was only approximate, as will be appreciated from his own words, in which he refers to his work and some of the difficulties encountered. He wrote in his *Seaman's Practice*, 1637, "Now touching the experiment, I confesse, that to have made it so exactly as were requisite, would have required much more time and expence than mine ability would reach unto: Yet, having made observation at York, as aforesaid, I measured (for the most part) the way from thence to London, and where I measured not, I paced; (wherein, through custome, I usually come very neer the truth) observing all the way as I came, with a circumferentor, (theodolite), all the principal angles of position or windings of the way (with convenient allowance for other lesser windings, ascents and descents) and these I laid not down by a protractor after the usual manner, but framed a table much more exact and fit for this purpose . . . . Now touching the angles of ascent and descent of hills and valleys, to have observed them exactly, would have required more time and charge than I could of myself bestow; yet I made allowance for such of them as were of most moment."

It will be seen that Norwood's approximate figure of 367,200 feet to one degree, or 6120 feet to one geographical mile, agreed fairly closely with Snellius's measure of 352,347 feet, which gave about 5,872 feet to the mile. These two experiments proved, without doubt, that the measure of 5000 feet, used in navigation, was erroneous and misleading. In spite of this, however, many navigators stuck, in their conservative way, to the old measure and continued to knot their log lines at every 42 feet, instead of every 51 feet which the revised measurements called for. A writer on navigation, almost a hundred years later, after describing Norwood's experiment, remarked that English sailors (or some of them) were so bigoted to custom that they still spliced their knots at intervals of only 42 feet.[1] Later writers, even at the beginning of the nineteenth century, had occasion to remark on the same thing, though it would appear that most of the "bigots" had by that time made some concession to the truth by reducing their sand glasses from 30 seconds to 24 or 25 seconds.

There were still some navigators of experience during the seventeenth century who preferred to rely upon their own estimation rather than trust even to the revised log line. Notable among these were Captain John Smith, sometime Governor of Virginia and Admiral of New England, who wrote in his *Seaman's Grammar*, which passed through several editions during that century, "Some use a log line and a minute glasse to know what way she makes, but that is so uncertain it is not worth the labour to trie it."[2] Another writer who had little faith in it was a naval lieutenant, Edward Harrison who, in a treatise upon longitude, expressed the opinion that the log was but a false supposition to find the distance run. It had been experienced, he said, in

[1]John Collier, *Compendium Artis Nautical*, 1729.
[2]*The Seaman's Grammar*, Revised Editions 1652, 1691.

one fleet that some ships had logged 70 miles in twenty-four hours, and others 80 miles, while still others showed a run of only 40 miles, although all the ships were not above one league apart during that period.

There were several reasons why the earlier navigators did not question the old measure of 5000 feet to a geographical mile, which were summed up by Norwood at the end of his account of his own labours. He suggested three reasons which had contributed to the error being persisted in.

Firstly. The error counteracted to some extent the contrary error introduced into navigation by the general use of the plane chart, in which every parallel of latitude was made equal in length to the equator. The result of this was that, except at the equator, the measurement of distance shown on the chart was greater than it ought to be. The excess so caused was greatly mitigated by accounting the distance by log less than it in fact should have been. To illustrate this he remarked that it could be shown on a globe that all meridians converged towards the poles, and if two meridians were 10° (or 600 miles) apart at the equator they would be found only 490 miles apart in the latitude of 35°, or about 3,000,000 feet. In other words 300,000 feet to 1°, which was the old measure used by navigators. Thus, to seamen navigating in a mean latitude of 35° N. or S. upon a plane chart, the old measure answered perfectly well when they sailed upon more or less easterly or westerly courses. There is something to be said for this contention, especially when it is remembered that a great deal of the shipping in those days navigated upon such courses in such latitudes in crossing the Atlantic from the Spanish coast to the West Indies or in running eastwards from the Cape of Good Hope. As Norwood pointed out, too, the navigator was not greatly concerned then about logging his distance when his course lay approximately upon a meridian, for under such conditions he had a much more certain way of reckoning, namely by observing daily for latitude when the sun or stars were on the meridian.

Secondly. The navigator as a rule preferred to have his reckoning somewhat ahead of the actual position of the ship, so that he did not fall in with the land unexpectedly. Such a result was obtained when the distance run by the log was in excess of the true distance sailed.

Thirdly. Up to that time there had been no reliable evidence that the old measure of one degree was wrong. Though, doubtless, many navigators had found errors in their reckonings, they could not know with certainty where the fault lay. They might have been due to bad steering, currents, leeway, the variation of the compass, faulty charts or to a combination of these causes or others, most of which were the result of the paucity of reliable information.. Another reason, hinted at by Norwood, why old seamen often disdained to use the log at all, and preferred to judge their speed from experience, was lest they should be thought young and inexperienced. This extreme prejudice, however, gradually disappeared and, by the middle of the seventeenth century, the log in one form or another was generally adopted at sea.

After Norwood's approximate determination of the magnitude of the earth, further and more elaborate investigations were made during the century which followed his experiment. Chief among these investigators were several eminent French astronomers and mathematicians, the near agreement of whose measures taken at the same place was proof of their accuracy, and the comparison of whose measures taken at different places confirmed Newton's theory that the earth was not a sphere but a spheroid.[1]

Eventually, in 1756, the Royal Academy of Sciences of Paris appointed a number of astronomers to measure the length of a degree of latitude between Paris and Amiens. Their measurements, reduced to English units, showed that a nautical mile contained 6080 feet. Though this figure is not exact for all latitudes, owing to the spheroidal shape of the earth, it is exact enough for all purposes of practical navigation, and represents a mean between the maximum and minimum quantities observed or calculated since.[2]

Towards the end of the eighteenth century, therefore, accurate navigation was practised and speed was measured with reference to the new figure, 6080, and the log line was graduated accordingly. Thus with a 30 second glass the interval between two adjacent knots on the line was $50\frac{2}{3}$ feet, but because careful navigators preferred to have their reckoning ahead of the ship they usually reduced the interval to about 48 feet. Other slight variations were also resorted to in order to achieve the same object, but they were comparatively unimportant and do not call for any special mention.

The increasing desire for accuracy in navigation during the latter half of the eighteenth century was reflected in many contemporary works upon the subject. All said very much the same thing, and all seemed to be agreed that a properly marked log line was the best practical method of calculating speed at sea. While this was agreed, many writers drew attention to the several errors to which this method was subject, and warned navigators to be on their guard against them. It was observed that a new log line was prone to contract considerably, and that one part of it might shrink more or less than another part, according to whether it was more or less exposed

---

[1]Further reference to these attempts is given in a tract entitled, *Improvements in the Doctrine of the Sphere*, 1765, by Samuel Dunn, Professor of Mathematics.

[2]For many years, a nautical mile has been accepted in the U.K. as 6080 feet, this is an approx. average of the length of 1′ latitude at the Equator and at the Poles, the values being 6046·4 feet and 6107·8 feet respectively.

An International Nautical Mile is a fixed length of 1852 metres (6076·1 feet). This value was suggested by the International Hydrographic Bureau in 1929, it has been adopted by most maritime nations. It has replaced the nautical mile of 6080 feet.

to the action of water. To avoid this source of error the navigator was advised to use a log line of cotton yarn, which would not be liable to shrink. Failing such a luxury, he was strongly urged to examine his line frequently and check the distances between the knots, an operation which was facilitated in most ships by having permanent marks of nails driven into the deck. The sand glass, too, was affected by moisture, and in very dry weather might register as much as 3 seconds less than 30, whereas in a damp atmosphere it tended to be sluggish and take about 33 seconds to run out. This latter source of error could often be overcome by taking the sand out of the glass and warming it, but, in order to avoid errors arising from whatever cause, the prudent seaman was advised to test his glass periodically in the following way:—
"On a round nail hang a string that has a musket ball fixed to one end, carefully measuring betwixt the centre of the ball and the string's loop over the peg $39\frac{1}{8}$ inches, being the length of a second pendulum; then swing it and count one for every time it passes under the peg, beginning at the second time it passes: and the number of swings made during the time the glass is running out shows the seconds it contains."[1]

Other sources of error, which were not so easily corrected, were the friction on the reel, upon which the line was wound, while the log was running out, and the lightness of the wooden log, both of which tended to bring the log home while it was being used, thereby showing less than the actual speed.

It was the usual practice in ships of the Royal Navy, East India Company and in some other well conducted ships on long voyages to heave the log at the end of every hour, while in coasters and those on short voyages once every two hours was deemed sufficient. The speed shown by the log at these times was not necessarily taken to be the average speed made good by the ship during the preceding hour or hours. It was usually left to the officer of the watch to arrive at the mean speed, basing his estimation upon that shown by the log, and taking into account the variable force of wind, temporary calms or passing squalls, and the amount of extra sail set or that taken in between the intervals of heaving the log. Other allowances were also made in order to arrive at an accurate rate, for example, when the ship was running before the wind with a heavy following sea the log was liable to indicate less than the true speed. In these circumstances, therefore, it was customary to allow one mile in ten to the distance run in order that the ship should not overrun her log distance.[2]

The care and interest which some navigators of the late eighteenth century took in the measurement of their distance run is well illustrated in the journal of Captain Phipps, R.N., who undertook a voyage towards the

---

[1]*Falconer's Marine Dictionary.*
[2]John Hamilton Moore, *The New Practical Navigator*, 1800.

North Pole, at His Majesty's command, in the year 1773. On the 6th June of that year he made the following entry:—"At five in the morning, the wind at S.S.W. weighed, and stood out to sea, finding I might lose two tides by going through Yarmouth Roads. Examined the log line, which was marked forty-nine feet; the glass was found, by comparing it with the time-keeper, to run thirty seconds."[1] The observations of this scientific navigator upon the respective merits of the different spacings between the knots on the log line are worthy of attention, for two reasons. Firstly, he was deeply interested in the subject and, secondly, as his course often lay upon a meridian he was ideally situated to check his log distances by frequent observations for latitude.

He experimented with log lines knotted at intervals of 45 feet, 49 feet, and 51 feet respectively, besides testing other forms of logs, which will be referred to later. His considered opinion upon the earlier spacing of 42 feet and the later spacings already mentioned, was that had the errors in distance been only attributable to faulty markings of the line nothing would have been easier than to have had that difficulty removed by carefully comparing the different measures with observations, and adopting that which was found to correspond best with them. The distance measured by any log, however, was rendered so uncertain by many accidental circumstances that it was difficult and almost impossible, to find any length of line which would show invariably the true distance run by a ship. In addition to the sources of error in the log already referred to by Falconer, he enumerated several more, which either, affected the log itself or interfered with the finding of a mean speed from it. These were: 1. The effects of currents. 2. The yawing of the ship with the wind aft or upon the quarter, under which circumstances the ship was seldom steered within a point on either side of the course. Though the ship would make good her intended course, provided she yawed equally on either side, yet the distance made good would be considerably reduced. 3. The ship being driven on by the swell.

Taking into account all the circumstances which affected the log and the distance run he came to the conclusion, upon this voyage, that, using a 30 seconds glass, the errors of the log marked at every 45 feet would keep the navigator on the safe side, i.e., his reckoning ahead of the ship, and the lines marked at the greater intervals would always indicate a run less than that actually performed.

Various attempts were made, from about the middle of the eighteenth century onwards, to overcome some of the errors inherent even in the most accurately marked log line. The first departure from the normal, which called

[1]Constantine John Phipps, *A Voyage towards The North Pole*, published 1774. This expedition was undertaken by two ships, *Racehorse* and *Carcass*. One of the midshipmen in H.M.S. *Carcass* was young Horatio Nelson who, during the voyage, experienced his fight with a bear; the story of which has often been told.

forth much comment and trial, appears to have been an improved form of log line, which was invented by a French scientist, M. Bouguer, about 1747. The principal object of this improvement was to counteract the effect of wind and sea upon the surface of the log ship, and to overcome the tendency of the friction on the log reel to cause the log to come home, *i.e.*, be dragged along with the ship. Bouguer's log consisted of a cone of varnished wood to which was attached a metal sinker of a weight sufficient to allow only the top of the cone to appear on the sea surface. These two parts were connected to each other by a line of about 50 feet in length. The ordinary log line, with knots spaced at intervals of 51 feet, was attached to the cone, and the whole was hove and used in the customary way. Captain Phipps, who experimented with this improvement, warmly recommended it to seamen. He found it much more reliable than the common log and found that, to a great extent, it overcame the errors it was designed to rectify.

By the beginning of the nineteenth century, other forms of logs, the forerunners of the modern mechanical logs, had made their appearances, but there is little record, in contemporary treatises on navigation, that such were used extensively by the practical navigator. Two of these new types had, indeed, been tested by Captain Phipps in 1773. They were named perpetual logs, because they were designed to be streamed throughout a voyage, and by mechanical devices showed the total distance run from the time of streaming. Both logs, the one invented by Russell and the other by Foxon, were constructed upon the principle that a spiral in moving its own length in the direction of its axis, through a resisting medium, makes one revolution about its axis. If, therefore, the revolutions of the spiral were registered, the number of times it moved its own length through the water would be known. In Russell's log the motion of a half spiral, of copper, with two threads, was communicated to clock work inboard by means of a line, one end of which was secured to the spiral, and the other to a spindle, which set the clockwork or mechanical recording apparatus in motion. The log then being towed astern of the ship recorded its revolutions upon a dial easily accessible to the observer, and the distance run was easily calculated whenever it was required. Foxon's log, on the other hand, was a whole spiral, made of wood with a single thread, which also registered its revolutions inboard. By means of larger mechanical devices, however, three dials were supplied, two of them to mark the total distance run, and the other, divided into miles and fathoms, to be used in conjunction with a 30 seconds glass to enable the observer to calculate the actual speed of the ship at any moment.

Phipps's opinion on this type of log was that though it would be, in some degree, affected by the same exterior forces as the common log, yet it would have "the advantage of every other in smooth water and moderate weather, when it is necessary to stand on one course for any particular distance, especially in the night, or a fog, as it measures exactly the distance run. It will also be very useful in finding the trim of a ship when alone, as well as in surveying a coast in a single ship, or in measuring distances in a boat between headlands or shoals, when a base is not otherwise to be obtained; both which it will do with the greatest accuracy in smooth water, with a large wind, and no tide or current." Notwithstanding these advantages, which made it useful and worth having, he doubted whether it would ever wholly displace the common log, his reason being as he so aptly said: "Machines easily repaired or replaced (such as the common log) have advantages at sea, which should not lightly be given up for others more specious."

Other types of logs in existence at this time mentioned by a well-known writer, in a book on navigation, were "The Marine Surveyor", designed by Henry de Saumarez of Guernsey; "The Navivium," by Joseph Gilmore, Gottlieb's Perpetual log, and the "Nautical Dromometer" or "Way-Wiser", another type of perpetual log by an inventor named Benjamin Martin. "The Marine Surveyor" and the "Nautical Dromometer" call for no particular mention as their construction was somewhat similar to the recording logs of Russell and Foxon. The "Navivium" and Gottlieb's log were, however, novel, in that instead of being towed astern of a ship, they were attached to the structure of the ship well below the water line. "The Navivium" was composed of a wheel and pinion fastened to the underside of the keel, to which a rod was connected. As the ship progressed the wheel was set in motion, and by means of the rod and suitable gearing its revolutions were transmitted to a dial, inside the ship, where they were recorded in miles of distance run. Gottlieb's log consisted of a perforated box, fixed to the side of the keel, through which the water had a passage. Within the box a small water wheel was supported on bearings, and when the ship moved ahead the revolutions of the wheel were transmitted, by means of pinion and rod, to gearing, which in turn reduced the revolutions to the number of nautical miles traversed, since the log was set in motion.[1]

A similar type of log was patented in America, by a merchant of New York State, in which a small vane was enclosed in a brass cylinder fixed to the keel of a ship.[2] Indeed, about this time there seems to have been a steady stream of inventions, and variations upon inventions, to record the distance run by a ship, but few of them seem to have been adopted by seamen for any

---

[1]Andrew Mackay, *The Complete Navigator*, 1804; with reference to these forms of log, Mackay said, "It may be observed that the preceding methods of applying wheelwork to the mensuration of a ship's way is not a new invention. Vitruvius (a Roman architect, who flourished before the Christian era) recommended an axis to be placed through the side of a ship, which being connected with wheels, would by their revolution, give the distance run in a given time."

[2]Lieut. Andrew Wilson, R.N., *Naval History of the United Kingdom*, 1807. (Appendix— Mr. Chester Gould's Sea Log.)

M

length of time or proved to be serious rivals to the old common log. The reason for this was not from any defect in principle, but probably because of the propensity for newly invented mechanical inventions to fail, either through faulty construction, inadequate instruction of the user or from lack of proper care and attention.

By degrees, however, the defects of mechanically recording logs and the prejudices against them were gradually overcome, and during the early years of the nineteenth century their use attained an ever increasing popularity in the art of navigation. An improved type of log was introduced, called the Massey log, whose principle was similar to its predecessors, but whose construction varied in several important particulars. This log consisted of a more sensitive and reliable form of rotator, which was attached to a geared recording instrument by a short length of line, usually about 6 feet, both parts being streamed overboard on a line of a length sufficient to keep them beyond the eddy of the ship's wake. The rotator was in the form of a hollow metal cylinder, exhausted or partially exhausted of air, so as to make its specific gravity about equal to that of sea water, which resulted in its revolving just below the surface so long as the ship had any appreciable headway. In order to impart a rotary motion to the cylinder four metal vanes were fixed obliquely upon it so that as the ship progressed they would turn it in a constant direction.

The following properties were claimed for this instrument and were proved in practice to an extent not found in any other form of mechanical log:—

1. Every occasional or momentary acceleration or retardation of the ship from irregularity of wind or other causes, which were either altogether passed over or very vaguely guessed at, were accurately registered upon the dials.

2. It gave the true distance sailed through the water from steerage way to any speed at which the swiftest sailing ship could move.

3. It was attended with less trouble than the common log and no mistakes could arise from the result it gave.[1]

There seems to be little doubt that this log gave very satisfactory results to those who used it, and the chief objection to it appears to have been not against its efficiency but its price. Raper, in his classic work on navigation published about the middle of the last century, remarked that it was highly approved in practice, but added that it was greatly to be desired that the patentee could manufacture, at a moderate price, an instrument which afforded a method, at once so simple and accurate, of measuring a ship's

---

[1] *Falconer's Marine Dictionary*, Revised Edition, 1830.

way, and which could not fail to come into extensive, if not general, use.

This log, and others of a similar type, continued to enjoy the confidence of navigators until a more convenient form was introduced about 1879, when the rotating log, which registered the distance upon dials placed in the ship, was reverted to. The Massey type of rotator was retained, but the inconvenience of having to haul the log in whenever a reading was required was obviated. Captain Lecky, writing shortly after this improved form was introduced, while not doubting its convenience, expressed doubts about its durability, because unless great care was exercised in repeatedly oiling the mechanism of the recording portion it would be liable to overheat at a high rate of speed. The Massey types of log, on the other hand, were towed in the water, and so getting plenty of "fisherman's grease", were not exposed to that danger. He found nothing to complain of in principle and his only criticism was the lack of durability which would result from the absence of careful and systematic lubrication.

Though refinements and improvements have been made in this and the other types of mechanical logs, the principles of the measurement of distance and speed at sea remain the same, and all in turn rely upon the accurate determination of the earth's dimensions, from which the measure of a nautical mile is derived.

One further system of distance measurement, however, calls for some reference, though it does not differ in principle from the system referred to above and that is the increasing practice of calculating speed from propeller revolutions. The advent of steam as a method of propulsion for ships during the first half of last century gave navigators still one more means of learning their speed and distance run, and some were not slow to profit by it. Captain Lecky wrote upon this, in 1881, as follows: "In certain paddle steamers, probably the best measure of speed is obtained by the revolutions of the wheels. Most of the cross-channel boats depend upon this method of making their runs in thick weather, and the captains of the coast boats of the Pacific Steam Navigation Co. make an invariable practice of tabulating the revolutions between their various ports of call. In vessels such as the Holyhead mail boats, where the passage is short, the vessels of great power, *and their immersion always the same*, the method is susceptible of considerable accuracy. Again, men who are going constantly backwards and forwards on a short run, acquire by long experience the knowledge necessary to enable them to make allowance for wind and sea, according as it may be in their favour, or against them. The slip of a screw-propeller is so variable under *apparently* the same circumstances, that in boats so driven the method is of inferior value. Experience shews that the revolutions of a paddle steamer are to be depended upon fully as much as the best patent log yet invented, with the advantage, that the revolutions do not wear out, and the patent log does."[1] Lecky's objections to the use of propeller revolutions as against paddle revolutions have been lessened to some extent in twin screw ships where the smaller propellers, placed at the side, are less likely to be only partially submerged at times, but experience and care is still necessary, as in Lecky's day, before reliance can be placed upon this method of distance measurement, in many ships of ever changing trim and variable disposition of cargo.

JOURNALS AND LOG BOOKS.

It has always been the practice of ocean navigators to keep some record of their voyages, indeed, it is probable that some of the very.early seafarers, long before the fifteenth century, kept some kind of account of their passages in the Mediterranean and elsewhere. Because of the many difficulties peculiar to deep water voyaging, especially in the earlier days when no records or sailing directions existed to aid the mariner in uncharted oceans, it was most necessary to keep a permanent record of all that concerned the navigation of the ship. All navigators and discoverers of eminence of the fifteenth and following centuries were careful to note in their journals such observations as might be of use to them in the future or which might serve as a guide to those who followed them. These early journals were in narrative form and had therefore to be examined closely to find the points of purely navigational importance. As time went on, however, these points were tabulated in a more methodical and exhaustive manner so that the navigator had both a convenient record of his progress and a ready book of reference for the future. Writers on navigation from the sixteenth to the eighteenth century were at pains to impress their readers with the importance of keeping such records and often gave examples in their books to show how such should be kept. The two

ANNO. 1593[2]

Monthes and daies of the month.	Latitude G.	M.	Corse	Leages	Winde	The 23 of March, Cape S. Augustine in Brasill being 16 leags east from me, I began this accopt.
March 24	7	30	N.N.E.	25	East	
25	5	44	N. by E., norly	36	Eb.N.	Compasse varied 9 deg. the South point westward.
26	4	1	N. by N. (?)	35	E.b.N.	Compasse varied 8 deg. the South point westward.
27	2	49	N.	24	E. × N.	
28	1	31	N. easterly	26	E. × N.	
29	1	4	N.N.W.	9	N.E.	Compasse varied 6 deg. 40m the South point westward.
31	0	0	N.b.W.	21	E.N.E.	Observation, the Pole above the Horizon.

[1]*Lecky's Wrinkles in Practical Navigation*, 1881.
[2]John Davis, *The Seaman's Secrets*, 1594.

examples given below show how little the form of such records changed, and comparison with any modern record will show that, in this matter, the practice of navigators has altered little during the last four centuries.

Extract from the Journal of a Voyage from London to Madeira and Teneriffe in the *Francis*, of London; William Johnson, Commander; kept by Joseph Mills, Mate. Begun April 1, 1799[1].

Hours	Knots	Fathoms	Courses	Winds	Leeway	Remarks on Board, Friday, April 17, 1799.
2	—	—		Calm	—	The first eight hours calm and foggy.
4	—		—	—	—	
6	—		—	—	—	
8	—		—	—	—	
10	3	5	W.S.W	South	1	Fresh gales and Clear.
12	4	4	—	—	—	Cape Finisterre S39° 57′ E., dist. 54 M.
2	4	6	—	—	—	Hoisted the boats out, and tried
4	4	8	—	—	—	the current, found it to set N.W. by N.
6	4	6	—	—	—	1 mile per hour all day.
8	4	8	—	—	—	
10	4	8	—	—	—	Variation 1¼ Point Westerly.
12	4	5	—	—	—	

COURSE	DISTANCE	Diff. of Latitude	DEPARTURE	D. R. Latitude	Latitude observed
S.80°W.	84	15	83	43° 49′	43° 34′

Diff. Long.	LONG. IN	BEARING & DISTANCE
1° 55′	10° 2′	EUNCHAL S.27°W. DIST. 735 MILES

It will be noted that in the earlier example only one line was devoted to each day, whereas in the later one the record was fuller, one line being given to every two hours. This additional detail is representative of the general trend towards greater accuracy as compasses, charts and logs became more reliable, but the habit was by no means universal, for some of the earlier journals were fuller than the example given and many of the later navigators contented themselves with a very brief account for every day.

The later extract also gives an additional column for leeway, and its remarks column indicates that care was being taken to discover what currents were to be expected at sea. It had become the practice, too, in those later years, to append to the account a recapitulation of all that was important in the navigation for the previous 24 hours. These additions were of gradual growth during the seventeenth century. The great increase in shipping and ocean trading during that period called for greater knowledge and more detailed information of the oceans and the lands which lay beyond them. Greater knowledge, in turn, begat a greater volume of shipping, and the two

[1] John Hamilton Moore, *The New Practical Navigator*, 14th Edition, 1800.

placed at the disposal of those who made it their business to supply Pilot books to navigators, a mass of information which, after sifting, redounded to the benefit of all.

The attitude of many who wished to further nautical science, towards the end of the seventeenth century, is well expressed in a letter written during that time by Mr. Graves, a contemporary of Dr. Halley, to the Earl of Northumberland. After urging the establishment of a properly organised school of navigation, he suggested "That the master and mates of every ship should diligently keep a diary of their voyage, wherein besides ordinary observations they shall write down what variation of compass they find, what winds, tides and currents. What soundings taken and where suitable anchorages, and dangers to navigation, shoals and by what landmarks those dangers might be avoided, and their compass bearings. Also they shall give information of those errors and defects which are in books of navigation, especially in Rutters and Waggoners, that more exact books may be printed and better charts drawn . . ."[1]

Leeway.—With the advent of steam leeway became a matter of less importance than it was in the days of bluff bowed sailing ships. Little mention was made of it during the earliest days of ocean navigation, but during the seventeenth century navigators regarded it as a very important matter and gave it their serious attention. "Besides", wrote a text book writer, "a good judgment in estimating the ship's way (speed) 'tis absolutely necessary before an account of the ship's place can be given, that you should not omit any possible opportunity in observing the latitude and variation; as also the tryal for the discovery of currents, and to be well experienced in the trim and qualifications of the ship whereby you may be the better able to allow for leeway. But in all these cases (*i.e.*, allowing for leeway) respect must be had to the smoothness of the water, or the seas running high; and then the allowances may be rectified by setting the ship's wake by the compass or quadrant, which is usually placed on each rail of the ship's quarter for that purpose."[2]

It is obvious from the above quotation that navigators had for some time taken steps to ascertain their leeway, and to make adjustments to their courses on its account, in order to attain greater accuracy in their navigation. In fact, the Dutch writer, Wagenhaur suggested in his *Mariner's Mirror*, 1583, that it was sometimes advisable to cast out a weighted line astern in order to observe the angle of leeway by compass, so that the course could be corrected. Several other ways were also adopted or suggested to assist them in arriving at a fair estimation of the necessary allowance to be made. If the ship

---

[1]British Museum. ADD. MSS. 30221.
[2]William Jones, *A New Compendium of the Whole Art of Navigation*, 1702.

was in sight of land the angle of drift, made by it through the force of wind on one side or the other, was taken between the keel line and that point of land which remained on a constant compass bearing. The more usual method, however, whether in sight of land or not, was to take the angle, by compass or wooden quadrant fixed on the taffrail for that purpose, between the keel line and the ship's wake. Such angle was also similarly observed, sometimes, between the centre line and the log line when it had been hove, as the one indicated the direction of the ship's head and the other the course being made good.

It was the common practice during the Eighteenth century for most works on navigation to include a table of leeway to assist the navigator in making his allowances. Though these tables were not identical they agreed substantially in their contents. The following table is given as the one recorded to have been most generally used during the eighteenth century.

Allowances for Leeway.[1]

    I. When a ship is close hauled, has all her sails set, the water smooth, and a moderate gale of wind, she is then supposed to make little or no leeway.

    II. Allow one point, when it blows so fresh that the small sails are taken in.

    III. Allow two points, when the top sails must be close reefed.

    IV. Allow two and a half points, when one top sail must be handed.

    V. Allow three and a half points, when both top sails are to be taken in.

    VI. Allow four points, when the fore course is handed.

    VII. Allow five points, when trying under the main sail only.

    VIII. Allow six points, when both main and fore courses are taken in.

    IX. Allow seven points, when the ship tries a hull, or all sails handed. (Bare poles.)

The seaman was warned, probably needlessly, that all ships did not make the same quantity of leeway, and that some made a great deal more than others, owing to the different forms of their hulls. He was usually told that experience was the best guide but the table would at least be of some assistance to him on joining a new ship.

Current.—It has already been remarked that observations for current became more numerous and systematic during the period of maritime enterprise and growing insistence upon greater accuracy. The extract from the

---

[1] J. Robertson, *The Elements of Navigation*, 1754. A similar table is given in A. Mackay's *The Complete Navigator*, 1804.

journal of 1799 shows that when off Cape Finisterre the boats were hoisted out to find the set and drift of the current. This practice had been followed in some ships for many years, and was carried out as follows. When weather conditions were suitable a boat was put out, equipped with a compass, log-line, half minute glass and some form of sea anchor. The sea anchor, for this purpose, was often a piece of wood heavily weighted with lead, though some seamen were content to use their iron kettle, attached to a line anything up to 120 fathoms in length. When the boat was pulled clear of the ship the sea anchor was lowered over the side, and when it was stationary, the log was hove and its rate of drift from the boat ascertained by means of the half minute glass. At the same time the set of the line was observed by the compass, and the boat then returned to the ship with its results.[1] This method was near enough for practical purposes, for although the set and drift observed only showed the difference between the current at the surface and that at the depth to which the weight had been lowered, the drift at such a depth would be of little moment.

The growth of oceanographical knowledge and marine meteorology during the late seventeenth century, and the years which followed, was fairly rapid, though it suffered from lack of proper co-ordination. Various attempts were made by scientists, among whom may be mentioned Dr. Halley, to place these subjects upon a more systematic footing, both by direct observation and by analysing the journals of others. A summary of their findings was usually given in contemporary treatises.

Rough Logs.—In order that the ship's journal might be neatly and safely kept, the practice grew up during the seventeenth century, of keeping a rough record of all that affected the navigation of the ship and copying it into the journal at the end of every day's run, which was reckoned from noon to noon. This rough record was generally kept upon a blackboard, upon which were ruled columns for every hour or two hours of the day, according to how often the log was hove, and space was given in these columns for the recording of the speeds, courses sailed and winds experienced during those intervals. This board, known as the log board, was probably first introduced solely for the recording of speeds shown by the common log, but it quickly developed into a rough daily account of the reckoning of the ship. In the course of time it gave its name to the navigational journal of the ship, which, as early as the later years of the seventeenth century, was called by some, the log book.

Another name sometimes applied to the board was the traverse board, because it contained, in addition to the distance run, a record of the courses

---

[1] W. Emerson, *Navigation, or The Art of Sailing upon the Seas,* 1764

steered during the previous 24 hours. The traverse board, proper, which was of an earlier period, was a board upon which an account was kept, of the times spent upon each course, by the steersman.

The following account of the steering and recording of courses was given by Captain John Smith, in his *Seaman's Grammar*, about three hundred years ago, when describing how a ship should be built and equipped. "The Stearage roome is before the great cabin where he that steereth the ship doth always stand, before him is a square box nailed together with wooden pins called a bittacle, because iron nails would attract the compass, this is built to close (*i.e.*, shut), that the lamp or candle only showeth light to the steerage, in it always stands the compasse, which every one knows is a round box and in the midst of the bottom a sharp pin called a centre whereon the fly (compass card) doth play . . . Upon the bittacle is also the Travers, which is a little round board full of holes upon lines like the Compasse, upon which by the removing of a little stick they keep an account how many glasses (which are but ½ hours) they steere upon every point . . ."

Use of Data recorded in Log Books.—From these log books, journals and records, compiled upon numerous voyages, the oceans, their currents and weather systems, were gradually revealed to those who searched for their secrets. The Pacific became more generally known chiefly through French and British explorers during the eighteenth century; ships of the British and Dutch East India Companies contributed much to the sum of knowledge of the Indian Ocean; and even convict ships to the settlements in Australia added their quota to the general knowledge of the route thither, and the weather and currents to be expected. Ships of the Royal and foreign navies, both singly and in squadrons, which cruised to almost every navigable part of the world, and privateers and individual traders by the hundred made their records, from which was gleaned information of use to future voyagers. As we have seen, in an earlier chapter, the sifting of the detail and its systematic collection was a gradual process, executed principally by the private publishers of sailing directions during the eighteenth century, and later by the hydrographic departments of the Admiralties of the principal maritime nations.

CHAPTER V.

NAVIGATION BY LATITUDE AND DEAD RECKONING.

THE origin of the term "Dead Reckoning" is obscure, though several attempts have been made to explain it. It is even difficult to ascertain when it was first used, but there are good grounds for believing that it came into being shortly after the introduction of the common log line. William Bourne who gave one of the first descriptions of the log, in 1574, in his *Regiment of the Sea*, used the term "deade reckening", which in those days meant the same as it does to-day, *i.e.*, the estimation of a ship's position solely from the distance run by the log, and the courses steered by compass, corrected for variation current and leeway, and without any reference to astronomical observations.

One writer suggests that the term was derived from the expression "Deduced Reckoning," which was abbreviated in the narrow columns of log books to "Ded: Reckoning." He argues that, before 1650, printed log books were not supplied by the Admiralty, and that captains were in the habit of entering their runs in a journal ruled into different columns. Through lack of space, the column that indicated the latitude, deduced from the ship's course and distance, sometimes bore the heading Ded: Latt:, and this abbreviation gradually came into general use, and was adopted, without question, by English and American seamen throughout the world. Thus, in the course of time, the true meaning of the words was obscured, a circumstance that was contributed to by the greater illiteracy of seafarers in those days, and which was further aided by the frequency of naval wars with the Dutch, French and Spaniards, and the many hostile encounters occurring with privateers, pirates and smugglers. The effect of these continuous struggles was to sever friendly relations and the interchange of ideas between the parties and to prevent the growth of a common language of the sea. The Dutch equivalent, "ruwe berekening" (rough estimate) and the French "route estimée" both convey, with much greater clarity, what their users are referring to.[1] Support for this suggestion is derived from Captain Samuel Sturmey, who, in his *Mariner's Magazine*, 1669, instructed the mariner how to correct the account when the "Dead Lat:" differed from the observed latitude.

---

[1]*Notes and Queries*, 12th Series, Vol. 6.

It is probable that the explanation given above is the true one, and that the term was in fairly common use during the first half of the seventeenth century, for in Richard Norwood's *Seaman's Practice*, 1637, the following instruction appears, "For he that runnes any course near the meridean . . . hath a more certain way of reckoning (than by using the log): namely his latitude, which he finds daily by observation of the sun or stars, upon which he will depend, either neglecting or at least not regarding his dead reckoning".[1]

Thus far we have seen that certain elements were necessary to the navigator before he could find his way at sea. Most of these were in being during the fifteenth century to assist him in his voyagings out of sight of land, and were in fact put into use, towards the end of that century by Columbus. These elements together made up a system of navigation, which may be described as the conducting of a ship from one place to another by dead reckoning and latitude. The component parts of this system have already been described in some detail, but a recapitulation of them is useful to show how little the principles of such navigation have altered during the last five hundred years.

1. To find the latitude by observation. This called for the knowledge and use of some instrument by which the altitudes of celestial bodies could be taken, and for tables of declination of such bodies.

2. To be able to set and steer a course. An operation which demanded a chart, a compass, the ability to find the variation of the compass, by amplitude or azimuth, and a knowledge of leeway and ocean currents.

3. The means of measuring the ship's run, either by estimation or some form of log.

STEERING A COURSE.

One further point, which did not rest upon learning or technical knowledge, commended itself to the earlier navigators and was frequently impressed by them, in their writings, upon others. This was the necessity for a careful watch upon the steering of the ship. It seems a little strange that such advice should have been necessary, especially in an age when it was difficult enough to make good a desired course, and that navigators had to be repeatedly reminded of the necessity for ordinary seamanlike care in this matter. Yet such care was often lacking, both in the open sea and within sight of land.

---

[1]Captain Basil Hall, R.N., expressed himself upon this subject, in his *Fragments of Voyages and Travels*, 1831, as follows: "The log of which, of course, takes account only of the relative motion between ship and water is the foundation of what is called Dead Reckoning—I do not know very well why, unless it be that, to a certain extent, its operations must be made in the dark, and, at best, in great uncertainty."

In the first case, careless steering caused many unnecesssary difficulties in the plotting of the ship's position, and in the second case grave risk of stranding and loss. With regard to ocean navigation, John Davis, in his *Seaman's Secrets*, 1594, said that one of the reasons why the results found in navigation so often differed from those expected was "the stredge (steerage) may be so disorderly handled so that thereby the Pylote may be abused."

The more pressing dangers which might result from lack of proper vigilance of the helmsman, when near the land, were graphically described by Sir Richard Hawkins in his account of his voyage to the South Sea in 1598.[1] "The coast from Santos to Cape Frio lyeth west and by south southerly. So we directed our course west south west. The night comming on, and directions given to our other Shippes, we sett the watch, having a fayre fresh gale of wind and large. My selfe, with the Master of our Ship, having watched the night past, thought now to give Nature that which shee had beene deprived of, and so recommended the care of Steeridge to one of his Mates; who with the like travell past being drowsie, or with the confidence which he had of him at the Helme, had not that watchfull care which was required; he at the Helme steered west, and west and by south, and brought us in a little time close upon the shore; doubtless, he had cast us all away, had not God extraordinariiy delivered us; for the Master being in his dead sleepe, was suddenly awaked, and with such a fright, that he could not be in quiet: whereupon, waking his youth, which ordinarily slept in his Cabin by him, asked him how the watch went on; who answered, that it could not be above an houre since he layd himselfe to rest. He replyed that his heart was so unquiet. that he could not by any meanes sleepe, and so taking his Gowne, came forth upon the Decke, and presently discovered the Land hard by us. And for that it was sandie and low, those who had their eyes continually fixed on it, were dazeled with the reflection of the Starres, being a fayre night. and so were hindered from the true discovery thereof. But he comming out of the darke, had his sight more forcible, to discerne the difference of the Sea, and the shore. So that forthwith he commaunded him at the Helme, to put it close a starbourd, and tacking our Ship, wee edged off; and sounding found scant three fathome water, whereby we saw evidently, the miraculous mercie of our God; that if he had not watched over us, as hee doth continually over his, doubtlesse we had perished without remedie."

This narrow escape from destruction prompted Hawkins to review the question of steerage generally, which he did to the detriment of English seamen, in the following words:— "In this poynt of Steeridge, the Spaniards

---

[1] *The Observations of Sir Richard Hawkins, Knight, in his Voyage into the South Sea*, A.D. 1593 (1622 Edition). Reproduced by the Argonaut Press, London, 1933.

and Portingalls doe exceede all that I have seen, I meane for their care, which is chiefest in Navigation. And I wish in this, and in all their workes of Discipline and reformation, we should follow their examples; as also those of any other Nation."

"In every Ship of moment, upon the halfe deck, or quarter deck, they have a chayre, or seat; out of which whilst they Navigate, the Pilot or his Adiutants (which are the same officers which in our Shippes we terme, the Master and his Mates) never depart, day or night, from the sight of the Compasse; and have another before them; whereby they see what they doe, and are ever witnesses of the good or bad Steeridge of all men that take the Helme. This I have seene neglected in our best Shippes yet nothing more necessary to be reformed. For a good Helme-man may be overcome with an imagination, and so mistake one poynt for another; or the Compasse may erre, which by another is discerned. The inconveniences which hereof may ensue, all experimented Sea-men may easily conceive; and by us take warning to avoyd the like".[1]

Upon reading the journals of later navigators it becomes apparent that English seamen continued to neglect the proper supervision of the steering and that helmsmen were careless. One further result of such carelessness is quoted at length from Dampier, on account of his interesting description which at the same time bears out the suspicion that many ships have been bewildered in their reckoning at sea or lost upon the coast through neglect of this elementary precaution. Drowsiness, or a mistaken reading of the compass at night, owing to the imperfect illumination of the card, a common fault in the days of candles, can easily be understood, but the absence of frequent checking of the course steered, by those responsible for the navigation, is not without significance when considering the difficulties of ocean navigation in those earlier days.

William Dampier recorded, in 1689, that when about four leagues short of Diamond Point, in Sumatra, "Captain Minchin desired me to set the Land, and withal prick the Card, and see what Course we ought to keep all night; for it was now about 6 a-Clock, and we had a fine gale at W.S.W. our course yet being E.S.E. After I had set the Land, I went into the Cabbin to look over the Draught to see what course we must steer after we cambe about the Point. Mr. Coventry followed me, and when I had satisfied myself, he asked me what course we must steer? I told him E.S.E. till 12 a-clock, if the gale

---

[1]Captain Samuel Sturmey, in his *Mariners' Magazine*, 3rd Edition, 1684, also observed that great errors were frequently committed by helmsmen through bad steering and careless looking at the compass. See also the remarks of John Collier in his *Compendium Artis Nautical*, 1729, which he concludes with, "for the best may often mistake the compass, and so may have run upon a wrong course a glass (½ hour) or more before the discovery be made, this must necessarily produce an error in computing the true course."

stood, and then we might hale more Southerly. He seemed to be startled at it, and told me, that the Captain and he had been pricking the Card, and thought that S.E. or S.E. by S. course would do well at 8 a-clock. I said it was a good course to run ashore; he argued a long time with me, but I persisted in my Opinion, and when I told Captain Minchin of My Opinion, he was well satisfied. Presently after this we had a pretty strong Tornado out of the S.W. which obliged us to hand our Topsail. When the stress of the weather was over, we set our sails again, and went in to Supper, and ordered the Man at Helm not to come to the Southward of the E.S.E. We stayed in the Cabbin till about 8 a-Clock, and then we came out to set the Watch. It was now very dark, by reason of a Thunder-Cloud that hung rumbling over the Land: yet by the flashes of lightning we plainly saw the Land, right a-head of us. I was much surprised, and ran into the Steeridge to look on the Compass, and found that we were steering S.S.E. instead of E.S.E. I clapt the Helm a Starboard, and brought her to N.E. by E. and N.E., and we very narrowly escap'd being cast away. When we first went to Supper we were 3 leagues off Land, and then E.S.E. was a good course, the Land lying E.S.E. parallel with our course. But then the man at Helm mistaking his Compass steer'd S.S.E. which runs right in upon the Shore."[1]

The human element is still present in navigation, even in this more mechanical age, and bad steering may still contribute to the imperfection of the true course made good. The chances of it so doing are however, slight compared with earlier days. The improved lighting of the compass card at night, a feature which first received attention about the beginning of the nineteenth century, increasing intelligence, magnifiers, and a greater vigilance on the part of those responsible for the safe navigation, have all assisted in reducing the errors attributable to careless steering.

PRICKING THE CHART AND SETTING THE COURSE.

The pricking of the card or chart, referred to by Dampier, in the quotation given above, was the first operation carried out in the navigation of the ship upon leaving the land. This simple operation was described by most of the early text book writers, and has, in effect, been practised in every age of ocean navigation, including the present day. An example often given in the sixteenth century was for a voyage from the Lizard to Spain, and another, which attained equal notice was from the Lizard to the Azores or Madeira. both of which were, and still are, well frequented routes.

Upon taking his departure from the Lizard, the navigator was instructed to guess or calculate his distance from it, and to observe its bearing by compass.

[1]*Voyages and Discoveries*, by William Dampier (A supplement to the *Voyage Round the World*), Argonaut Press, London, 1931.

and then prick the chart in the position so obtained. From this prick he had to lay his course towards his objective, and thereafter prick the chart every day at noon to denote his position. The pricking was done with a blunt needle or the point of the dividers, and the pricks were effaced, when no longer required, by applying chalk to them.

These positions were arrived at by a consideration of the true courses steered and the distances run upon them during the previous 24 hours. Should an observation for latitude be obtained at noon and the result be different from that shown by the dead reckoning, certain rules were applied to adjust the one to the other. These rules were no more than guides based upon probabilities, reliance being placed upon each element of them in order of probability. Though such guides must have proved most misleading on many occasions, and were condemned by some of the later writers, they enjoyed a large degree of popularity until the close of the eighteenth century, when more reliable methods for the finding of longitude were introduced. As every component of the only system of ocean navigation open to seamen, before the nineteenth century, was subject to very uncertain errors, such guides were generally adopted for want of something better.

Cortes, the Spanish writer, whose *Art of Navigation* became popular in England, during the latter half of the sixteenth century, laid down no rules but the very simplest, but other writers who followed him adopted the method of probabilities already referred to.

Cortes's method was as follows. If after sailing for a day the latitude by observation was the same as on the previous day, then the true course made good was east or west, and the distance along that course, was, presumably (although he did not say so) that which the navigator estimated, either from experience or by using the log line. If, however, the latitude by observation was found to be different at the end of a day, then the ship's position lay at the intersection of the estimated true course line with the parallel of the newly found latitude. As rulers and pencils had not then been introduced for use on board, the operation of pricking the position on the chart had to be carried out with two pairs of dividers, or compasses, as they were called. The foot of one pair had to be placed in the departure position while the other leg had to be extended along the direction sailed. At the same time, one foot of the second pair had to be placed in the latitude scale in the margin, at the point which marked the observed latitude, while the other foot rested upon the nearest parallel drawn on the chart. "So," said Cortes, "with both the compasses, one in the one hand and the other in the other, let him goe joyning them together, taking good heed that the point of the compass do not move from the direction he has sailed, neither the point of the other from the East and

West line. And following those 2 compasses by these 2 lines until the points join, that is the place where the ship is."[1]

From the above rule it will be seen that Cortes preferred to rely upon his course, on every occasion, rather than the estimated distance, except when the course made good was along a parallel. The later writers, however, adopted a different view, and advised the navigator when the dead reckoning latitude did not agree with that observed, to consider whether the course or distance was more likely to be in error. The more reliable of the two had then to be used in conjunction with the observed latitude to find the position, while the unreliable component had to be adjusted to agree with it.

In deciding whether the true course or distance should be so used, the following argument was generally put forward as a guide to the navigator. As will be seen from the three cases given below, the degree of reliance to be placed upon either depended primarily upon the true course, whether it was laid nearer a meridian than a parallel or vice versa.

To Correct the Course and Distance Found by Dead Reckoning by an Observation of the Sun.

Case 1.—Suppose a ship sailed N.N.E. from *Y*, and by the following noon her Dead Reckoning position, according to the distance run was *C*. By observation her latitude was found to be along the parallel *AB*.

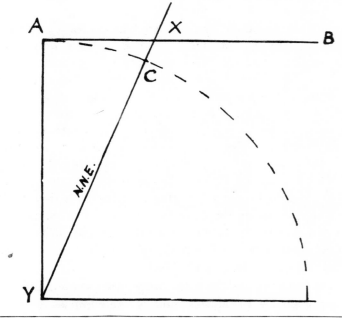

---

[1]Edens Translation, 1561.

If the course were correct she would be at *X*.

If the distance were correct she would be at *A*.

Unlikely that the course would be 2 points in error, although the distance could easily be *CX* miles out.

Therefore, when the course was nearer a meridian than a parallel, reliance was placed upon it rather than upon the distance.

Case 2.—Suppose a ship sailed E.N.E., and by the following noon her Dead Reckoning position, according to the distance run was *G*. By observation her latitude was found to be along the parallel *DE*.

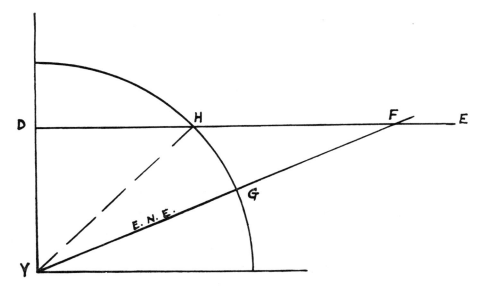

If the course were correct she would be at *F*.

If the distance were correct she would be at *H*.

Unlikely that the distance would be in error by as much as *FG* but possible for the course to be in error by the angle *HYF*.

Therefore, when the course was nearer a parallel than a meridian, reliance was placed upon the distance rather than upon the course.

Case 3.—Suppose a ship sailed N.E., and by the following noon her Dead Reckoning position, according to the distance run was *O*. By observation her latitude was found to be along the parallel *KL*.

If the course were correct she would be at *M*.

If the distance were correct she would be at *N*.

In this case the errors in both course and distance would be within
reasonable limits, and both were assumed to contribute, in equal
degree, to the erroneous position. The correct position was
therefore placed, between N and M, at P.

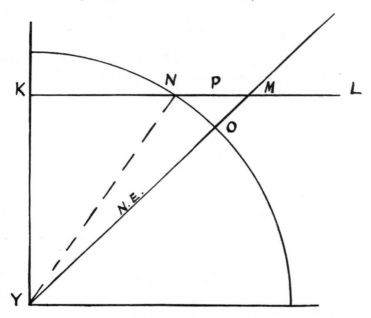

Such were the rules followed by many navigators in order to arrive at
their daily positions. Some navigators preferred to take a position somewhere
between A and X, in Case 1, and F and H, in Case 2, allowing such errors with
regard to course and distance, respectively, as they thought reasonable.
Again, for example, if after steering a supposed course of N.N.E. (True), they
had reason to suspect that their allowance for variation was incorrect then
they would place more reliance upon their distance, although the course
lay nearer a meridian than a parallel.

When the corrected position had been pricked on the chart, according
to the new longitude assigned to it, under the rules, a new course was set,
if necessary, and in this manner the ship progressed until she reached her
objective or, as will be seen, the latitude of her objective.

The way in which the course was laid off on the chart in the early days
of ocean navigation has already been described, in the chapter on charts,
where the use of the radiating rhumb lines, drawn on the earlier charts, was
explained.[1]

For some unexplained reason the sliding parallel ruler, so familiar to-day,

[1] *Vide.* pp. 22 and 24.

was not generally adopted for use at sea until the early years of the nineteenth century, although it had been used by surveyors, and the like, ashore, for many years. The method of course laying generally used, during the eighteenth century, scarcely differed from that used by the Elizabethan navigators. It was performed by laying the edge of a ruler between the point of departure and the destination; and holding the ruler in that position, taking a pair of dividers and extending them between the edge of the ruler and the centre of the nearest compass rose engraved upon the chart. The points of the dividers being held in a line perpendicular to the edge of the ruler, one point of the dividers was then slid along the ruler until the other point cut the edge of the rose. Such point of intersection denoted the true course required between the two places.

THE OBLIQUE MERIDIAN USED TO FACILITATE LAYING OFF THE COURSE.

Considerable light is shed upon the practice of some navigators, and the charts used by them, during the sixteenth century, by William Burrough, in his *Discourse of the variation of the Cumpas*, which he published in 1581, It appears from him that some charts which portrayed the regions of the North Atlantic, where the variation of the compass was greatest, were subject to "great errors and confusion", on account of neglect to allow for the variation in the drawing of them.[1] An examination of these charts shows that the trend of the coastline of the Gulf of St. Lawrence, Newfoundland and Labrador followed the compass direction and not the true, a factor which accounted for the almost unrecognizable configuration of the land shown in them. At the time when Burrough wrote, the variation in Newfoundland was about 2 points westerly, while that in London was about 1 point easterly. Off the Scilly Isles it amounted to about ½ point easterly and in the vicinity of the Azores it was nil.

In order to facilitate the laying of a compass course from the Scillies to Cape Race in Newfoundland, whereby the taking into account of the considerable difference in the variation, between the two places, could be overcome, some of the charts of the North Atlantic, designed for the voyage to North America, were constructed with two scales of latitude. On the eastern side of the chart the European seaboard was plotted with each place in its correct latitude, while on the western side, the points on the American seaboard were placed in false latitudes, so that Cape Race lay due west (true) of the Scilly Isles, in latitude about 50° N., instead of in its correct latitude of 46° 40′ N.

The reason for this was, according to Burrough, that seamen had found

---

[1]This source of error was also referred to by Wright in his *Certain Errors in Navigation, 1599.*

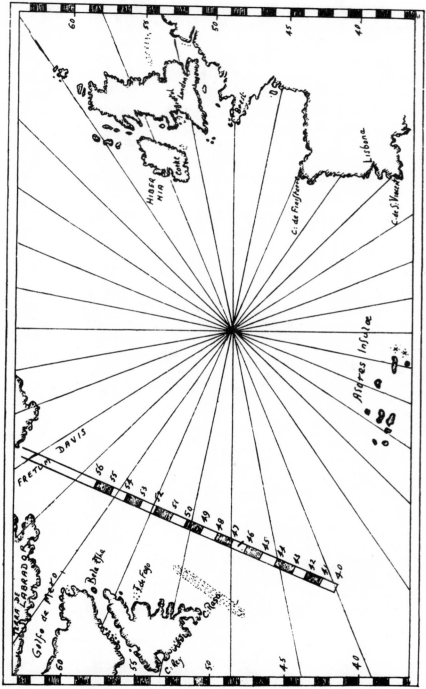

The Oblique Meridian.

that by sailing due west by compass from the Scillies and presumably maintaining that course, they arrived in due time at Cape Race, although it was, in fact, over 3° of latitude further south. The compass in use was the one popular at that time, whose needle was set half a point east of the true axis of the card, to make it a true compass at the mouth of the Channel.

By using this type of chart the navigator had no difficulty in laying off his course from England to Newfoundland, he knew it was due west and he sailed accordingly, without troubling about the changes in the variation. The consequences of his so doing were as follows:—Upon leaving the Scillies, steering west by compass, the ship sailed along a parallel for some time, until the decreasing easterly variation, and later, the increasing westerly variation, made the true course actually achieved turn gradually more and more south of west. The result was that by the time the ship reached the longitude of Cape Race she was in fact in her proper latitude, or nearly so, although she had been steered continuously upon a compass course of west.

Although the points on the American seaboard were placed in false latitudes, and their bearings from Europe were entirely fictitious, a means was provided to overcome these defects by drawing a second scale of latitude on the chart, a little to the eastward of the Newfoundland coast. This scale, or oblique meridian as it has been called, was drawn at an angle to the eastern meridians of the chart, equal to the variation, and in the direction of true north in that region, relative to the coast whose trend was shown in the magnetic direction. The effect of this was that the meridians on the chart represented the direction of true north, in the eastern parts, whereas they showed the direction of magnetic north in the western parts.[1]

The true latitude of any place in the western North Atlantic could be found by dropping a perpendicular from that place to the oblique meridian upon which the true latitude scale was marked.

In some cases the second scale of latitude was not drawn obliquely to represent the compass bearing of true north, but upon the vertical western margin of the chart. In such cases the latitude in the western Atlantic had to be read from that margin and in the eastern Atlantic from the eastern margin.

Though the method of charting those regions by compass direction, instead of true, may have been of some benefit to mariners unskilled in allowing for variation, when coasting along Newfoundland and the other parts affected, it is questionable whether the clumsy method of avoiding such allowance, by providing two distinct scales of latitude was of much assistance in ocean navigation. Such scales must have been almost as bewildering to them as the allowance for variation, and to those who knew the rudiments of their

---

[1]Further on the oblique meridian *vide Imago Mundi*, 1937, Vol. II.

art, nothing but a nuisance. William Burrough's opinion of such a method was, "But how farre the same hath beene from reforming the error or giving any helpe to Navigation you maie easily judge."

Upon reading Burrough it is evident that some seamen of his day relied solely upon their compasses, without observing for latitude or correcting their courses for variation. Apart from those, already mentioned, who used a compass corrected for the Channel, there were others who, though they used compasses which indicated magnetic north, made no allowance for any alteration in the variation as they progressed westward. They simply sailed west by compass, taking no trouble to observe for their latitude, and usually made their landfall in Newfoundland, about 50 leagues North of their objective which was generally Cape Race. When it is recalled that the prevailing winds in the North Atlantic ocean were between south and west, and that the ships would seldom have a favouring wind for their entire voyage from the Scillies to Newfoundland, it becomes all the more a matter for conjecture how unskilled mariners succeeded in making the land within such a limit. It is probable that when the wind favoured they steered west, and when the wind was unfavourable they steered as close to it as possible, making what westing they could in the conditions which prevailed.

THE PLANE CHART AND PLANE SAILING.

The first chart to be used at sea, and which did not wholly lose favour until long after the more accurate chart upon Mercator's projection had been introduced was the Plane chart.[1] This chart, in which the earth was regarded as an extended flat surface, was described in the earliest books on navigation. In it all meridians were drawn as parallel straight lines, equally spaced; and the parallels of latitude were drawn at right angles to the meridians, equally spaced in the same degree, regardless of the latitudes they represented. The result of this has already been described in an earlier chapter, but its bearing upon the accuracy of course laying and distance measurement has not been considered.

In considering the plane chart, or indeed any chart used by navigators before the later years of the eighteenth century, it is necessary to inquire how they were built up, and what reliance could be placed on the information contained in them. What applied to one chart could be applied to all, and therefore one example will suffice to illustrate the errors which, of necessity, arose from them in laying the course for a ship. Suppose a discoverer sailed in a westerly direction from Europe, and, in the course of time, made a landfall somewhere in America. Upon arrival there he observed for latitude, and marked that place upon his blank chart, assigning to it such a longitude to

---

[1]Further on this see the chapter on charts.

the westward of his place of departure as he could best judge from the estimated distance run. Tnereafter, he or later discoverers surveyed the new coasts by means of compass bearings, sometimes corrected for variation and in other cases not. The bearings and estimated distances of one point from another, coupled with frequent observations for latitude, enabled these discoverers to build up, by degrees, rough charts of hitherto unknown coasts, which were the only guides for future navigators. It was by no means uncommon for those early seamen to be several hundred miles in error in their distance after sailing some weeks without a sight of land, and, consequently, the bearings of places in America from points on the European coast varied considerably from the truth. The result of this was that whatever form of chart was used, the direct courses between points in the Old and New Worlds were in error, to greater or lesser extents, according to the degree of accuracy in the estimated distances apart of the two continents. As time went on more and more distances were checked and revised, and the errors from this source were gradually lessened, until, with the general adoption of the chronometer they practically disappeared during the earlier decades of the nineteenth century.

These errors were further accentuated by using the plane chart which by taking no account of the convergency of the meridians towards the poles caused the bearings of points and the distances between them to be exaggerated. The deficiency of the plane chart in regard to these particulars is best illustrated by comparng courses laid upon it with similar courses plotted on Mercator's Chart, whose projection satisfies most of the requirements of navigation. (See page 190).

In Case A. From the Scillies to Cape Race, the course by Plane Chart is 2° in excess of the correct course, while the distance is 2800 miles instead of the true distance by Mercator Chart of 1875 miles.

In Case B. From the Lizard to Corvo, in the Azores, the course by Plane Chart is about $7\frac{1}{2}$° in excess of the correct course, while the distance is 1700 miles instead of the true distance, by Mercator Chart, of 1264 miles.

In Case C.—From Madeira to Barbadoes, the course by Plane Chart is 2° in excess of the correct course, while the distance is 2800 miles instead of the true distance, by Mercator Chart, of 2614 miles.

The above cases do not necessarily represent the errors made in practice by the users of the plane chart during the sixteenth and following centuries, because as we have already seen, the longitudes of places were assigned by taking a mean of the reliable distances between them and other points whose positions were more accurately established. What they do show is the tendency to exaggeration in both course and distance when the plane chart is used, especially in the higher latitudes. It would be impossible to show the real effect

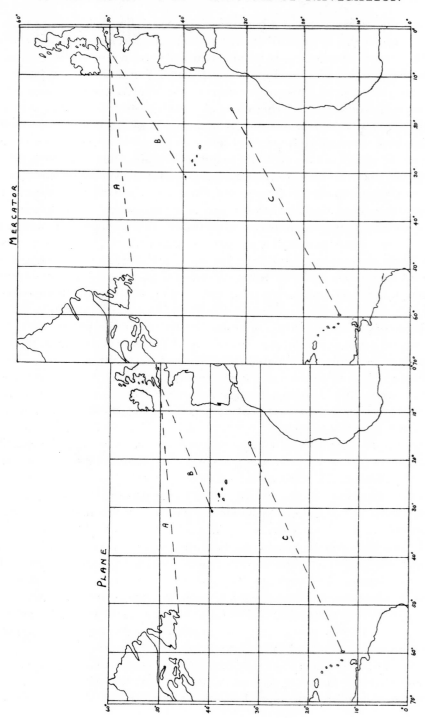

of the Plane Chart, experienced by the earlier navigators, upon their navigation in every case, because all their charts suffered from errors in distance which were by no means uniform. In some cases the very errors in the assigning of longitude doubtless helped to cover up the errors inherent in the plane projection, whereas in others they served to augment them.

There is no doubt that the use of the plane chart did serve to increase the difficulties which beset the navigator and caused him many moments of bewilderment and danger. Many writers of great practical experience condemned its use and warned the navigator against placing much reliance upon it. One of the best examples of the imperfections arising from it was given by Captain Samuel Sturmey who, in 1669, wrote as follows:— "After a long voyage the ship supposed to be near the shore the commander or master requires from his mates an account of their judgment how the land or cape bears from them and the distance from it. He that comes nearest the Truth is supposed to have kept the best reckoning. I have known some that have scarce been able to number 5 figures have gone nearer the truth than the best artist in the ship, but they have been wonderfully mistaken (to my knowledge) in other voyages. I went a voyage to Barbadoes in the *Rainbow* and took out reckoning from Lundy ... in the ship were 12 practitioners that kept an account—eleven of them kept it by plain chart and myself made use of Mercator and Mr. Wright's projection. When we came in the latitude (which was 400 leagues from the island) every man was ready to give his judgement of his distance off the Barbadoes. But they all fell wonderfully short of the truth; for he that should have had the best reckoning was 300 leagues short and most of all the rest was 268 and 250 leagues, and he that was accounted an excellent artist was 240. But by the reckoning kept by Mercators Chart there wanted but 3 leagues short of the true distance of the island. In the same ship, going thence to Virginia they also fell short by the same way of account by the Plain Chart 90 leagues the nearest, but those that were advised to keep it by Mercator found it to come but 4 or 5 leagues short of the Cape of Virginia."[1]

The practice of sailing by plane chart was exhaustively treated by Doctor Halley in a long letter to Mr. Pepys, in 1695, where he remarked that one of the greatest faults of the ordinary navigators was the absurd way they kept their reckonings by the plane chart, which supposed the meridians to be parallel. By using the chart they were never able to assign the true course and distance from one port to another. Though the error was negligible in the Tropics, in voyages where there was a great difference in latitude, such as the Barbadoes voyages, experience constantly showed them the necessity of keeping their account by Mercators Chart. It was the practice for all outward

[1] *Mariner's Magazine.*

bound ships to steer to the southward in order to pick up the N.E. trade winds as soon as possible, after which they ran down all their westing in low latitudes, where there were about 20 leagues to one degree of longitude. On their return they always stood close hauled to the northward till they passed Bermuda and picked up the prevailing westerly winds. The result was that whereas on the outward passage there were about 20 leagues to the degree, on the homeward run all their easting was made between the fortieth and fiftieth parallels where there were not more than 15 leagues to a degree of longitude. "Whence", wrote Halley, "they commonly find Barbadoes above 100 leagues more to the westward of the Lizard than the Lizard is to the eastward of Barbadoes.. And whenever they meet with easterly winds to the northward this difference is always greater. These errors the saylers excuse under the pretext of a constant current setting eastwards and will allow no other reasons for their mistakes."[1]

A further instance of the result of navigating by a plane chart was given by Halley, which showed the added difficulties when the mariner chose to consider the earth as a flat surface. He took the case of a master of a ship, who by previous experience had found the Barbadoes to lie about 900 leagues to the westward of the meridian of the Lizard, and who on a later occasion was bound first to Newfoundland and then to the Barbadoes. In this case, wrote Halley, "He shall certainly find Newfoundland about 500 leagues west of the Lizard by his Plain Sailing and consequently he will conclude Barbadoes to be 400 leagues more westerly and having the difference of Latitude between Barbadoes and Cape Rez (Race) 660 leagues he will steer a way nearest S.W. by S., which point will bring him upon Hispaniola. Whereas the True Course he ought to steer is S. × W. But a master finding himself thus mistaken will here conclude a very strong current setting westwards. Thus they shut their eyes against the truth and will not be prevailed upon to use those ready helps which have been long prepared for them. Of this we have a very eminent instance in Captain John Wood who went to seek the N.E. Passage, who, though he were in Latitudes where 5 or 6 leagues made a degree (of longitude), yet in his journal lately published he has kept his account by plain sailing, and that Captain was generally esteemed one of the best artists of his time."[2]

A consideration of the foregoing examples shows that navigation upon a plane chart was only free from material errors in the following circumstances.

---

[1]It is probable that the Gulf Stream and the N.E'ly Atlantic drift were partly responsible for the discrepancies and the "saylers" were not wholly wrong in their contentions.

[2]Letter of Mr. Halley to Mr. Pepys, touching the yet imperfect measure of knowledge in our ordinary navigators. Brit. Mus. ADD. MSS. 30221.

(*a*) When the courses were small or very large, *i.e.*, either upon or near the meridian or a parallel, or

(*b*) When the distances to be sailed were short, or

(*c*) When navigating in low latitudes.

Plane Sailing.—Plane sailing is the art of sailing a ship upon principles deduced from the notion of the earth being an extended plane. Because of this notion it followed that even in the earliest days of its application the navigator was able to solve all problems connected with it by simply drawing a plane right angled triangle from the data he possessed, and obtaining the required result by direct measurement. This graphic solution could be performed upon the chart itself, if it were of a sufficiently large scale, or upon any flat surface, provided the operator was possessed of a ruler, a protractor of sorts and the wherewithal to draw a line.

In considering all cases of plane sailing the navigator was told to take into account the following elements necessary for the construction of the plane right angled triangle.

(*a*) Rhumb Line. A straight line drawn from the centre of the compass to the horizon, which is named after that point of the horizon which it cuts.

(*b*) Course. The angle which any rhumb line makes with the meridian, which is sometimes reckoned in degrees, and sometimes in points of the compass.

(*c*) Distance. The number of leagues or miles between two places upon a rhumb line; or the way or length a ship has gone on a direct course in a given time.

(*d*) Departure. The east or west distance of a ship from the meridian of one place, reckoned on its parallel of latitude in the plane chart; and therein it is the same as the difference of longitude.

It is perhaps not surprising that the ordinary navigator found some difficulty in understanding exactly what was meant by some of the definitions given to him by those who wrote for his benefit. Many of the earlier writers failed to convey to the learner in simple words the true significance of the most elementary rudiments of the art of navigation. They bear no comparison with the later writers who substituted clarity for obscurity, and expressed the above definitions in a more direct form, which told the practical man exactly what each element in the plane triangle meant in his navigation. It was not until the nineteenth century that such a necessary improvement in the exposition of the subject made itself apparent, and such essential definitions were presented in a more concrete manner as follows:—[1]

---

[1]Raper's *Practice of Navigation,* 1840.

(*a*) Rhumb Line. The track of the ship while preserving the same angle with all the meridians as she crosses them in succession.

(*b*) Course. The course steered is the angle between the meridian and the ship's head. The course made good is the angle between the meridian and the ship's real track on the surface of the sphere. The course is reckoned from the north, towards the east or west, when the ship's head is less than eight points from the north point. The same applies to the south point.

The course is measured in points of 11° 15′ each, or in degrees and minutes.

(*c*) Distance. The distance between two places, or the distance run by the ship on a certain course, is measured in nautical miles of 60 to the degree of latitude. Three such miles make a league.

(*d*) Departure. The departure is the distance in nautical miles, made good by the ship due east or west; or the distance between two places measured along their parallel. Departure is marked east or west, according as it is made good towards east or west, and is accordingly called easting or westing; such easting and westing being, however, expressed in miles, and not, like longitude, in arc.

The figure below, taken from an eighteenth century treatise, serves to

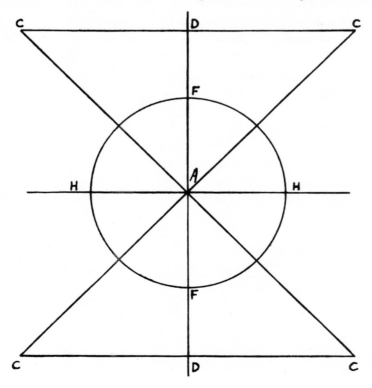

explain the whole principle upon which many ships were navigated, for about four hundred years, by the art of plane sailing.

Suppose the circle *FHFH* to represent the horizon of the place *A*, from whence the ship sails.

AC the rhumb she sails on, and *C* the place come to.

Then *HH* represents the parallel of latitude she sailed from, *CC* the parallel of the latitude arrived in.

So that *AD* becomes the difference of latitude, *DC* the departure, *AC* the distance sailed.

The angle *DAC* is the course.

These particulars will be alike represented whether the ship sails in the N.E. or N.W., S.E. or S.W. quarters of the horizon.

Hence it is evident that the difference of latitude, departure and distance form the sides of a right angled triangle, whose angles are the course, its complement and the right angle; therefore among these four things, course, distance, difference of latitude and departure, any two of them being given, the rest are to be found by plane trigonometry.[1]

The writers of the sixteenth century did not avail themselves of the benefits of plane trigonometry, but almost without exception adopted the graphical method for the solution of all their problems. It was customary for them to include in their books a diagram which showed the number of leagues that

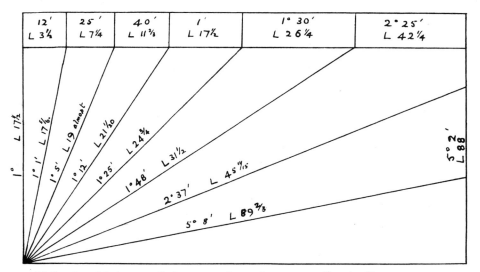

Of the Spanish leagues that are run for a degree according to divers courses.

[1]Robertson's *Elements of Navigation*, 1754.

had to be run on every full point of the compass in order to make a difference of one degree in the latitude.

It will be seen from the above diagram that the navigator could tell by inspection the departure made good upon every course, to the nearest point, after altering his latitude by one degree, and by rough interpolation, his difference of latitude and departure upon any course for any reasonable distance. It could not be claimed that there was any great accuracy in this method, but in an age when nothing was accurate in navigation it doubtless served its purpose and was, in fact, the forerunner of comprehensive tables by means of which all plane right angled triangles could be solved with speed and accuracy.

These tables known as "Traverse Table" which were introduced during the seventeenth century, were quickly adopted by navigators, to be used by them in the calculation of their positions, whether they had sailed upon one or many courses during each noon to noon period of their voyages.

In the absence of observations for latitude and when only one course had been steered during the day, one reference to the Traverse Table was sufficient to obtain the difference in latitude and departure, to be applied to the previous position, in order to calculate the latest dead reckoning position. So long as the plane chart was in use there was no need to convert the departure into difference of longitude (measured along the equator) because the distance made good east or west was more important to the earlier navigator than difference of longitude and, in any event, in such a chart, the two amounted to the same thing.

When several courses had been steered during the day the ship was said to have steered upon a Traverse, the definition of which was given by John Davis, in 1594, as follows:—"A Travers is the varietie or alteration of the Shippes motion upon the shift of windes, within any Horizontall plaine superficies, by the good collection of which Traverses the Ship's uniforme motion or Corse is given."

The solution of this form of sailing, called Traverse Sailing, so necessary when the wind was the sole means of propulsion, was well understood by Elizabethan navigators. In fact it was their sole method of keeping a dead reckoning account, though the results they obtained by using the rough diagrams, explained above, compared unfavourably with those arrived at by later seamen with their accurate Traverse Tables.

The method of setting out the solution of a traverse sailing has not altered since the early seventeenth century, when the departure and difference of latitude made upon each course and distance was tabulated in the following manner.

E.g., From noon to noon a ship sailed upon the following courses, S.E. 40 miles; N.E. 28 miles; S.W. × W. 52 miles; N.W. × W. 30 miles. Required the difference of latitude and departure.

Course	Distance	D. Latitude		Departure	
		N.	S.	E.	W.
S.E.	40		28·3	28·3	
N.E.	28	19·8		19·8	
S.W. × W.	52		28·9		43·2
N.W. × W.	30	16·7			24·9
		36·5	57·2	48·1	68·1
			36·5		48·1
	D. Lat.		20·7 S	Dep.	20·0 W.

The difference of Latitude of 21 miles south and the Departure of 20 miles west were then applied to the previous noon position to obtain the new position to be pricked on the chart.

The introduction of logarithms during the seventeenth century, and their use in trigonometrical calculations, prompted many writers to incorporate into their works numerous problems of both practical and academic interest, all of which could be solved by plane trigonometry. During the latter half of the seventeenth century navigators were encouraged to resolve their traverses, or Day's work as they were often called, by such means, but it is doubtful whether many availed themselves of the tables of logarithmic sines, tangents and secants, supplied for that purpose.

OBLIQUE SAILING.

During the eighteenth century a variant of plane sailing was expounded by many writers called Oblique Sailing, so called because in it the plane triangle to be solved was not a right angled triangle as in the case of plane sailing. There is no doubt that many of the problems in oblique sailing were intended purely as mental exercises, and had nothing to do with ocean navigation. On the other hand, to those who cared to master the elements of trigonometry, they offered great scope for ingenuity and, at times material benefit. The material benefits to be derived were of two kinds, and are of considerable historical interest. The one was the information that could be obtained and used when sailing to windward, and the other, most useful in those days of frequent naval engagements, the possibility of intercepting another ship or escaping from her.

Windward Sailing was the term applied when a ship endeavoured to gain headway towards that point of the compass from which the wind blew. It frequently happened that the master of a ship wanted to sail into a port or in a direction when the wind was wholly or partially against the direct course, and he was compelled to reach his objective by sailing first on one tack and then on the other. As a general rule sailing ships of the eighteenth century sailed close hauled within six points of the wind, though sloops, yachts and similar craft could lie much nearer. To know how near the wind a ship would lie the seaman observed the courses she sailed on each tack when close hauled, and halved the number of points between the two courses.

With this information, and a knowledge of plane trigonometry, the seaman was equipped to solve all cases of windward sailing, an example of which, taken from a contemporary treatise, is given below.

"The wind at north, and I am bound to a port 25 miles directly to windward, being on the starboard tack and lying within 6 points of the wind; What must be my course and distance on each of two tacks (the least number possible) to reach my port?"

The primary rule to be followed was to construct a figure to illustrate the problem, upon the following general rules:—

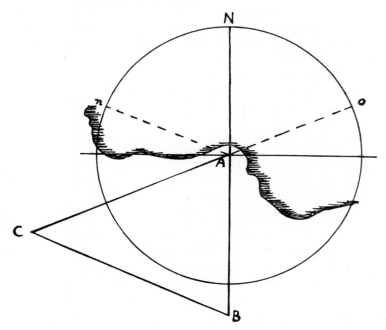

"Draw the meridian and parallel of latitude of the place *A*, within a circle which represents the horizon, placing *A* at the centre.

Mark upon the horizon the direction from which the wind blows, *N*, and on each side of this point measure in degrees the nearness to the wind at which the ship will sail, *o* and *n*. Then draw two diameters through these points to show the two courses which can be sailed upon close hauled.

Let B represent the position of the ship and join BA which is the course to be made good.

The first course BC will lie parallel to An (on the starboard tack) and the second course, on the port tack, along the diameter oA produced, which cuts the first course at C.

Solution. BC being parallel to An $\angle ABC = \angle NAn$. (6 points)

And $\angle BAC = \angle NAo$. (6 points)

$\therefore$ $\angle ACB = 4$ points.

$\therefore$ as $\angle ABC = \angle BAC$; $BC = CA$ (ABC is an isosceles $\triangle$)

In the $\triangle ABC$, all the angles and one side (AB) are known.

$\therefore$ By Plane Trigonometry the other two sides, BC and CA may be found."

An interesting example of fleet work was provided by the following problem, which could be solved by an elementary knowledge of geometry and trigonometry.

"A fleet of ships steering S.W. $\times$ S., 4 miles an hour, on seeing a sail, detached a cruiser who gave chase S.E. 5 hours at the rate of 7 miles an hour,

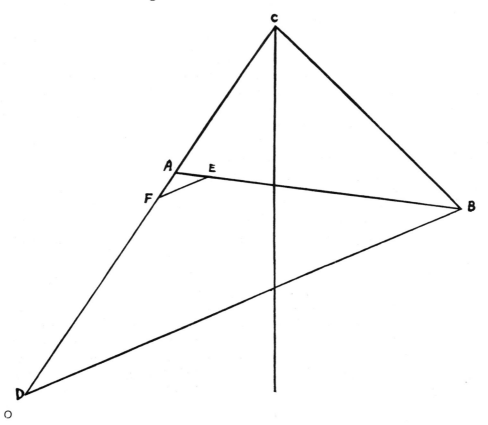

comes up with and takes the chase (being a privateer); and after an hour's time spent in adjusting matters on board the prize, she steers for the fleet who still kept on the same course and rate: Required the course the cruiser must shape, and the distance she must run at 7 miles an hour, to join them .

Solution. Let C be the first place of the fleet, draw CD, S.W. $\times$ S. and CB, South East; make $CB=35$ (7×5), $CA=24$ (4×6) and draw AB; then B is the place where the cruiser took the chase, and A the place where the fleet was when she left the chase: Make $AF=4$, $FE=7$, draw BD parallel to FE, and D is the place where the cruiser joined the fleet.

In the triangle ACB find (by trigonometry, given two sides and the included angle) $\angle CAB$ and $\angle CBA$, and AB.

$$\angle CAB=63° 25'$$
$$\angle CBA=37° 49'$$
$$AB=38 \cdot 39$$

Then $\angle FAE=116° 35'$ (being the Supplement of $\angle CAB$)

In $\triangle FAE$, find $\angle AEF$ (30° 44') and $\angle EFA$ (32° 41')

In $\triangle ADB$ (whose angles are similar to $\triangle FAE$, and whose side AB equals $38 \cdot 39$) find BD (which equals $63 \cdot 58$ miles).

Answer. The cruiser must steer S.66° 27' W., and run $63 \cdot 58$ miles.

Because of the uncertainties of navigation in general, and the further uncertainties added to it by using the plane chart, a form of sailing was adopted by many seamen, during the sixteenth century, to reduce the difficulties experienced in ocean sailing. It would not be true to say that they, with one accord, realised the errors inherent in the plane projection, though some did, but rather that they found by experience that the whole art of ocean sailing was beset with difficulties, and that they could obtain the best results by adapting their methods to the charts and instruments at their disposal.

Parallel Sailing.—The one element in their navigation upon which they could place reliance was the latitude by observation, and the one reliable feature of their charts was the latitudes of the places marked thereon. Upon this firm basis, therefore, they built their method of navigation, which became known as Parallel Sailing, and used it whenever prudence demanded and circumstances made possible.

The tendency to exaggeration in the distance measured on the plane chart has already been shown, and its effect upon navigation considered. To the examples given may be added those quoted by Edward Wright, in 1599, when he clearly described the origin of parallel sailing and defined its application. "Hereto", he wrote, "accord the often experiments and usual practice of many well experienced and judicial mariners and seamen of our time, who confess that in sailing from the West Indies to the Azores they have often fallen with those islands, when by their account according to the chart they should have been 150 or 200 leagues to westward of them. The like hath been found in sailing from Azores to Ushant, as I have also partly seen in the little experience I have had at sea, when we were come within sight of that island, when by account of the ordinary chart we should have been fifty leagues short of it. And as concerning the courses from place to place I have observed that some masters take a wise course in not trusting to those courses which are showed by their charts. But first getting themselves into the height or parallel of the place to which they are going and withal knowing assuredly whether they be more eastward or westward than that place; they then proceed always heedfully keeping themselves under that parallel till they come to the place desired. Than which way of sailing there is none more certain and infallible for the sure finding of the place assigned: but it hath this inconvenience, that it maketh the way longer than otherwise".[1]

There was everything to be said for this method of sailing, for the comparative ease with which the approximate latitude could be found by observation, and the absence of error in laying off the east or west course on the plane chart, usually saved more miles than were, in theory, lost by sailing indirectly to the objective.

A very good illustration of the methods of navigation, during the sixteenth century, which showed the uses of traverse sailing and parallel sailing, in a voyage across the Atlantic, was given in the instructions, issued by Sir Humphrey Gilbert, to the commanders of his squadron, upon his expedition to Newfoundland, in 1583. Part of the instructions were as follows:— "The course first to be taken for the discovery is to bear directly to Cape Race, the most southerly cape of Newfoundland; and there to harbour ourselves either in Rogneux or Fermons, being the places appointed for our rendezvous, and therefore every ship separated from the fleete to repair to that place as fast as God shall permit, whether you shall fall to the southward or to the northward of it . . . Beginning our course from Scilly, the nearest is by west-south-west (if the wind serve) until such time as we have brought ourselves in the latitude of 43 or 44 degrees, because the ocean is subject much to southerly winds in June and July. Then to take traverse from 45 to 47 degrees of latitude, if we be inforced by contrary winds; and not to go to the northward of the height (latitude) of 47 degrees of septentrional (north) latitude by no means, if God shall not inforce the contrary; but to do your endeavour to keep in the height of 46 degrees, so nere as you can possibly, because Cape Race lieth about that height."[2]

---

[1] *Certain Errors in Navigation*, 1599.
[2] Hakluyts Voyages, 1600, Vol. III.

The growing appreciation by navigators, during the seventeenth century, of the spherical shape of the earth, and their gradual adoption of the more accurate Mercator projection, which took the sphericity into account, led them to apply the principles of plane trigonometry, upon which the Mercator projection was based, to the calculation of the difference in longitude between two places, whose distance apart along a parallel was known or estimated. By means of the necessary formula the number of miles sailed along any parallel of latitude could readily be translated into degrees and minutes of longitude, measured along the equator.[1]

Though Mercator's projection contributed to the increasing accuracy in navigation which took place during the seventeenth and later centuries, it did little to abate the practice of parallel sailing which, after all, was based upon tried experience and sound commonsense. Though navigators could set and steer better courses, and obtain more accurate latitudes, they were unable to calculate their longitude at sea with any degree of accuracy until the end of the eighteenth century. Consequently the positions assigned to many places, especially those less frequented by ships, were often grossly in error, and parallel sailing had to be employed to avoid missing the desi   d port altogether. Thus we find that most text book writers advised the employment of parallel sailing whenever possible, especially on long voyages, and that practical seamen sailed to the latitudes of their destinations as soon as possible, provided the wind served, and then continued along those parallels until they reached their objectives.

There were two objections to the wholesale adoption of parallel sailing, which Doctor Halley, who was ever anxious to improve the standard of English navigational practice, remarked on, in a letter to Mr. Pepys, in 1695.[2] The first objection was that such a comparatively sure method of sailing caused the navigator to be well satisfied with himself if he knew enough of the doctrine of the plane triangle as to be able to take his ship to the latitude of his port and sail due east or west until in due time he arrived at it. It was not the method which Halley criticised but the complacent state of mind it bred, which caused the navigator to take no further steps to attempt more or to learn more of his art, which was so greatly in need of the improvements which progressive minds could give.

Though the method was certain in theory, in practice it often happened that clouds or fog obscured the sun at noon, for many days together, and the navigator, uncertain of his latitude, had no other guide, unless he was in shallow water when soundings gave him some indication of his position. The

---

[1] For the formula, Difference of Longitude = Departure × Secant Latitude, See Chapter on Charts.

[2] Brit. Mus. ADD. MSS. 30221.

very complacency of mind bred by the method, which Halley so strongly condemned, caused the navigator to neglect any other means to find his latitude although latitude was the foundation upon which the practice of parallel sailing rested. "Whereas", wrote Halley, "if they were well acquainted with the stars and knew the doctrine of the sphere, any clear glare in the night-time would suffice to give them their latitude with even greater certainty than the sun at noon, which vulgarly is esteemed the only moment when the latitude can be taken. Hence appears a necessity for the sailor to know the stars and how to use them, lest he be destitute of the succour of his latitude. Which he must allow to be absolutely necessary yet he cares not to know any more ways than one to come by it. For want of this knowledge many ships bound up the Channel of England have been lost, some on the Welsh and Devonshire coasts and others run on shore upon the coast of France".

The second objection to parallel sailing applied in time of war, when enemy frigates and privateers were on the watch to work every possible havoc with British merchant ships, especially those laden, homeward bound, off the mouth of the Channel. Halley tells us that many ships were taken by the enemy because of the "erroneous manner of keeping the account". These ships being very doubtful as to the distance and bearing of the land which they were approaching, for their convenience and safety (from the navigational point of view) were obliged to get into the latitude of the Lizard long before it was necessary, and then sail along the parallel until they made the land. As a result the enemy ships kept near to that parallel, and had no need to search or disperse over a wider area, to intercept and capture many a richly laden British ship. "Whereas", wrote Halley, "if they could come directly in upon a North East course they would have a very good chance to escape".

In times of peace, at any rate, the advantages of parallel sailing outweighed any objection to it and it was generally practised by those who, in later years, were above the strictures of Halley. It was the only practical method in times of uncertainty. How uncertain such times could be, even about the middle of the eighteenth century, was well illustrated during Anson's expedition to the Pacific, in 1741. After his squadron had been dispersed in stormy weather off the coast of Chile, and his men and ship were so enfeebled that he could no longer stay at sea to look for it, the chronicler of the voyage wrote, "Our deplorable situation then allowing no room for deliberation, we stood for the island of Juan Fernandes; and to save time, which was now extremely precious (our men dying four, five and six in a day) and likewise to avoid being engaged again with a lee-shore, we resolved, if possible, to hit the Island upon a meridian. And, on the 28th of May, being nearly in the parallel which it is laid down, we had great expectations of seeing it: but not finding it in the position in which the charts had taught us to expect it, we began to fear that we had got too far to the westward; and therefore, though the Commodore himself was strongly persuaded that he saw it on the morning of the 28th, yet his Officers believing it to be only a cloud, to which opinion the haziness of the weather gave some kind of countenance, it was, on a consultation, resolved to stand to the eastward, in the parallel of the Island; as it was certain, that by this course we should either fall in with the Island, if we were already to the westward of it; or should at least make the main-land of Chili, from whence we might take a new departure, and assure ourselves, by running to the west-ward afterwards, of not missing the Island a second time."[1]

The common use of parallel sailing continued until well into the nineteenth century, when an ever increasing number of navigators were able to find their longitude at sea by means of the recently introduced chronometer. This increasing ability gave the navigator a greater confidence in sailing directly to his objective, whose position was also known with greater accuracy. The decline of parallel sailing was foreshadowed by Captain John Vancouver R.N., in the introduction to the description of his voyage round the world, at the close of the eighteenth century.[2] He remarked that by the introduction of nautical astronomy into marine education the navigator was taught to sail on the hypotenuse, instead of traversing two sides of a triangle, which was roughly the case in parallel sailing. "By this means", said he, "the circuitous course of all voyages from place to place is considerably shortened: and it is now become evident that sea officers of the most commonrate abilities, who will take the trouble of making themselves acquainted with the principles of the Science, will on all suitable occasions, with proper and correct instruments, be enabled to acquire a knowledge of their situation in the Atlantic, Indian or Pacific Oceans, with a degree of accuracy sufficient to steer on a meridional or diagonal line to any known spot: provided it be sufficiently conspicuous to be visible at any distance from 5 to 10 leagues".

Whereas, in the old days, navigators sailed to the desired latitude as soon as convenient and practicable, and then progressed along the parallel often several hundred leagues, until their port was reached, the better equipped navigator of the nineteenth century was able to, and did, take the more direct route. In times of doubt, however, the prudent man adopted the method of his predecessors, and carried out the old maxim of good seamanship, which Raper placed first among the essentials in making the land, as follows, "When confidence cannot be placed in the correctness of the longitude, it is proper, if circumstances permit, to make the latitude of the port, and then to

[1]Richard Walter, *A voyage round the world by George Anson*, 1740-1744. Published 1748.
[2]Vancouver's *Voyage Round the World*, 1790-95. Captain Vancouver died shortly before the publication in 1798.

run on the parallel for it."[1]

Middle Latitude Sailing.—Although parallel sailing was extensively used in the early days of navigation, already described, there were occasions, even then, when the mariner felt justified in adopting a more direct course. In any case, he seldom sailed along a meridian to his required latitude, but took a diagonal course from the point of departure to some point on his required parallel, short of his objective, and then continued, as we have seen, by parallel sailing. In order to invest this diagonal sailing, as it may be called, with more accuracy, and to assist the navigator to find his change of longitude while so sailing, a method was evolved by the beginning of the seventeenth century, called Middle Latitude Sailing.[2] This sailing was no more than a combination of the other two forms already practised, Plane and Parallel. It was the intelligent application of Parallel Sailing, which took account of the sphericity of the earth, to Plane Sailing, in which the earth was regarded a plane surface. By Plane Sailing it was possible to obtain the total difference in latitude, and distance made good east or west, (departure), after sailing on any number of different courses during a day; and by Parallel Sailing it was possible to convert departure, in any given latitude, into difference in longitude. Therefore, by taking the mean of the latitude sailed from and the latitude sailed to, in the diagonal sailing, the difference of longitude made good could be found by the formula used to convert departure in parallel sailing. Though this reasoning was not strictly accurate, the results obtained by it were accurate enough for distances up to about 600 miles. It was adopted by all text book writers by the end of the seventeenth century, and remains to this day the means whereby the practical navigator calculates his dead reckoning longitude, and course and distance made good day by day, in preference to the exact calculations of the more refined Mercator's Sailing which takes account of the meridional parts.

Great Circle Sailing.—That a great circle (*i.e.*, one whose plane passes through the centre of a sphere) is the shortest distance between two points on a sphere was known to ancient mathematicians long before the days of Columbus. The idea of sailing upon a great circle was certainly present in the minds of many nautical writers of the sixteenth century, but there is little or no reliable evidence that such a course was ever followed by the navigators of that time. The Portuguese writer Pedro Nunez alluded to it in 1537, and Martin Cortes, shortly afterwards, wrote that, according to the cosmographers, the course from one place to another ought to be by the arc of a great circle, for such was the shortest distance between them. Repeated reference to the

---

[1] *The Practice of Navigation*, 1852.

[2] A mathematician named Ralph Handsen is credited with its invention in 1614. *Vide* Robertson's *Elements of Navigation*, 4th Edition, 1780.

theory of sailing upon a great circle, and the desirability of so doing, by sixteenth century writers, leads to the conclusion that they were copying what the earlier cosmographers had said, without giving it any great consideration and without any practical experience of the subject.

There were many difficulties which prevented the navigators of the sixteenth and seventeenth centuries, from contemplating the use of such a method of sailing. Firstly, it was impossible to plot an accurate Great Circle course on either a globe or chart unless the longitudes, as well as the latitudes, of the two places were known, and it was seldom that the difference of longitude between places two or three thousand miles apart was known within five or even ten degrees.

Secondly, it was seldom that the wind was favourable for long enough to enable a ship to maintain the Great Circle course.

Thirdly, the lack of fresh food, water and fuel often compelled ships to prosecute their voyages by stages, from point to point, to refresh the crews and restock the larders.

Fourthly, the distance likely to be saved on voyages of 2000 to 4000 miles, in the higher latitudes (for there was little or no saving in the tropics) was only between 50 and 200 miles, and was not justified by the greatly increased chances of missing the objective altogether, a contingency unlikely when parallel sailing was adopted some hundreds of leagues short of it.

Fifthly, in the trade wind belts, in both hemispheres, the prosecution of a voyage to the westward upon a Great Circle was likely to take the ship out of the belt into a higher latitude, where the anti-Trades blew, although it might be an advantage to ships bound to the eastwood. For example, in a voyage from Madeira to Florida, a Great Circle course would keep a ship to the northward of the Trade Winds altogether, whereas by adopting parallel sailing, she would get them for practically the whole of her voyage.

Ships were much more concerned with finding and keeping a fair wind than saving a few hundred miles of distance at the most, which might just as easily be lost in tacking against head winds, or in searching for the destination at the end of the course. There may have been isolated instances of Great Circle sailing, during the sixteenth and seventeenth centuries, especially in the higher latitudes when the wind served. John Davies, who was one of the foremost and most progressive practical navigators of his day wrote. "Great Circle navigation is the chiefest of all the 3 kindes of sayling, in whom all the others are contained, and by them this kinde of sayling is performed . . and also when with favourable windes the Pylote shall shape a corse . . . as the best meane to attaine his porte, he shal by this kinde of sayling finde a better and shorter corse".[1] The detailed and practical manner in which Davis

[1] *Seaman's Secrets*, 1594.

treated of Great Circle sailing leaves the impression that he had attempted it on occasions, although no mention was made of it in the accounts of his voyages. On the other hand, it is possible that his practical mind grasped how it should be applied when more reliable charts should be produced, and, until then, was content to rely upon the plane sailing, "which kinde of sayling," he wrote, "is now of the greatest sort only practised".

The first evidence that Great Circle sailing was more than theoretically desirable was given by Richard Norwood, who, it will be remembered, was the first Englishman to calculate the accurate measure of 1° of a Great Circle by measuring the arc of the meridian between York and London.

In giving an example of the use of the newly invented Traverse Table he illustrated its application to Great Circle sailing. It had long been appreciated that such a form of sailing was made up of a series of straight courses, and to show the resultant differences of latitude and longitude, on the plane chart, which arose from steering such courses, he appended the following table, for a voyage upon a Great Circle from Sumners Islands (Bermuda) to the Lizard.

Course	Rhumb from North	Distance	N.	S.	E.	W.
N.E. ½ E.	4½ Points	600	380·6	—	463·8	—
N.E. × E.	5 Points	300	166·7	—	249·4	—
E.N.E. ½ N.	5½ Points	495	233·3	—	436·6	—
E.N.E.	6 Points	390	149·2	—	360·3	—
E.N.E. ½ E.	6½ Points	264	76·6	—	252·6	—
E. × N.	7 Points	210	41·0	—	206·0	—
E.	8 Points	951	—	—	951·0	—
		3210	1047·4		2919·7	

1047' = 17° 27', which to be added to the latitude of:

Sumner I.	32° 25' N.	
	17° 27' N.	
Gives	49° 52' N.	Latitude of Lizard

And her longitude altered to East 2920 miles, of such miles whereof 60 make a degree of a Great Circle.

Therefore if you set down this reckoning on the plane chart you must make a point in the chart that may be in latitude 49° 52' and to East of Sumner Is. 2920 miles.

If set down on Mercators, find latitude 49° 52' and make a point and may likewise be to East of Summer Is. 2920 miles.[1]

An examination of the above table reveals that according to the accepted longitude of Bermuda, west of the Lizard, the Great Circle distance between them was 3210 miles, whereas the actual distance, taken from more accurate

[1]*The Seaman's Practice*, 1637.

longitudes is 2812 miles. In this particular instance the error in distance of about 400 miles would not have caused any embarrassment to the navigator, because the last leg of the Great Circle course was true east for 951 miles. It would simply have meant that in approaching the Lizard upon its parallel (for it so happens that the final course on this route, is, in fact, S89° E.) the landfall would have been made sooner than expected.

The danger of relying upon Great Circle sailing when the difference in longitude between two places was imperfectly known is well illustrated if the above courses and distances are laid on the chart in the reverse direction, for a voyage from the Lizard to Bermuda. In this case the error of 400 miles would have led to a most bewildering result, because the final course in this direction was not upon a parallel but about S. 50° W., and upon reaching the latitude of 32° 25′ N., the ship would have been within two days' sailing of the Carolina coast instead of in sight of Bermuda.

Norwood did not say that the above courses had actually been sailed by any ship, but it may well be that they were, and that the distances run were over-estimated. There would be nothing remarkable, in those days, in such an error, but what is remarkable is that if his was a purely theoretical example he should have chosen Great Circle courses to illustrate the use of the Traverse Table.

The general attitude towards such a form of sailing during the seventeenth and eighteenth centuries seems to have been that its theories produced some very pretty problems for those who found pleasure in spherical trigonometry for its own sake, but it really wasn't worth the trouble to those who had little interest in mathematical conundrums. Captain Samuel Sturmey, whose *Mariners Magazine* passed into several editions during the seventeenth century, and who appears to have been a man with a very advanced outlook for his day, described the theory of Great Circle sailing, and added, "He that will take pains will find great delight in this Great Circle Sailing. Yet I conclude, that although it is the nearest way, it is not always the convenient way for seamen, for several reasons known to them that can keep an account of the ship's way, both by Mercator's and Great Circle sailing, which I could lay down here, but in regard it is needless—I leave every one his discretion, and shall show you the way how I did keep my account at sea by Mercators Chart".

It is safe to assume that had Great Circle sailing been desirable and possible in a general way, during this period, it would have received greater notice from Dr. Halley, who, besides being an eminent mathematician, was well informed in practical maritime affairs. There is no mention of it in his letters to Pepys, though he referred to it somewhat loosely at a later time, in giving his blessing to a new set of charts, published in 1728 by Messrs. Harris, Senex and Wilson.[1] Some of these charts were on Mercators projection, but

_____

[1] *Atlas Maritimus et Commercialis.*

the greater part of them were drawn "according to a New Globular Projection adapted for measuring distances (as near as possible) by scale and compass". They added little to the simplicity of ocean navigation and never attained any great popularity with seamen.

The chief merit of these charts was, in Halley's opinion, the greater accuracy of the longitudes shown, which was an improvement upon any previously published. With reference to the projection he wrote, "The undertakers have made choice of this Globular projection purely for the sake of measuring distances", and he recommended its use in charts when the distances to be measured did not exceed 400 to 500 leagues. He concluded by saying, "I am of opinion that this sort of sea chart, showing both the true distances and bearings of places by the help of the rhumb lines drawn thereon may be of good use to navigators, more especially to such as shall be desirous to sail by the arch of a Great Circle"

It is obvious that Halley had either not thought a great deal about the use of this projection in great circle sailing or he did not regard such sailing very seriously, for there was little advantage to be gained in using it when distances did not exceed 500 leagues. The globular projection was one in which the parallels of latitude were arcs of circles, spaced equally, which had the pole for their common centre, and the meridians curvilinear, similarly spaced, which converged at the pole, or common centre of the parallels. As all meridians and parallels were curved, except the central meridian and the equator, it will readily be appreciated how difficult it was for the navigator to read his great circle courses with either ease or accuracy. Such a projection had little to recommend it for practical navigation, but it had the merit of showing the different parts of the earth in their proper proportions. For this reason it was never generally accepted at sea though it was, and still is, adopted in large area geographical maps.

Text book writers, contemporary with Halley, did not devote much space to great circle sailing. Some did not mention it at all, while others, after explaining its theory devoted their attention to plane and Mercator sailing, which they regarded as much more practical propositions.

For the purpose of this inquiry it is a little unfortunate that the voyages undertaken by the principal navigators of the eighteenth century were voyages of discovery, sponsored by the governments of the maritime nations, in which the leaders were bound to follow some prearranged tracks or to conduct their inquiries within certain defined limits. Such sailing orders circumscribed the routes taken and the methods of sailing adopted by those best fitted to exploit and investigate the practicability of Great Circle sailing. For this reason there is little conclusive evidence that the practice was ever seriously considered or used by those navigators whose names now adorn the islands, headlands and straits of the oceans.

It may be said with some force that Great Circle sailing did not come into its own until the nineteenth century, when as a result of the increased knowledge of the seasonal and prevailing winds over the navigable oceans, the seaman could follow some preconceived track with a measure of confidence that had been denied to his predecessors. In the realm of marine meteorology, as in other branches of nautical research, the accumulation of information by individual shipmasters, and the observations by navigators and scientists equipped by organised societies and governments, began to bear fruit which every seaman could enjoy, if he so desired.

Doctor Halley had been at some pains to gather information about the winds in the Atlantic and Indian oceans, and his conclusions were included in many books on navigation during the eighteenth century.[1] This information was confined to the Trade winds in the North and South Atlantic, the Doldrums, and the Monsoons in the Indian Ocean where, for the reasons already given, Great Circle sailing was seldom advantageous or practicable.

It was not until the nineteenth century that the great Southern ocean, where the westerly winds blow round the world unimpeded by land, received any detailed attention. Australia was practically unknown to merchantmen until the early decades of the nineteenth century, and, as a result, the route thither had been subjected to little systematic investigation.

The whole subject of marine meteorology was finally put on to a proper footing about the middle of the nineteenth century, chiefly through the efforts and patience of an American naval officer, of whom it has been written, "The late Commander M. F. Maury, of the United States Navy, may rightly be deemed the founder of scientific Marine Meteorology. He first gathered the strands of the subject, laid them up into a coherent whole, and eventually arranged the result so as to be useful to seafarers for all time. By force of his indomitable energy, and his infinite capacity for taking pains, Maury induced shipmasters of the merchant navies all the world over, to co-operate with him in the good work. They supplied carefully kept observations of the wind, weather, temperature of air and sea, atmospheric pressure, and other items of interest, taken at specified hours by day and by night at well defined geographical positions during the voyage. Maury's brilliant deductions from the scattered data, obtained from thousands of observations, have seldom been equalled and never surpassed in value . . .[2] As the result of that

---

[1]Reference must also be made to William Dampier's *Discourse of Winds, Breezes, Storms, Tides and Currents of the Torrid Zone*, which was compiled during the latter half of the seventeenth century.

[2]They form the basis of the present-day monthly pilot charts of the oceans issued by the American Hydrographic Office.

illustrious American seaman's efforts, the United States Government convened an international maritime conference, which met at Brussels in 1853 and drew up a scheme for the record of observations of Marine Meteorology. Ever since that gathering of seamen the collection of data has been steadily proceeded with by the state-supported departments of all nations . . ."[1]

Of his labour Maury himself wrote, "Ever since log books have been kept at sea and preserved in old sea chests and garrets on shore, the materials for such a system of investigation, as this is, have existed. But the labour of collecting from such records . . . appeared a Herculean task, which no one before had offered to undertake."[2]

One of the first results of these investigations was the recommendation of the use of the Great Circle track from New York to Cape San Roque, in Brazil, by all ships bound to South America or round Cape Horn to California. By means of elaborate pilot charts of the oceans Maury showed the most advantageous routes to be followed by ships where they would, in the main, experience the greatest percentage of favouring winds. Up to that time it had been the common practice for ships bound to South America from North America to sail south easterly as far as the C. Verde Islands before they steered south for the Equator, but Maury showed that by adopting the Great Circle route, not only would great distances be saved, but more favourable winds would be experienced. Upon his chart of the North Atlantic, published in 1848, was engraved the actual Great Circle to be followed, together with the advice, "Great Circle from New York to the Equator at 31° W. longitude DISTANCE 3370 miles. The distance by the route usually pursued is upwards of 4100 miles. Outward bound vessels are recommended to try this route to Rio Janeiro. The tracks of vessels on this chart shew the average passage from the United States to the Line to be 38 days, and to Rio 55 days. There is reason to believe that the prevailing winds along the route here indicated will be found more favourable, steadier and stronger than they are by the usual route and the distance is nearly 1000 miles less. Hence I respectfully invite the attention of navigators to this route, under the expectation that by taking it, they will shorten their average passages several days."

Maury never advised the adoption of Great Circle sailing unless there was a reasonable prospect of the winds aiding its execution, but he pointed out the benefits which would accrue, in the shortening of the distance, by keeping as near to the track as possible when the winds were unfavourable along the track itself, or when other impediments barred the navigator from following it. Upon no route was this advice so welcome as from Europe to Australia,

---

[1] William Allingham, *A Manual of Marine Meteorology.*
[2] Maury's *Sailing Directions to accompany Wind and Current Charts*, 1851.

for coincident with the publication of Maury's *Sailing Directions* came the news of the discovery of gold in Australia.[1] Then the need was for quicker and yet quicker passages to what Maury referred to as the "Great Gold Continent", and it may be said with truth that this coincidence caused the navigators of the world to consider the possibilities of Great Circle sailing as they had never considered it before.

In considering the routes to and from Australia Maury remarked that the United States and Australia were nearly antipodal, and consequently if the meridians of many places in America were followed to the South Pole and thence onward the course would lead directly, by the shortest way to Australia. Such a course was manifestly impossible, not only on account of the impenetrable ice barrier, which more or less followed the parallel of the Antarctic Circle, but also by reason of the numerous bergs which broke off from it and drifted as far north as about the 50th parallel. For these reasons Maury wrote, "Let us, however, look for one (route) which being practicable will be found to deviate as little as possible from the Great Circle and which moreover, all things being considered, offers to vessels in the Australian trade from Europe, as well as from the United States, the fairest prospect of the most speedy passages". As a result of this reasoning the method of sailing on a Composite Great Circle track was born.

This method was a combination of Great Circle and Parallel sailing, by means of which the navigator followed a Great Circle course until he reached the highest parallel to which he could go with safety, and then ran his easting down along that parallel with the aid of the "brave west winds", until he reached a position where he could again sweep towards his objective upon a second Great Circle in the lower latitudes. By such means was Maury's guiding principle, of sailing as near as possible to the Great Circle, achieved. Not only was the actual sailing distance shortened but, on the Australian route, by traversing in the higher latitudes, a steadier westerly wind was assured than that which obtained when ships followed the older route of passing close to the Cape of Good Hope. No change of principle was involved in his recommendation of the track to be followed by ships homeward bound from Australia. Here again he impressed upon the navigator the fact that all Great Circles between places in the higher latitudes curve towards the relevant poles when drawn upon a Mercator Chart, especially when their differences of longitude are considerable. His directions to homeward bound ships were as follows:— "Returning by way of Cape Horn homeward the best route is to get south of the parallel 45° or 50° S., as soon as you can, by a S.E. course. Do not hesitate if winds favour to pass south of New Zealand.

---

[1]For a full description of its effect upon British shipping the reader is referred to Basil Lubbock's, *Colonial Clippers*, 1924.

But whether you pass south of these islands or not as soon as you get clear let the course be shaped direct for Cape Horn, recollecting that the further you keep south of the middle of the straight line on your chart from Van Dieman's land to Cape Horn, the nearer you are to the Great Circle route, and the shorter the distance—the difference by the Great Circle and by the straight course on the charts being upwards of 1000 miles".[1]

The attention which Maury, and others drew to the theory and practice of Great Circle sailing, and the results which were achieved by its application, carried conviction, and thus we find that a knowledge of it became more and more important to every navigator who hoped to compete successfully with his rivals. Nor was this the only cause of the increased attention paid to it, for, during the nineteenth century, the propulsion of ships by steam removed the last objection which could be levelled against it. A well known textbook writer aptly reviewed the question in his introduction to the subject in the following words:— "Within these last forty years, the marine steam engine has been brought to such perfection that many long voyages are now performed by its aid; thus, having a means of propelling our vessels independently of the wind. Great Circle Sailing has come into greater prominence. The increased intelligence of many of our masters has, no doubt, contributed largely to its more general use".[2] How much the intelligence was quickened by the changed circumstances of ocean travel, and by Maury's happy discovery that the principles of Great Circle sailing could be practised with advantage by sailing ships, upon many long voyages, would be difficult to assess, but there can be no doubt that these two factors helped much to put into practice what to the majority of seamen had been but a theorist's trigonometrical problem.

The latter half of the nineteenth century witnessed the gradual adoption of Great Circle routes, whenever advantageous, in every navigable ocean, with the result that, to-day, to quote one example only, there are no fewer than twelve such principal routes radiating from Honolulu, in the centre of the Pacific, to the Americas and the Far East, for distances which vary from 2000 to 5000 miles.

Various tables and diagrams were compiled to assist the navigator, of last century, over the mathematical difficulties of Great Circle Sailing, but the most popular and simplest was that proposed by Mr. Godfray of St. John's College, Cambrdge, who suggested a chart on the Gnomonic Projection.[3]

---

[1] One further use of the principles of great circle sailing was demonstrated by the above instruction. Suppose a ship, upon leaving port, to experience a head wind on the direct Mercator course to her distant objective; by adopting the tack which took her to the polar side of it she would in effect, make good some considerable distance towards her destination, whereas by adopting the opposite tack she would often be sailing away from it. This was known as Windward Great Circle sailing.

[2] *Navigation and Nautical Astronomy*, by John Merrifield and Henry Evers, London, 1873

[3] F. C. Stebbing, *Navigation and Nautical Astronomy*, 1896, whose explanation of the Gnomonic Polar Projection is given below.

This projection, the invention of which is ascribed to Thales (B.C. c.600) was adopted for this purpose because any Great Circle could be represented upon it by a straight line.[1] In it a tangent plane is supposed to touch the earth at the pole, or at some other more convenient point, called the tangential point, when portraying lower latitudes, the eye of the observer being supposed to be at the centre of the earth. When the tangential point is the pole the meridians appear on the tangent plane, as straight lines radiating from the pole; all great circles are represented by straight lines (because the planes of the meridians and all Great Circles pass through the centre of the earth); and the parallels of latitude appear as concentric circles whose radii are proportional to the cotangent of the latitude.

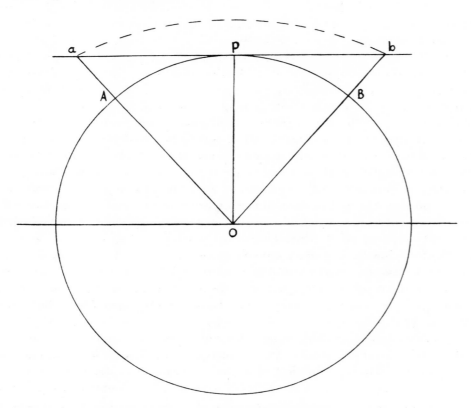

Let *ab* be a portion of the tangent plane, *P* the pole, *O* the observer at the centre of the earth.

Then $Pa = PO \tan \angle POA$.

$\qquad = PO \cot$ latitude of A.

---

[1]For further remarks on this *vide Map Projections*, A. R. Hinks (1921).

By the means of this chart the great circle between any two places could be drawn as a straight line, and it could at once be seen if the course was interrupted by land or other impediments. The latitude and longitude of various points along the great circle could then be read off from the chart and plotted on the Mercator chart, and, a free curve being drawn through those points, the great circle could thereby be transferred to it, and the various courses and distances which made up the track laid off in the usual way.

It may be that the fullest use of Great Circle sailing has not yet been made and that, in the course of time, such a method will be practised across regions which are permanently closed to shipping, either by land or ice. A glance at any globe will show that the direct courses between many great trade centres lie across continents or the ice bound Arctic and Antarctic regions, which, though unattainable by surface vessels are, and will be increasingly possible to aeroplanes of high speed.

Jet aircraft frequently follow Great Circles when they are engaged in flying over polar routes in the Northern Hemisphere. There is a considerable saving in distance when flying from the British Isles or Scandinavia to the West Coast of the U.S.A.

The Lead Line.—Making the land, especially strange or previously undiscovered land, after weeks at sea, has always held a certain element of romantic adventure, which even in these days of many scientific contrivances, still retains, to some degree, its ancient uncertainty. In spite of all mechanical invention, making the land is still not devoid of danger, and it is still a source of pride and gratification to the true navigator to make a good landfall after a difficult passage or in difficult circumstances.

Numerous signs, many of which were known to ancient seamen, have been used to indicate the approach to land. The presence of birds, weeds and trees, dust and fine sand in the air, the scent of vegetation, discolouration of the sea, an appreciable fall in the violence of the sea upon making the leeward side of the land, cloud low on the horizon in an otherwise cloudless sky, field ice, and changes in temperature have all aided the seaman, at some time or another or warned him to be on the lookout for land. Yet none of these natural signs has been of such unfailing assistance to the mariner, in making the land, as the lead line.

There is no doubt that some form of lead line was used by seamen very early in the history of navigation. In the familiar account of the wreck of the ship in which St. Paul was being taken to Rome, 62 A.D., we read "But when the fourteenth night was come, as we were driven up and down in Adria, about midnight the shipmen deemed that they drew near to some country; and sounded, and found it twenty fathoms: and when they had gone a little further, they sounded again, and found it fifteen fathoms." (The Acts of the Apostles, Chapter 27, verses 27-28).

It seems that the fathom (of 6 feet or thereabouts) was often used as a measure of depth long before the Christian Era, though it is doubtful whether its length was then a standard measurement of 6 feet. It was usually taken to be the distance between the outstretched arms, and was peculiarly easy of measurement to seamen, who passed the sounding line through the hands in the way familiar to them to this day.

Whether the lead line was marked at intervals, or the depth was taken, in those early ships of low freeboard, by measuring the line from the height of the leadsman, is immaterial. One thing is certain, the lead is one of the oldest implements known to seamen, and it is safe to assume that the hand lead and the heavier deep sea lead have altered little, except perhaps in the method of marking, during the last few thousand years.

We are told that Columbus, after leaving the Canary Islands, proceeded carefully to the westward, with astrolabe and sounding lead, and that Ferdinand Magellan, in the circumnavigation of the world, sounded the depths of the sea with the plumb line.[1] In the description of the first voyage of John Davis to discover the North West Passage, in 1585, frequent references are made to soundings taken in both deep and shallow water, and from the information given, it is obvious that, in his day, the lead was often armed to bring up a sample of the bottom. Thus we read, "In sayling 20 leagues within the mouth of this entrance we had sounding in 90 fathoms, faire gray osie sand, and the further we ran into the westwards, the deeper was the water, so that hard abord the shoare among these yles we could not have ground in 330 fathoms".

Many great navigators of the sixteenth century recorded the soundings taken during their voyages, and it is not surprising to find that, during this period, soundings were frequently recorded on charts or in the sailing directions to assist seamen in making the land or finding a good anchorage.

Though deep sea and shallow water sounding was practised by seamen generally, from the beginning of ocean navigation, few accounts of the lead were given, probably because it was so well known that any description of it was considered superfluous. An interesting description of its use in making the land was given, however, by Captain John Smith, sometime Governor of Virginia, during the seventeenth century, in *The Seaman's Grammar*, where he wrote as follows:— "Rockweed doth grow by the shore and is a signe of land, yet it is oft found far in the sea. Lay the ship by the lee to trie the

---

[1]See Herrara's description of Columbus's first voyage (Dec. 1. Lib. 1. cap. IX) *Journal of Columbus*, Hakluyt Society, Volume 86, and Harris's *Complete Collection of Voyages and Travels* (Ferdinand Magellan), London, 1744.

Dipsie (Deep Sea) line, which is a small line some 150 fadome long with a long plummet at the end, made hollow, wherein is put tallow that will bring up any gravell; which is first marked at 20 fadome and after increased by tens to the end; and those distinguished by so many small knots upon each little string that is fixed at the mark through the strands or middle of the line showing it is so many times 10 fadomes deep where the plummet doth rest from drawing the line out of your hand; this is only used in deep water when we think we approach the shore, for in the maine sea at 300 fadomes, we find no bottome. Bring the ship to rights, *i.e.*, again under sail as she was . . One to the top to look out for land, the man cries out Land To; which is just as far as a kenning or a man may discover or see the land . . . A good landfall is when we fall just with our reckoning, if otherwise, a bad landfall: but however it bears, set it by the compass and bend your cables to the anchors."

Smith then procedeed to describe the hand lead for use upon closing the land, "Fetch", said he, "the sounding line—this is bigger than the Dipsie line and is marked at 2 fadome next the lead with a piece of blacke leather, at 3 fadome the like but slit, at 5 fadome with a piece of white cloth, at 7 with a piece of red in a piece of white leather, at 15 with a white cloth. The sounding lead is 6 or 7 lbs. weight and neer a foot long. He that doth heave this lead stands by the house or in the chains and doth sing fadoms by the mark..."

Comparison with the modern system of marking both deep sea and hand leads shows how little the old system has changed during the last 300 years.

MODERN SYSTEM OF MARKING THE LEAD LINES.

	Hand Lead.	*Deep Sea Lead.*
2 fathoms	— Leather with two tails.	The same as the hand
3 ,,	— Leather with 3 tails.	line up to 20 fathoms,
5 ,,	— White rag.	then for every addi-
7 ,,	— Red rag.	tional ten fathoms add
10 ,,	— Leather, with a hole in it.	a knot to the cord,
13 ,,	— Blue rag.	and at every 5 fathoms
15 ,,	— White rag.	a piece of cord with
17 ,,	— Red rag.	one knot only, or a
20 ,,	— Cord with two knots in it.	piece of leather.
Weight of hand lead 7 to 14 lbs.		Weight of deep sea lead 28 lbs.

The great disadvantage in using the long established deep sea lead was that the ship had to be stopped before any considerable depth could be sounded. Such a necessity was always inconvenient and sometimes dangerous. Thus we find that from the beginning of the nineteenth century efforts have been made to introduce more convenient and accurate means of sounding without reducing the speed of even the fastest ships.

The first improvement to receive any marked attention from seamen was the Massey Fly, which was proposed by the inventor of the Massey log and worked on much the same principle. It was attached to the deep sea lead line, a few feet above the lead, and consisted of a small fly or fan, which was set in motion by the descent of the lead, and by means of suitable gearing measured the depth of water. Provided the line was paid out without checking the vertical descent of the lead it mattered little if the ship had considerable headway, though the task of hauling in the line under such conditions was not without its difficulties.

It is difficult to say to what extent the Massey Sounding Fly was used in ordinary navigation. Raper remarked, in 1852, that it had long been approved and added that Captain Bayfield, R.N., in his survey of the River St. Lawrence, had reported that in depths exceeding 100 fathoms, the fly was liable to be crushed. Sir William Thomson, in a lecture on navigation, in 1875, spoke of it as follows:— "If the depth is to be found simply by the quantity of rope carried out by the lead before it reaches the bottom, the ship's way through the water must be as nearly as possible stopped if the depth is anything more than twenty fathoms. But by the introduction of a "Massey Sounding Fly" a few feet above the lead, and in line between it and the rope, the distance travelled by the lead through the water may be measured with considerable accuracy, and thus soundings may be taken from a steamer going at full speed, even when the depth is as much as fifty or sixty fathoms. Suppose the ship is going at 12 knots, and it is important not to lose time by heaving to, or even by reducing speed, the lead, with Massey fly and rope attached, is carried forward as far towards the bow as possible. Two or three coils of the rope are carried outside of the rigging, and several men, at different places along the ship's side, stand by, each with a coil or two of it in his hands. The foremost man casts the lead; when the next man feels the rope beginning to pull he lets go, and so on. By the time the ship's stern has passed lead may have reached the bottom, or it may not have reached the bottom until a considerable distance astern of the ship. It is very hard work pulling in 150 to 200 fathoms of the thick deep-sea sounding rope, with 56 lbs at the end of it, when the ship is going at any such speed as 12 knots through the water, even with twenty or thirty men employed to do it; but a careful and judicious navigator will not spare his ship's company. He will keep them sounding every hour or every half hour rather than run any unnecessary risk, and (if to lose no time is important) he will only reduce speed when he cannot, at full speed, take the soundings required for safety".[1]

The Massey Sounding Fly was followed by other devices which were more or less well known about the middle of the nineteenth century. Though

[1] *Popular Lectures and Addresses.* Vol. III. (1891).

there is little evidence that any of them were used extensively in ordinary practice, there is no doubt that the rotating fly type attained a certain measure of popularity.[1] Raper referred to Burt's Buoy and Nipper as a simple and well known instrument for use in sounding without stopping the ship's way. In this device the lead line was reeved through a spring catch in a small buoy. The lead was heaved and the buoy was dropped into the water immediately afterwards. The line was then allowed to run freely through the catch till the lead reached the bottom, when the catch seized the line and prevented further running and attached it to the buoy. The length of line between the lead and the buoy indicated the depth of water.

One further type, referred to by Raper, was Ericcson's lead, which measured the depth of water by the space into which the air contained in a glass tube within the lead was compressed by the pressure of the water. This type, which worked on the pressure principle, was first seriously considered during the early years of the nineteenth century, when it was known as the Self-acting Sounder. It was then described, in *Falconer's Marine Dictionary*, as a contrivance consisting of a glass tube, having one end open and the other shut, with a valve at the open end, which opened inwards by the pressure of the water as it descended. Upon descent the air was gradually compressed, and a quantity of water, proportionate to the depth, ascended the tube, and moved an index which indicated the depth of water in graduations marked on the tube. When the descent of the lead was stopped, the valve closed and sealed the open end of the tube, retaining the index at the height on the scale which indicated the depth of water at that time.

It will be appreciated that such a depth indicator functioned quite independently of the amount of line that was run out, or of what angle it assumed during its descent while the ship progressed. It was superior to Massey's Fly, which was easily damaged, and more reliable than Burt's Buoy and Nipper which could not always be depended on to bite the line securely when the lead reached the bottom.

As in several branches of nautical science, so in this, it was left to Sir William Thomson to investigate the whole problem of deep sea sounding

---

[1]This type received some attention from Captain Lecky in his *Wrinkles in Practical Navigation*, 1881, when he wrote as follows:— "The other kinds of sounding machines vary in certain minor details, but they nearly all depend upon the principle of the rotating fly. A small cylinder, protected by brass guards, is caused to rotate in its descent through the water by vanes or blades set obliquely to its axis; this communicates motion, by an endless screw or worm, to a train of toothed gearing. On the machine reaching the bottom, an arm falls and locks the rotator, so that it cannot revolve the back way as it is pulled to the surface. An index points to figures on a graduated dial, which indicate the depth of water reached".

"These instruments are very good, but they nearly all possess what may be termed an Index Error—*i.e.*, they either show too much or too little. When quite new they are generally correct, but, through wear of the working parts—or more likely from knocks under the counter in hauling in—they seldom remain so. However, their error is easily determined, and an account of it, with date . . . should be kept in a small pass-book in the box containing the machine."

and to produce a method at once simple and reliable. By his description already quoted, of taking a cast with the deep sea lead, with the Massey Fly attached, it is obvious that he was fully conversant with the difficulties and delays attendant upon such an operation. He was a keen sailor and appreciated the difficulties under which the navigator worked with an understanding born of experience and, what is more, grasped the essentials with his brilliant scientific mind, and solved the problem of deep sea sounding in fast steam ships.

There were three difficulties to be overcome. The first was to get the lead or sinker to the bottom; the second, to get sure evidence as to the depth to which it descended; the third, to haul in the line and lead quickly without stopping the ship.

Up to this time the only line used in sounding was a hemp rope, whose rough and comparatively large surface prevented the lead from descending, with the rapidity necessary to get a deep cast at speed, and made it almost impossible to haul it in when the cast was taken. After several experiments he decided that pianoforte wire was superior to every other medium, for it was strong enough to carry a heavy lead, flexible enough to be wound on a drum, small enough in area and smooth enough in surface to offer little resistance to the water as the lead descended and ascended. The advantages of wire over rope were quickly confirmed by experience in ocean-going steamships, and, in 1878, he introduced his sounding machine to the United Service Institution, after repeated tests at sea. "It may indeed be said," he wrote, "to be a practical impossibility to take a sounding in 20 fathoms from a ship running at 16 knots, with the best and best managed ordinary deep-sea lead. Taking advantage of the great strength and the small and smooth area for resistance to motion through the water, presented by pianoforte wire, I have succeeded in over-coming all these difficulties; and with such a sounding machine as that before you the White Star Liner *Britannic* (Messrs. Ismay, Imrie and Co., Liverpool), now takes soundings regularly, running at 16 knots over the Banks of New-foundland and in the English and Irish Channels in depths sometimes as much as 130 fathoms. In this ship, perhaps the fastest ocean-going steamer in existence, the sounding machine was carefully tried for several voyages in the hands of Captain Thomson, who succeeded perfectly in using it to advan-tage; and under him it was finally introduced into the service of the White Star Line".

This sounding machine, which was rapidly adopted by navigators of all maritime nations, was the forerunner of the sounding machines in use to-day. It consisted of a wire drum mounted on a galvanised iron frame, which was enclosed by a wooden box to protect it from the weather when not in use. It was placed at the stern of the ship, the wire being led over a pulley secured to the taffrail. To the wire was attached the lead and depth recorder, the wire being released by taking the brake off the drum when a cast was required. The nature of the machine is too well known to require any detailed description here, and it is sufficient to repeat that the machine introduced by Sir William Thomson over 100 years ago was, with various constructional refinements, the sounding machine that was fitted until a few years ago. Because of the reliability of echo-sounders, there is no longer any need to fit this machine.

The type of depth recorder favoured by Sir William Thomson was that which relied upon pressure and its resultant compression of air in a tube. Though he fully approved of Ericcson's and similar pressure devices, he recommended his own invention as being more certain, probably because the valves in the other types might occasionally stick and fail to seat properly. His own invention was a masterpiece of scientific simplicity in which the risk of failure was cut to an absolute minimum. It consisted of a thin glass tube, sealed at its upper end and open at the other, and coated internally with a preparation of chromate of silver. This tube was then placed in a brass sheath perforated at its lower end, which was attached to the line near the lead. As the tube descended the air was compressed as the sea water gradually rose up it until bottom was reached. Between the salt of the sea water and the chromate of silver a double chemical action took place. The chlorine left the sodium of the common salt and combined with the silver, while the chromic acid and oxygen left the silver and combined with the sodium. Thus chloride of silver, white and insoluble remained on the glass in place of the orange-coloured chromate of silver, lining as far up as the water had been forced into the tube and the chromate of sodium dissolved in the water was expelled as the air expanded when the tube was brought to the surface.

By applying the tube to a graduated depth scale, supplied for the purpose and noting where the sharp line of discoloration cut the scale, the depth of water was immediately obtained.

Captain Lecky in his *Wrinkles in Practical Navigation* 1881, enumerated the advantages of Sir William Thomson's sounding machine as follows:—

"1st. Let the speed of the ship be anything up to 16 knots, or even upwards, bottom can be obtained at a depth of 100 fathoms without slowing or deviating from the course.

2nd. Instead of requiring all hands 'to pass the line along', two men and an officer are sufficient to work it under all circumstances.

3rd. A cast can be taken in 100 fathoms, and depth correctly ascertained in from 4 to 7 minutes, according to the speed of the ship.

4th. This great saving of labour and time admits of soundings being much more frequently taken than formerly, resulting in greater safety to life and property.

5th. A regular 'chain' of soundings, with correct time intervals, is now not only possible, but easy; and this latter is the sole method which can be depended upon to give the place of the ship with any degree of certainty, since a single cast is not only useless in the majority of cases, but is apt to prove mischievous in the extreme."

There is no doubt that the increased rapidity, certainty and regularity with which soundings could be taken, by using Thomson's machine and depth meter, greatly assisted the navigator in his approach to land, and, as Lecky remarked, made it not only possible but easy in many cases, to plot the ship's position with some confidence, by means of a chain of soundings, applied to the chart at their proper intervals (measured in distance run between each cast).

Echo-Sounding.—This is based on the principle that sound travels through sea-water at a nearly uniform rate. The velocity is usually taken as 1500 metres per second. The actual velocity being a function of temperature, pressure and salinity.

In 1911, an account was published of an experiment which timed the echo of an underwater explosion. High frequency sounds in water were produced by Pierre Langevin and in 1918 he used the principle for echo depth finding. The first practical echo sounder was developed in 1922.

An echo sounder which operates within the range of audible sound (say 20 to 20,000 Hz), may be called a sonic depth finder. One which uses sound waves of higher frequency (20 to 100 kHz) may be called an ultra sonic depth finder.

The basic elements are shown in the figure. The electrical energy of the transmitter is converted to acoustic energy by the transducer which beams it down to the sea bed. After reflection by the sea bed, the returning pulse is converted back to electrical energy by the transducer. The receiver then measures the time difference between transmission and reception and converts this directly into depth in metres or fathoms.

Various forms of display are used, the most common being a paper recorder, a stylus passes along the paper and makes a mark which corresponds to depth. Sometimes two bottoms are displayed, this could be due to a layer of hard rock covered by a layer of soft mud. Shoals of fish will also give a mark on the display, very sensitive echo sounders are used by fishermen to help them track their quarry. A flashing strobe display was very popular at one time in American vessels, but the paper recorder type has the advantage of a permanent record and the rate of change of depth can easily be seen.

Even small yachts are now being fitted with small echo sounders, these will be of the electronic type giving an analogue or digital display of the depth.

William Thomson's (Lord Kelvin) machine has now become obsolete with the advent of electronics.

Principle of Echo-Sounding

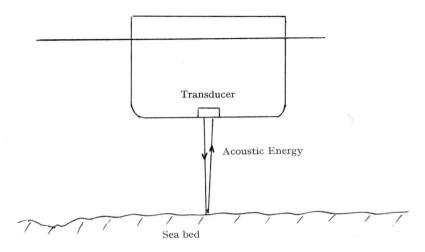

Transducer

Acoustic Energy

Sea bed

Depth in metres = $\frac{1}{2}$ (1500 × time difference in seconds)

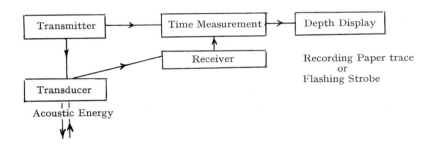

Transmitter

Time Measurement

Depth Display

Receiver

Transducer

Acoustic Energy

Recording Paper trace
or
Flashing Strobe

CHAPTER VI.

LONGITUDE.

The longitude of a place is the arc of the Equator or the angle at the Pole between the Prime Meridian, which is zero, and the meridian of that place.

The ancient astronomers had no difficulty in defining longitude, the difficulty lay in finding a reliable method of measuring with accuracy the angular difference between the two meridians.

The finding of latitude has always been relatively simple since it is the arc of the Meridian north or south of the Equator. All celestial bodies culminate on every meridian during the Earth's daily revolution and provided the angular height of one of those bodies (usually the sun) above the equator was known and its altitude above the horizon could be observed at culmination, the latitude could be found.

No such facility existed for the finding of longitude, but since the Earth apparently made one full revolution of 360° at a uniform rate within a constant period of time called a day, the ancient astronomers appreciated that the determination of longitude depended upon their ability to find the difference in time between the meridian of one place and another.

The daily indication of noon by the sun on the meridian and the occasional eclipses of the sun or moon prompted the astronomers of the pre-Christian era to suggest their use in the calculation of longitude. In about 150 B.C. Hipparchus observed that the only means they possessed of becoming acquainted with the longitudes of different places was afforded by the eclipses of the sun and moon.[1] Provided the astronomer could keep some account of the passage of time from noon he could observe the local time of the eclipse which, compared with the local time of eclipse at another place gave him the difference in longitude.

A further stage was reached when as a result of the observations and calculations of astronomers the times of lunar, and solar eclipses and the occultations of planets by the moon were tabulated in advance for a particular place and the observer, armed with this information, could note the local time of any of them at another place and determine the difference in time.

---

[1]Strabo, Book I.

Such, in broad outline, was the only way in which the navigator of the Age of Discovery could attempt to find his longitude. It is reported of Columbus that on the 12th January, 1493, "he advanced thirty leagues farther . . . he discovered a vast Bay which was three leagues in breadth and in the midst of it a small island. He stayed there to observe the Conjunction, which was to be on the 17th, and the opposition of the moon and Jupiter with Mercury, and the sun in opposition with Jupiter, which occasions high winds."

This was a beginning but the method never found favour with navigators who required more frequent occasions than occultations or eclipses to find their longitudes at sea. They lacked accurate time recorders and were, in the main, ill equipped with the knowledge, instruments or accurate astronomical information necessary to apply the theory with success.

The attitude of seafarers to what was to them an unsatisfactory method was well described, at the end of the 17th century, in a letter to the Earl of Northumberland by a Mr. Graves, who in discussing the ways proposed for the finding of longitude wrote, "By Lunary Eclipses, and this as the most absolute way has been recommended to us by Ptolemy and the Ancients. But because they happen seldom and when they happen are not always seen by reason of cloud or if seen are but rarely observed with fit instruments this can be of no use at sea, but only at land. And yet at land too there may be this objection made, if there be an error but of 1 minute of time committed (as who can promise to come so near) there will be an error of a quarter of a degree in the true longitude".[1]

From the beginning of ocean navigation the seaman was awaiting the invention of an accurate timekeeper wherewith to carry with him the local time of his adopted prime meridian so that he could at any time compare it with the local time of wherever he might be. Provided he was supplied with the essential astronomical tables and knew enough trigonometry he was able to calculate his local time whenever the altitude of a celestial body could be observed; the accuracy of the result depending upon the exactness of his observation, instruments and tables.

Cranks and charlatans made extravagant claims to have found ways of discovering the difference of longitude between places by means of sun dials, sand glasses and water clocks of their own design. The credulous seaman was warned against them in Hues Treatise on the Globes (1592) in the following terms:— "But all these conceits long since devised, having been more strictly and accurately examined, have been disallowed and rejected by all learned men (at least those of riper judgments) as being altogether unable to perform that which is required of them. But yet, for all this, there are a kind of trifling

---

[1]Brit. Mus. Add. Mss. 30221.

Imposters that make public sale of these toys or worse, and that with great ostentation and boasting, to the great abuse and expense of some men of good note and quality, who are perhaps better stored with money than either learning or judgment. But I shall not stand here to discover the errors and uncertainties of these instruments, only I admonish these men by the way that they beware of these fellows, lest when their noses are wiped, as we say of their money, they too late repent them of their ill bought bargains. Away with all such trifling, cheating rascals!"

Finding the longitude at sea by the observation of eclipses of the moon was, for the reasons already given, never seriously attempted though, on occasions, comparatively good results were obtained from them by navigators in fixing the longitudes of places at which they touched. They appear to have attained a certain amount of popularity for this purpose during the seventeenth century. It is recorded that, in 1631, such an attempt was made by Captain Thomas James in his voyage to discover the North West Passage. The astronomer Gellibrand described this attempt in an appendix to the record of the voyage in which he also compared the ease with which latitude could be found with the difficulty in finding the longitude. "For the exact setting of latitudes" he wrote, "we have many and absolute helpes so that the error if any happen ought to be imputed to the imperfect handling of the artist. But *the longitude of a meridian is that which hath and still wearieth the greatest masters of geography.* Nevertheless hath not the wise Creator left man unfurnished of many excellent helpes to attaine his desire: For besides Eclipses, especially of the moone (whose leasure we must often waite and perhaps goe without it, if the Heavens be not propitious to us) we have the concourse of quicke pac'd inferior Planets, with superior slow ones, or their Appulses with some fixed starre of knowne place, or else some other Artifice derived from their motions and positions. As for the magneticall needle to argue a longitude from its variation is altogether without ground. And though well furnished seamen are able by the D.R.s (as they terme them) to determine the Diff: of Meridians somewhat neere, yet by reason of the unknowne quantity of a degree in a given measure (which is the rule of the ships way) varieties of adverse winds, different sets of tydes and other involved incombrances, they come often wide of the mark they aim at. The best way yet known to the world is that which is deduced from the Celestiall Apparences, which being performed by judicious artists, may in short time rectifie our geographicall and hydrographicall charts hitherto in most places fouly distorted. It is my intent here to give an instance from two observations drawn from the Celestiall Bodyes by the author of this discourse in his discovery for the N.W. at the bottome of the Bay,[1] being his wintering place and called by the name of

---

[1]Hudson Bay. Capt. James gave his name to the smaller bay at the South Eastern end.

Charleton which for judgment, circumspection and exactness may compere with most. The first from the Eclipse of the Moone; the second from the Moones mediation of Heaven, or Her comming to the plane of his meridian of Charleton".[1] Gellibrand then went on to show how Captain James knowing that a lunar eclipse was to take place on the 29th October, 1631, awaited it with his instruments but was prevented by clouds from observing its immersion. James was more fortunate on the emersion of the moon and was able to take its altitude from which he calculated his local time. Simultaneously Gellibrand with some friends, using a quadrant with a 6 feet radius cut to divisions of 1' of arc, made a similar observation at the Moon's emersion in London which upon later comparison with James's calculation showed the longitude of Charleton to be 78° 30' west of the meridian of London. Gellibrand concluded his description with the hope that English seamen and others would make similar observations "in forraine parts as the heavens shall be offered unto them".

James's computation was, in fact, about 1° of longitude in error and probably represents the most accurate result obtainable in the middle of the seventeenth century even when the conditions were favourable.

During the latter half of the seventeenth century the longitudes of some places were calculated in the same way, and though they may have been of indirect assistance to navigators in that they enabled chart makers to produce slightly more accurate charts, the method was of little or no assistance at sea.

In the *Compleat Modern Navigator's Tutor*, published in 1720, the lunar eclipse was one of the methods mentioned for the discovery of longitude but the reader was advised not to confide too much in it.

Daniel Defoe, the author of *Robinson Crusoe*, in the Preface to "A General History of Discoveries and Improvements in Useful Arts" wrote, in 1726, "The World has been long perplexed about an intricate affair which some have promised mankind they shall one time or other be much better for, and that it shall be fully discovered to them. I mean the Longitude, or the settled distance of East and West; we shall in the process of this work endeavour to put an end to the importance of that search, by setting two things in a clear light about it.

I. That it can never be fully and finally ascertained and perhaps very little more than it already is, and that therefore 'tis to no purpose to spend any farther time about it.

II. That it is not so very essential to the World as some would have us believe, and in short, that as to the great Article of human Knowledge 'tis not one Farthing matter whether it be more fully discovered or no".

---

[1]The Strange and Dangerous Voyage of Captaine Thomas James, 1633.

Later on, with a touch of humour, he wrote, "How may they hereafter, when some effectual method for ascertaining the Longitude of the Globe shall be discovered to them, admire at our stupidity in not being able to find it out sooner?

It was used occasionally by navigators of the eighteenth century to fix the position of islands and points of land when their sojourn there coincided with the eclipse, notably by Anson, Cook and Bligh, but it is most unlikely that the ordinary navigator or shipmaster even troubled to inform himself of such an infrequent event.

Longitude by the Eclipses of Jupiter's Satellites.—It is apparent that astronomers from the earliest days had endeavoured in their search for the means of finding longitude to treat the Celestial Concave as a natural time-piece though it was always an infrequent and usually an inaccurate performer. The theory was correct but the difficulties in practice were that their knowledge of the motions of the moon and the planets was inexact and their predictions and results suffered accordingly. As the centuries rolled by their knowledge grew and its accuracy slowly increased until, as already seen, the great navigators of the eighteenth century were able occasionally to fix with tolerable accuracy a few places on the earth's surface.

The next stage in the evolution of the Celestial clock face was reached when the telescope was invented. At the beginning of the seventeenth century the four principal satellites of the planet Jupiter were discovered and Gallileo, who observed them closely, was probably the first astronomer to suggest their use in the discovery of longitude. Observation showed that these satellites revolved about their parent planet in orbits whose planes almost coincided with its equator and that they were frequently eclipsed or occulted by it or made their transit across its face. In due course tables were prepared, giving the times of the eclipses and, in 1696, this method of finding longitude was referred to by a naval Lieutenant, Edward Harrison, in his *Idea Longitudinis* in the following terms:— "As by lunar eclipses, so also by the eclipses of Jupiter's satellites, the difference of the observed movements of the occulation or emersion of a satellite from his shadow, noted carefully in two distant places, will be the difference of meridians betwixt these two places in time". It is doubtful whether by this time, the tables were either complete or very accurate though they were completed and improved upon during the eighteenth century.

Dr. Halley, in 1731, while acknowledging the use of the method ashore was of the opinion that it was "unfit at sea as requiring telescopes of a greater length than can well be directed in the rolling motion of a ship in the ocean".

This appears to have been the opinion of most people who during the following hundred years had experience of observing the eclipses at sea.

Wiliam Emerson, the English astronomer, in his treatise on navigation, in 1764, expressed surprise that this method was not more practised by seamen as nothing more was required than a common refracting telescope of three feet in length or a reflecting telescope one foot in length, and a clock or watch set to the true local time. "And these eclipses", he wrote, "happen very often; there being about four of them every week. It is true many of them happen in the day or when Jupiter is below the horizon; and sometimes clouds may interpose and prevent the observation. But there are frequent opportunities when none of these things happen". Emerson who had no sea experience continued, "I don't know whether this could conveniently be practised at sea; but ashore nothing is more easy. And one would expect that sailors, above others, should be more than ordinarily solicitous for making proper observations in distant countries". Emerson whose book contained tables of the times of the eclipses informed the reader that they were not so exact as could be desired.

About the same time Dr. Maskelyne, the British astronomer under whose superintendence the first official *British Nautical Almanac* was published in 1767, expressed his opinion that the immersion and emersions of Jupiter's satellites afforded the best general method known for determining the longitudes of places on land and hoped that they could likewise be observed at sea. He made several voyages in the interests of navigational science during which, among other things, by observations of the eclipses of the satellites, he fixed with accuracy the longitude of St. Helena as 5° 44′ W. of London. The longitude calculated in the usual method of fitting in the dead reckoning to the observed latitude, by the Officers of the East Indiaman in which he voyaged was 1° 28′ East of London showing an error of 7° 12′. Maskelyne reported that on this voyage many reckonings of longitude were no less than 10° in error. There is no doubt that the inferior telescopes of the day together with the ship's motion discouraged the ordinary navigator from exploiting this method to the full. An attempt was made to overcome the difficulty by fitting a Marine Chair which was slung in gimbals to enable the observer to remain in the true vertical regardless of the ship's motion, but the experiment was unsuccessful.

The method was used fairly frequently by astronomers, and occasionally by navigators, during the eighteenth century to fix the longitudes of places on land or when the ship was at anchor. Captain Christopher Middleton of His Majesty's Sloop *Furnace* in his attempt to discover the North West Passage in 1741-42 reported his observations for longitude at Fort Churchill in Hudson Bay as follows:—

	Hours.	Mins.	Secs.
"Having observed the apparent time of an Emersion of Jupiter's first satellite at Fort Churchill on Saturday the 20th March last at	11	55	50
I find the same Emersion happened at London, by Mr. Pound's Tables compared with some Emersions actually observed in England near the same time at	18	15	10
whence the horary difference of meridians between Fort Churchill and London comes out	06	19	20
which converted into degrees of the Equator gives for the distance of the same meridians.	94	50	00

"It follows that according to this observation Churchill is 94° 50′ in longitude west of London". Captain Middleton's longitude was in fact about 45′ of arc in error but the result was much nearer the truth than was possible by the methods then uniformly practised at sea. He made his observation with a fifteen foot refracting telescope and a two foot reflecting telescope and obtained the local time from a good watch which he could depend upon. He had previously made observations to discover its daily rate which he found to be 15 seconds losing. "This watch", he continued, "I kept in my Fob in the day and in bed in the night, to preserve it from the severity of the weather; for I observed that all other watches were spoiled by the extreme cold."

He concluded by expressing the hope that with a good telescope and a good watch seamen would probably be able to observe the eclipse of the first satellite of Jupiter to determine their longitude at sea.

Captain Cook made a similar use of the satellites some years later in the South Seas but there is little evidence that the good telescope which Captain Middleton had hoped for became a reality before the good watch, by which time the ordinary navigator had no need to rely upon the occasionally available eclipses of the satellites of Jupiter in order to find his longitude.

Longitude by an occultation of a fixed star by the Moon.—European astronomers of the early eighteenth century revived the old idea of obtaining longitude at sea by the occultations of planets by the moon. It had been attempted by Columbus, though his interest in the phenomenon was probably more astrological than astronomical, and a few others early in the sixteenth century, but, judging by the few occasions which were thought worthy of record, with unsatisfactory results. The increase of knowledge and the improvement in the accuracy of instruments and observation during the intervening two centuries had made it possible for those learned in astronomy to determine longitudes ashore with increasing confidence. It is recorded that Dr. Halley determined the longitudes of Oxford and Dantzic by observations of the occultation of Mars by the moon. To the planets these later astronomers, notably Cassini in 1705, added some of the fixed stars and of this method Halley observed, "of all the methods hitherto proposed for finding the longitude . . . none seems more adapted to the purpose than that by the occultations of fixed stars by the moon, observed in distant parts. For those immersions of the stars which happen on the dark semicircle of the moon, and their emersions from the same, are perfectly momentaneous, without that ambiguity to which the observations of the eclipses of the moon, and those of Jupiter's satellites, are subject".

This was one further step in the evolution of the Celestial Clock, in which the moon, with its monthly revolution about the earth, was the minute hand.

After Halley became Astronomer Royal he thought, in 1731, that the longitude at sea might be found, by this method, to within one degree. Though Sir Isaac Newton had given the true theory of the motions of the moon whereby the defects of all former tables had been amended, Halley realised the difficulty in getting the desired accuracy and advocated a continued investigation in order to produce tables of greater accuracy. "Now," he wrote, "the motion of the moon is so swift that were we able perfectly to predict the true time of the appulse or occulation of a fixed star in any known meridian we might, by comparing therewith the time observed on ships at sea conclude safely how much the ship is to East or West of the meridian of our calculation".

In spite of Halley's cautious optimism this method, as with the two which preceded it, all of which, apart from the necessity of accurate tables, called for an accurate observation of the moment of contact, immersion or emersion, and a dependable timepiece whose error on local time was known, never appealed to the practical every day navigator.

Raper, in his *Practice of Navigation*, 1852, summed up the seaman's attitude to occultations during the preceding hundred years in the following words:— "This observation affords, in favourable cases, the most decisive results, because it is both instantaneous and altogether independent of instrumental adjustments. On board ship the motion prevents the telescope, which is almost always necessary, from being kept steadily directed to the moon, and in consequence the method has been very rarely practised at sea".

Apart from the physical difficulties which attended the application of eclipses or occultations to the determination of longitude at sea considerable calculation was necessary before the result could be obtained.

These calculations, which were directed to finding the right ascension of the centre of the moon at the time of observation, called for a process to remove, by spherical trigonometry, the effects of parallax in right ascension of the moon and an allowance for the semi-diameter of the moon in right ascension.

It is possible that the practical seaman might have shown more interest

Q

in the problem had he been able to observe the occultations when he needed them and not when they occurred whether he wanted them or not.

Longitude by Lunar Observations.—The navigator's position differed from that of the astronomer. It probably mattered little to the astronomer whether he observed for his longitude on one day or the other. There was no urgency in his position where, on firm ground, with large and accurate instruments (and the larger, the greater accuracy) he could select his day and identify his star. On the other hand the navigator was afloat on an unstable element, subject to unbroken winds, and currents, always moving, when a day or a few hours might make all the difference between a good landfall and destruction. Unless some means could be found whereby he was able to observe, almost at will, a star of good magnitude which was easily recognisable, and from which his longitude could be determined without too tedious calculation, he would navigate as his forebears did.

The maritime nations of Europe in the Age of Discovery realised the advantage of being able to determine, within tolerable limits, the longitude at sea. It would be an exaggeration to say that the Heads of those States were solely animated by a desire to assist the navigator for, in the Age of Discovery, it was obviously desirable to stake the claims to new territories and define them with some degree of accuracy.

In order to solve the problem considerable monetary rewards were offered by some of these States to any person who produced a satisfactory method of finding the longitude at sea.

The first reward, of 1000 crowns, was offered by Philip III. of Spain, in 1598, which was shortly followed by the States of Holland who promised 10,000 florins. Even before the offers of these rewards were made, European astronomers were, as has already been seen, trying to find a satisfactory solution to the navigator's difficulty. John Werner, of Nuremberg, was probably the first of these to suggest a method which, 250 years later, was in almost daily use by seamen of all the western nations on all the oceans. In 1514, he proposed that longitude be found by observing the distance between the moon and a star. This idea was accepted by astronomers, notably Oronce Finé, Gemma Frisius and Kepler, for if it could be evolved into a practical and reliable method, the navigator's needs, as well as the astronomer's, would be met. During the next hundred years, English, Dutch and French astronomers laboured to produce the astronomical tables necessary to enable the theory to be put into everyday practice.

The theory of the lunar problem was an extension of the ancient Celestial clock-face, examples of which have already been referred to in describing the attempts to find longitude by observations of eclipses and occultations. It

is obvious to the most casual observer that the motion of the moon past the
fixed stars is appreciable and that it changes its position relative to any star
in a short interval of time.[1] From this it follows that for any and every moment
of time it has a particular fixed distance from any individual star. If these
angular distances are tabulated for the conspicuous stars, including the sun,
at known intervals of time for a place on a particular meridian then by measurement of the distance at any place the time at the particular meridian can be
ascertained by interpolation.

In practice various corrections have to be made to the observed angular
distance between the moon and any other celestial body. The calculation
and application of these corrections was known as Clearing the Distance.

Clearing the Distance.—All astronomical distances are calculated from
the centre of the earth and, therefore, all such distances observed from the
earth's surface have to be corrected for parallax. In addition, all observations
are subject to refraction, for which a correction must be applied. Because
of the moon's proximity to the earth her parallax though variable is always
greater than the refraction, whereas in the case of the sun or star, where the
distances are much greater, the refraction exceeds the parallax. The result is
that the apparent or observed altitude of the moon is always less than the
true, and with the other celestial bodies the true altitude is always less than
the observed.

The solution of the problem of clearing a lunar distance depends upon the
true and apparent altitudes of the moon and the other celestial body.

In the figure below:—

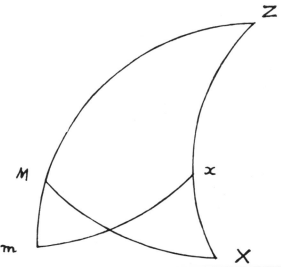

---

[1]Its motion relative to a star is about 30′ of arc in 1 hour, ½′ of arc in 1 minute of time.

Z represents the observer's zenith.

m   ,,   ,, apparent position of the moon.

x   ,,   ,,   ,,   ,, of a star.

M   ,,   ,, true position of the moon.

X   ,,   ,, ,,   ,,   ,,   ,, star.

Because the observed altitude of the moon
    is less than the true   ..   ..   .. **Zm** = The complement of the
    observed altitude (

and **ZM** = The complement of the
    true altitude (

Because the observed altitude of the star
    is more than the true ..   ..   .. **Zx** = The complement of the
    observed altitude of
    the *

and **ZX** = The complement of the
    true altitude of the *

In the △ Zmx

  Zm   Co: alt (Corrected only for Index Error, Dip, Semi Diameter.

  Zx = Co: alt * Corrected only for Index Error, Dip.

  mx = Obs: distance between (and * corrected for Index error and
    Semi Diameter.

By spherical trigonometry the angle **Z** (which is common to both triangles)
may be found.

In the △ ZMX

It is required to find **MX** the true distance.

∠**Z** is known.

ZM = Co. T. Alt. (or **Zm** corrected for Parallax in altitude and
  refraction.

ZX = Co. T. Alt. * or **Zx** corrected for refraction.[1] By spherical trigonometry the value of **MX** may be found.

The whole problem may be worked by looking up ten logarithms after
the appropriate corrections have been applied to the observed altitudes and
distance. By comparison with the true distances at specified times at say
Greenwich, and interpolation, the true time at Greenwich at the time of
observation may be obtained and this, compared with the ship's mean time
gives the longitude of the ship.

This was the theory which in due course, was put extensively into practice
during the closing years of the eighteenth century. The period from John

---

[1]In the case of a star, no correction for Parallax is necessary, as it is so minute.

Werner's idea, in 1514, to its adoption at sea was long and tedious. Little progress was made in the compilation of the necessary tables during the seventeenth century and in order to assist in the process, and possibly in competition with the French who were engaged upon it, the Royal Observatory at Greenwich was founded by Charles II., in 1675. Flamstead who was appointed Astronomer Royal was commissioned "To apply himself with the utmost care and diligence to the rectifying of the tables of the motions of the heavens, and the places of the fixed stars, in order to find out the so much desired longitude at sea, for perfecting the art of navigation." He was ill provided with instruments but set about his purpose observing that "the longitude might be also attained by observation of the moon, if we had tables that would answer her motions exactly; but after 2000 years, we find the last tables extant erring sometimes 12 minutes or more in her apparent place, which would cause a fault of half an hour, or $7\frac{1}{2}°$ in the longitude deduced, by comparing her place in the heavens with that given by the tables."

Dr. Halley, who succeeded him as Astronomer Royal, remarked that when he took over Flamstead had not carried out a full series of observations and the Observatory was wholly improvided with instruments. He carried out a long series of observations and, in 1731, in a paper before the Royal Society, he expressed the opinion, that he would be able in future, to compute the true position of the moon within $2'$.

England was somewhat tardy in following the examples of Spain and Holland in offering rewards to those who should produce a reliable method of finding longitude at sea, but in 1714 a Board of Longitude was established with power to pay out a sum not exceeding £2000 for the making of experiments, if success was probable, and to recommend rewards on the following scale.

To the first discoverer of a proper method of finding longitude—

£10,000 if determined to 1° of a great circle.

£15,000 if determined to 40' of a great circle.

£20,000 if determined to 30' of a great circle.

The preamble to the Act[1] authorising the setting up of the Board was indicative of the state of affairs at the beginning of the eighteenth century and began, "Whereas it is well known by all that are acquainted with the art of navigation, that nothing is so much wanted and desired at sea as the discovery of longitude, for the safety and quickness of voyages, the preservation of ships and the lives of men: and whereas in the judgment of able mathematicians and navigators, several methods have already been discovered, true in theory though very difficult in practice, some of which (there is reason to expect) may be capable of improvement, some already discovered may be proposed to the publick, and others may be invented hereafter. And whereas

[1]13 Anne C. 14.

such a discovery would be of particular advantage to the trade of Great Britain, and very much for the honour of this kingdom; but besides the great difficulty of the thing itself, partly for the want of some publick reward to be settled as an encouragement for so useful and beneficial a work, and partly for want of money for trials and experiments necessary thereunto, no such inventions or proposals hitherto made, have been brought to perfection."

The Commissioners of the Board of longitude included the Lord High Admiral of Great Britain, the Speaker of the House Commons, the first Commissioners of the Navy and of Trade, the Admirals of the red, white and blue squadrons, the Master of Trinity House, the President of the Royal Society, the Astronomer Royal and certain professors of mathematics at the Universities of Oxford and Cambridge.

One half of the reward was to be paid when the Commissioners were satisfied that the method "extended to the security of ships within 80 geographical miles of the shores", and the other half when a ship appointed by them actually sailed across the Atlantic from Great Britain to a port in the West Indies as nominated by the Commissioners "without losing their longitude beyond the limits before mentioned".

In 1716, the Regent of France, promised a reward of 100,000 livres for a similar purpose.

A number of mathematicians and astronomers applied themselves to the task of developing lunar tables to enable navigators to find their longitude within the prescribed limits. Notable among these was Professor Mayer of Goetingen who, in 1755, sent a copy of his lunar tables to the Board of Admiralty claiming some or one of the rewards which he might be thought to merit. Mayer's tables were examined and tested at the Royal Observatory and found to give the true position of the moon within 1' of arc. As, in the lunar problem, an error in observation of the lunar distance will produce an error about 30 times its amount in the longitude, the final report on the tables was that it was fairly certain that they were exact enough for finding the longitude at sea within half a degree, provided the necessary observations on board ship could be taken with sufficient exactness.

In a letter to the Secretary of the Admiralty, in 1760, the Astronomer Royal, Dr. Bradley, showed the accuracy of Mayer's tables by comparing observations made at sea in the years 1757, 1758, and 1759, when, on twelve different occasions, the longitudes so obtained and reduced to Ushant varied from the mean by no more than $+ 23'$ and $- 37'$.[1]

Unfortunately Mayer died, in 1762, before his labours received their due reward, but he left behind him a more complete and accurate set of lunar tables which was sent to the Board of Longitude. In an Act of Parliament,

---

[1] *The Theory and Practice of Longitude*, Andrew Mackay, 1810.

1765 (5 Geo. 3 c.20), which was passed to explain and make the earlier Act[1] more effective, he, among others who had improved the lunar tables, was recognised in the following words: "Whereas great progress has been made towards discovering the longitude at sea by a set of lunar tables constructed by Tobias Mayer deceased, late Professor of Goetingen in Germany, upon the principles of gravitation laid down by Sir Isaac Newton, in construction of which he was assisted from theorems furnished by Professor Euler of the University of Berlin, and whereas the tables are of considerable use to publick . . ." In the same Act a sum of £3000 was awarded to Mayer's widow and £300 to Professor Euler "upon assigning the Lunar tables to the Commissioners".

In another section of the same Act effect was given to the desirability of publishing Nautical Almanacs, compiled under the direction of the Commissioners, which would contribute to making the lunar tables more generally useful. The Commissioners were authorised to cause such Almanacs to be constructed printed and sold as they thought necessary and useful in facilitating the discovery of longitude at sea. As a result the first official Nautical Almanac was published in 1767 and its publication has continued, annually to this day. The Almanac contained, among other things, the lunar distances from several conspicuous stars and the sun for every three hours at Greenwich.

In 1763, Dr. Nevil Maskelyne, the Astronomer Royal published *The British Mariner's Guide*, "containing the complete and easy instructions for the Discovery of the Longitude at sea and Land, within a degree, by observations of the distance of the Moon from the Sun and Stars, taken with Hadley's Quadrant". In his Preface Maskelyne said that daily experience showed the wide uncertainty of a ship's position as inferred from the usual methods of keeping a reckoning, even in the hands of the ablest and most careful navigators. Errors of 5°, 10° or even 15° were not uncommon on long voyages and he now had good reason to think that by careful observation the longitude at sea could always be determined within 1° and generally within 30'.

Captain Cook on his first voyage 1768-1771 used Lunars to find the longitude. Thereafter, as instruments improved and the lunar tables increased still further in accuracy, the method came into general use. French, Dutch and Spanish scientists and astronomers all contributed to the further improvement in the tables and the presentation of the problem to the navigator and, by the end of the eighteenth century there were books on the subject in practically every European language.

The following is a description of the manner in which a complete set of lunar observations was taken at the beginning of the nineteenth century. "In order to take a set of lunar observations, in a regular and accurate

---

[1]13 Anne c. 14. See P. 234

manner, three assistants will be necessary, whereof two are to observe the altitudes of the moon, and of the sun or star, at the same time that the distance is taken by the principal observer; the other assistant, having a watch showing seconds, is to mark the time when these observations are made . . . this last assistant must be provided with a pencil and paper, to write down the observations as they are taken, which may be as follows:

"The sextant and quadrants being accurately adjusted, or the error of adjustments found, set their indices to the estimated distance and altitudes respectively. Now let the principal observer place his assistants in the most convenient situation possible, and desire them to be prepared when he is ready to observe the distance; then all are to begin to observe at the same time, and when the principal observer has brought the nearest limbs of the sun and moon, or the enlightened limb of the moon and a star into contact, he is to ask the other observers, if they are all ready; and being answered in the affirmative, then, as soon as he has obtained a perfect coincidence of the limbs of the objects, he is to make it known to his assistants, by calling out any particular word, as NOW, or DONE (the French call out TOP, which is to the same import). The person having the watch is immediately to write down first the second and then the minute of (the time) observation, the hour being previously marked; the principal observer is to read off the distance, using the magnifying glass, which he is to communicate to the time assistant, that it may be wrote after the time of observation."[1]

Thereafter the other assistants had to report their observed altitudes whereby one complete set of observations was obtained. The whole process was usually repeated four or five times and the lunar distance was calculated from the mean of the sets.

After referring to the eclipse and occultation methods of finding longitude Mackay said that the method of observing the distance between the moon, and the sun or a fixed star was now (1810) commonly preferred, both on account of its superior facility and because it could be practical at sea almost as often as necessary. "Yet", he continued, "as even this method is attended with a calculation that is, by many navigators, thought troublesome, various ways have been proposed, to shorten, as much as possible, the operations for reducing the apparent to the true distance; and it is now accordingly reduced to a tolerably simple computation. By this method the longitude may, in most cases, be determined within half a degree, which at sea is esteemed no very great error".

In spite of what was admittedly a great improvement in accuracy and facility on any previous method there is a good deal of evidence that in the early years of the nineteenth century the determination of longitude at sea was

---

[1] *The Theory & Practice of Finding the Longitude*, Andrew Mackay, 1810.

not as uniformly accurate as might have been expected. One example of many taken from the private log of the Captain of H.M.S. *Spencer* which sailed from Ceuta Bay for Jamaica on the 14th January, 1802, in company with three others, indicates the wide discrepancies which could and did occur in the estimation of longitude after a few days at sea. At noon on the 28th January the D.R. longitude of the *Spencer* was 46° 49′ W. and by lunar 46° 37′ W. Two days later the longitude of the *Spencer* at noon was 53° 22′ W., while the other ships in the squadron gave their longitudes as 56° 00′ W., 58° 30′ W., and 61° 30′ W. Either the other ships in the squadron had neglected to take lunars or their calculation of them was very wide of the mark. In the description of the taking of a lunar observation it will have been noted that three observers were required. Such conditions were not ideal where each observer would have his peculiar personal error, for which there was no correction. Though the working of the problem itself was very neat the operation of observing would always be clumsy and, in these circumstances, it is not surprising that considerable errors crept in.

The advent of the chronometer and its general adoption at sea during the nineteenth century outmoded the lunar method within a comparatively short period with the result that, in 1881, Captain Lecky was able to write. "To be able to place any reliance on Lunars, requires a really first class observer, and constant practice, and even then the results are at best but approximate. In the class of vessels most likely to need Lunars (namely, those small craft which, for sake of economy, carry but one chronometer), it is not likely that an expensive Sextant or Quadrant will be found; and if by chance it were, it is questionable whether the requisite expertness in observing and calculating would accompany it. Therefore, practically speaking, Lunars are out of date. Nor is there the same necessity for them as of yore".[1]

Their nominal existence flickered until the beginning of the present century when, in 1908, lunar distances were omitted from the nautical almanac. They had served a useful purpose but, so far as the navigator was concerned, the mechanical timepiece had superseded the Celestial clockface upon which the determination of time still depends.

The use of the Gulf Stream as an indication of longitude.—Before proceeding to the final stage in the determination of longitude it is of interest to refer to a commentary on eighteenth century navigation by the United States naval officer, Lieutenant Maury, who did so much in the nineteenth century to inform seamen of the winds and currents of the oceans.[2] In that commentary reference was made to the use of the warm Gulf Stream in the

---

[1]*Wrinkles in Practical Navigation.* First Edition, 1881.
[2]*The Physical Geography of the Sea*, M.F. Maury, U.S.N., 1855.

navigation of the North Atlantic in the eighteenth century. Maury observed that in earlier days the Gulf Stream controlled commerce across the Atlantic by governing vessels in their routes to a greater extent than it did in the middle of the nineteenth century, because ships were faster, nautical instruments better and navigators more skilful than formerly. "Up to the close of the eighteenth century", said Maury, "the navigator guessed as much as he calculated the place of his ship". This observation was probably true, in a general way, but there was a great deal of intelligent guess-work and a lot of it was based upon a fairly accurate knowledge of latitude, not only in the eighteenth century, but in the two which preceded it.

"Chronometers," continued Maury, "were an experiment sixty years before. The Nautical Ephemeris was faulty and gave tables which involved errors of 30' in the longitude." This is true for, as already remarked[1], the lunar tables with an error of $\pm$ 1' produced an error thirty times as great in the calculated longitude.

"The instruments of navigation erred by degrees quite as much as, in 1855, they did by minutes, for the rude cross staff and backstaff, the sea ring and mariner's bow had not yet given place to the sextant." This was an excess of gloomy retrospect on Maury's part for Hadley's quadrant was in fairly general use by 1750, when a good one could be purchased for less than five guineas, and many sixteenth century navigators found their latitude with commendable accuracy and sailed the five oceans successfully with only a cross staff and a table of the sun's declination.

According to Maury instances were numerous of vessels being 6°, 8° and even 10° of longitude out of their reckoning in as many days from port. That, of course, was true but, as we have seen, the dangers were largely obviated by Parallel Sailing.

Maury then proceeded to deal with the Gulf Stream as follows:— "Though navigators had been in the habit of crossing and recrossing the Gulf Stream almost daily for three centuries, it never occurred to them to make use of it as a means of giving them their longitude, and of warning them of their approach to the shores of this continent (America). Dr. Franklin was the first to suggest this use of it. The contrast afforded by the temperatures of its waters and that of the sea between the stream and the shores of America was striking. The dividing line between the warm and the cool waters was sharp and this dividing line, especially that on the western side of the stream, never changed its position as much in longitude as mariners erred in their reckoning".

It appears that when Dr. Franklin was in London, in 1770, he was consulted about a memorandum which the Board of Customs at Boston had sent to the Lords of the Treasury stating that the Falmouth mail packets generally

[1]Page 238

took two weeks longer to Boston than the ordinary merchantmen from London to Rhode Island. As the latter distance was considerably greater any difference in time should have been the reverse. Put upon inquiry, Franklin is reported to have discussed the matter with a Nantucket whaler captain, Folger, who chanced to be in London. Folger told him it was because the Rhode Island Traders were acquainted with the Gulf Stream while the masters of the Falmouth packets were not. On the westbound voyages the packets kept in the Stream which set them eastward 60 or 70 miles a day while the Rhode Island men avoided it altogether.

It is difficult to believe that in those latitudes the Gulf Stream exerted such an adverse effect and there must have been other reasons to account for the two weeks delay.

At Franklin's request Folger drew on a chart the course of the Gulf Stream from the Florida Straits which he said he had learned from the whalers. Franklin had copies made which he sent to the Falmouth Captains who paid no attention to it.

Franklin's discovery was looked upon as one of great importance and of considerable assistance in the determination of longitude on the North American seaboard, for on approaching the coast the difference in temperature between the warm water of the Gulf Stream and of the cold current to the westward of it, would enable the mariner "to judge with great certainty and in the worst weather, as to his position".

Another American, Jonathan Williams, in speaking of the importance of this discovery asked the question, "If these stripes of water had been distinguished by the colours of red, white and blue, could they be more distinctly discovered than they are by the constant use of the thermometer?"

From the Florida Straits to the latitude of Rhode Island the direction of the Stream trends parallel to the coast towards the North and East. It is probable that by using a thermometer many ships stood to the westward with much greater confidence in the knowledge that a decisive fall in the temperature of the sea indicated their distant approach to the American continent, but it is extremely doubtful whether it gave a better warning or determined their longitude with greater accuracy than their soundings.

Longitude by Chronometer.—Side by side with the investigation of the Celestial Concave as a timepiece, for use at sea, during the sixteenth and following centuries, clockmakers had been gradually evolving a mechanical timepiece which could be relied upon. The difficulties in producing such a machine were great, and for navigational purposes were enhanced principally by the violent movement of a ship in a seaway, and the many and sudden changes in temperature experienced in an ocean voyage of any appreciable duration. The latter difficulty was very real in the days of sailing ships when it often took weeks to make good a distance which, upon the advent of fast steamships, could be accomplished in as many days.

The use of the pendulum was debarred by the ship's motion and by the difference of gravity in different latitudes unless complicated precautions were taken. What was required was a kind of watch, slung in gimbals to obviate the risk of derangement, compensated for temperature and protected as far as possible from dampness and dust.

A large amount of ingenuity and labour was spent by clock-makers of England, Holland and France during the seventeenth and eighteenth centuries to produce the timepiece which navigators required.

The first real attempt was made, in 1662, when Lord Kincardine and the mechanically minded Dr. Hook suspended a pendulum clock, weighted with lead, near the centre of gravity of a ship and carried out trials at sea.

Shortly afterwards, the originator of the pendulum clock, Christian Huygens, a Netherlander, applied himself to the problem and produced a paper on the subject to the Royal Society. He recommended that two clocks should be carried in case one should fail and gave directions as to their care and rating. His pendulum clocks designed for sea use were without compensation for temperature and their trials at sea proved unsatisfactory.

Urged on by the reward offered by the British Government in 1714, an English artist, Henry Sully, who lived in France, applied himself to the improvement of watches for the discovery of longitude at sea. He received considerable encouragement from the French Court but died at Bordeaux while still engaged on his experiments and investigations.

Some years later John Harrison, a Yorkshireman, who had advanced the art of clockmaking by fitting his clocks with gridiron pendulums of his own invention turned his talents to the problem of keeping time at sea. After several years' work he produced his first marine clock, in which the pendulum was discarded in favour of springs. In 1735 Harrison's clock received the approval of Dr. Halley and other Fellows of the Royal Society who expressed the opinion that it promised a very great and sufficient degree of exactness.

In the following year he accompanied it on trial in H.M.S. *Centurion* on a voyage to Lisbon and on the return in another ship was able by its aid to correct the dead reckoning by about $1\frac{1}{2}°$. As a result of this success the Board of Longitude gave him some financial assistance and requested him to continue in his labours. A second and improved clock was completed for the Board by 1739 and the opinion was that its time keeping qualities were sufficiently regular and exact for finding longitude at sea within the limits of 30'. It was, however, never tested at sea.

Harrison proceeded to construct a third clock and received great encouragement from the Royal Society, twelve of whose Fellows delivered the following Memorandum to the Commissioners of the Board of Longitude in January, 1742. "We, whose names are underwritten, are of opinion, that these machines, even in their present degree of exactness, will be of great and excellent use, as well for determining the longitude at sea as for correcting the charts of the coasts.[1] And as every step towards farther exactness, and security, in a matter of such importance to the public, is greatly to be valued, we do recommend Mr. Harrison to the favour of the Commissioners appointed by the act of Parliament, as a person highly deserving of such further encouragement and assistance, as they shall judge proper and sufficient, to finish his third machine". This document was signed by M. R. Folks, P.R.S., Lord Macclesfield, Dr. Smith, Dr. Bradley, Professor Colson, Mr. George Graham, Dr. Halley, who had already done so much to improve nautical astronomy, Mr. William Jones, Dr. Jurin, Lord Charles Cavendish, Mr. de Moivre and Mr. John Hadley.

In 1753 a further Act was passed to replenish the original sum of £2000 authorised for expenditure on experiments, from the preamble of which it is evident that the Commissioners were satisfied with the progress made with the improvement in the lunar tables and with the probabilities of Harrison's chronometer. Out of the original £2000 the sum of £1250 had been paid to assist Harrison in his work, £500 to William Whiston to survey and fix the latitudes and longitudes of the chief ports and headlands of the British Isles, and only £250 remained. The Commissioners were authorised to expend a further £2000 on experiments as they thought fit.

The foregoing assistance, moral and financial, was referred to in the *Elements of Navigation*, 1754, by the author, John Robertson, F.R.S., who wrote "It has therefore been proposed to keep an account of longitude by a time keeper, or kind of clock, that should always shew the true time under the meridian of some one place; consequently was the time of the day, found in any other place, compared with the time then shewn by such a clock, the difference of the longitude between those places would be determined. But the difficulties attending the construction of such an instrument has been hitherto found too great to be overcome. Indeed the ingenious Mr. Harrison has removed some of, if not all, the capital obstructions; and his judicious friends suspect he will entirely perfect his most elaborate machine: He has received some gratuities from the public for the advances he has already made towards the solution of this intricate problem of the longitude; and it is wished he may

---

[1] In 1741 an Act (14 Geo. 2 c.39) had been passed "for surveying the chief ports and headlands on the Coasts of Great Britain and Ireland and the islands thereto belonging in order to the more exact determination of the Longitude and latitude thereof". The sum of £2000 was appropriated to this purpose.

merit the whole reward allotted by the Government for the discoverer of this so much desired acquisition in navigation." Robertson continued, rather surprisingly and yet with a foundation of good sense, that, on the whole, it appeared there were many ways by which a ship's position might be found at sea, nearly exact enough for navigating to places whose longitudes were almost as incorrectly known as the ship's. He can almost be heard saying "near enough for a sailing ship", an expression not unfamiliar in more advanced days than his. In conclusion, he admonished the navigator always to maintain a good lookout and keep his account by dead reckoning. If only seamen would practise all the precepts already given they would be able to proceed on their voyages (obviously by the three "L's", latitude, lead and lookout) and have very little concern about the perfecting of the discovery of the longitude.

John Robertson's words are probably a fair indication of the state of navigation in the middle of the eighteenth century. Meanwhile John Harrison was completing his third chronometer and constructing a fourth. In 1758 he completed the third timekeeper, which differed in design from his earlier instruments, and felt sufficiently confident in it to apply to the Commissioners of the Board of Longitude for the sea trial to some West Indian Port which in accordance with the Act of 1714 was necessary before the full reward of £20,000 could be claimed.

It was not until three years later, in March, 1761, that Harrison (who was then 68) received instructions for his son to proceed to Portsmouth with the third instrument to embark in H.M.S. *Dorsetshire* for Jamaica. Further delay ensued, as the *Dorsetshire* was ordered to another station, but, in November 1761, he finally sailed from Portsmouth in H.M.S. *Deptford*. As a result of the delays Harrison had completed his fourth chronometer. It was a large watch much more similar in appearance and size to the modern chronometer than his previous instruments which were cumbersome clocks.

The instructions received by Harrison from the Admiralty regarding the sea trial were very detailed and began, "That the watch be sent in charge of Mr. Harrison's son to Portsmouth; and that he proceed with it from thence in the *Deptford* to Jamaica". The case of the watch was secured by four different locks of which the key of one was kept by the younger Harrison and the other three by Governor Lyttleton (who was taking passage to Jamaica) the Captain and the first Lieutenant of the *Deptford* respectively. Then followed elaborate instructions as to the setting of the watch to the exact local time at Portsmouth before sailing and its comparison with true local time at Jamaica immediately upon arrival, by independent observers.

The *Deptford* reached Jamaica in January, 1762, and in the same month the watch began its homeward voyage in H.M.S. *Merlin*, which arrived at

Portsmouth at the end of March. In spite of a violent storm and substantial fluctuations in temperature during the voyage the error of the watch, from 6th November, 1761, to 2nd April 1762 was 1 minute 53 seconds or 28' of longitude, which, in the latitude of Portsmouth amounted to about 18 nautical miles.

An Act in 1763[1] made it clear that while the Board of Longitude were well pleased with the performance of the watch, and that they were disposed to show Harrison a marked preference over others who might emulate his achievements, they were not yet "satisfied" (the word of the 1714 Act) that it had proved to be the solution to the finding of longitude at sea. There are several reasons why the Board should have adopted this cautious attitude, but their treatment of Harrison, though possibly correct within the letter of the original Act of 1714, was ungenerous. The Act (1763) showed that the Board were mindful of Harrison's advanced age and failing sight, and that the ability of his watch had been proved in the recent voyage to Jamaica, but that they were not, at that stage, prepared to authorise payment to him of more than £2500. Of this sum he had already received £1500 and the remainder was not to be paid until after a further sea trial to the West Indies.

There were probably two principal reasons for what appears, in these days, to have been a niggardly attitude. A watch, however finely constructed, was an expensive mechanical device made by man and might develope some defect which a single voyage would not disclose. It was something new then, and the Commissioners had not, as we have to-day, over 150 years experience of the reliability of a chronometer, or the same convenient means of attaining its daily rate, or error, by visual or wireless time signals.

The lunar problem was also, at that time, engaging the skilled attention of astronomers who, in the nature of things, must have held decided views on the ultimate infallibility of the regular movements of the celestial clock. If only they could have a little more time to observe and predict these movements mathematically, all would be well and Science would be triumphant.

It is significant that Dr. Maskelyne, in his *British Mariner's Guide* (1763), one year after the successful trial to Jamaica, disdained even to refer to Harrison's chronometer but presented the Lunar Problem, at great length, for the discovery of longitude at sea within a degree.

A second sea trial was made in H.M.S. *Tartar* on a voyage from Portsmouth to the Barbadoes. Mr. Harrison, junior, sailed in March, 1764, with the watch, to which some further refinements for the correction for temperature had been made. On 18th April, Harrison found the mean time at ship from observations of the sun and by comparison with the watch concluded that the *Tartar* was 43 miles to the Eastward of Porto Santo. Course was altered direct for the Island, and, early the following morning, it was sighted. The

---

[1] 3 Geo. 3. c 14.

ship's position was fixed and the distance run from the previous day was found to agree with Harrison's calculation.

The *Tartar* reached Barbadoes, on the 13th May and by astronomical observations the error of the watch was found to be only 43 seconds. Mr. Harrison returned to London in July, 1764, when the total error for the outward and homeward voyages was found to be 54 seconds.

It was after this further trial that the Board of Longitude displayed a meanness which is difficult to understand. In 1765, a further Act[1] was passed, the relevant part of which was as follows:— "Upon a further trial of the watch or timekeeper a ship has sailed from Portsmouth to Bridgetown in Barbadoes, by means of said watch invented by John Harrison the ship did not lose its longitude beyond 10 geographical miles, *i.e.*, within ½ degree of great circle as laid down by 12 Anne C 15.[2] But doubts arise whether by the words of that Act the Commissioners can direct payment of the award of £20,000 to John Harrison upon a discovery of the principles of the said watch . . ." Significantly, but justifiably so far as the recipients were concerned, the Act then proceeded to reward Mayer's widow and Euler for their lunar tables as already described.[3]

The Act then proceeded,   "Be it enacted that £10,000 be paid to John Harrison so soon as the principles upon which his watch is constructed are fully discovered and explained to the satisfaction of the Commissioners and so soon as Harrison has assigned to them for the use of the publick the property of the 3 timekeepers, deducting the £2,500 already paid. The other £10,000 to be paid as soon as other timekeepers of the same kind shall be made and shall, upon trial, be found to be of a sufficient correctness to determine longitude to within ½° of great circle, provided discovery made within 6 months of the passing of this Act".

Eventually, after further trials and delays Harrison received, through the intervention of Parliament, in 1774, the balance of the full reward of £20,000 to which, under the Act of 1714, he was clearly entitled.

While John Harrison had been developing his chronometers, clockmakers in France had also been actively engaged improving the mechanism of timekeepers. Notable among them were M. Julien le Roy and his son, and M. Berthoud. About the same time as Harrison's watch was being tested on the second voyage, an instrument constructed by le Roy some years before was placed in the Royal Observatory at Paris, where, from December, 1763, until July, 1764, it was found to have a maximum error of 1 second. His son, who had been applying himself to the development of a timekeeper

---

[1] 5 Geo. 3, C. 20.
[2] Revised number 13 Anne C. 14, *i.e.*, The principal Act of 1714.
[3] Page 236

for use at sea, produced two marine watches which were tested in the French frigate *Aurora*, in the year 1767, with satisfactory results.

Other timekeepers, made by M. Berthoud, were also tested for sea use for over one year in two French frigates with results which never exceeded half a degree error in the longitude.[1]

Of the further chronometers required by the Board before they would authorise the payment of the final £10,000 to Harrison, one was made on instructions from the Board by Kendal, a London clock-maker. When Captain Cook proceeded on his second voyage, in 1772, to the Antarctic and South Pacific this instrument was one of the several timepieces which accompanied him. It was committed to the care of William Wales, one of the two astronomers sent by the Board of Longitude for astronomical duties on the expedition. During this voyage, which was not completed until 1775, the chronometer, often referred to as Mr. Kendall's watch, proved its worth as a timekeeper and, what was of equal value to the navigator, was used in weather and conditions when the clumsy operation of observing for lunars was impossible. So long as the observer could see one identifiable heavenly body and knew his approximate latitude he could, with one observation instead of three, simultaneously discover his longitude with far greater exactness than had previously been possible.

While Captain Cook was on his second great voyage another naval captain was also testing watches under rigorous sea conditions. In 1773, Captain Phipps, R.N., left the Nore with two ships, H.M.S. *Racehorse* and H.M.S. *Carcass* on a voyage of discovery towards the North Pole. Among the instruments provided for the voyage were "two watch machines for keeping longitude by difference of time; one constructed by Mr. Kendal on Mr. Harrison's principles; the other, Mr. Arnold". Captain Phipps also had a pocket watch, by Mr. Arnold, with which he kept the longitude to a degree of exactitude much beyond what he expected, for it accumulated an error of only 2 minutes 40 seconds in 128 days.

Mr. Lyons, who accompanied this expedition, as the representative of the Board of Longitude to make astronomical observations, was probably among the first to write from practical sea experience of the daily finding of the longitude by chronometer, in a manner which could readily be understood by practical seamen who had little learning in astronomy. The following extracts from his report are examples of clarity of exposition seldom attempted and never equalled by the English text book writers of his day.

"The observations for finding the time at sea were taken with a brass Hadley's sextant of eighteen inches radius, made by Dolland; and sometimes by Captain Phipps, with a smaller of four inches radius. The error of the

---

[1] *The Theory & Practice of Finding the Longitude*, Andrew Mackay, 1810.

R

sextant was generally found by observing the diameter of the sun; which if the same as double the semi-diameter set down in the Nautical Almanac, shewed that the instrument was perfectly adjusted; if it differed, the difference was the error of the sextant . . . As most of our altitudes were observed when the sun was near the prime vertical, a small error in the latitude will not produce any considerable change in the time; indeed, if it is exactly in the prime vertical, it will not make any change at all. To find the Longitude from these observations: to the apparent time found by calculation apply the equation of time according to its sign, which will give the mean time; the difference between which and that marked by the watch, will show how much it is too slow or too fast for mean time''.[1] It is of passing interest to remark that the method of finding longitude by chronometer in constant use at sea to-day, and the most advantageous bearing on which to observe for it, i.e., on the Prime Vertical, was practised at sea when Horatio Nelson was a boy and one of the youngest members of the expedition.

The two timekeepers sent for trial by the Board of Longitude were stowed in different ways which together amounted to the usual method common to-day. The one made by Kendal was laid between cushions and the other, made by Arnold was suspended in gimbals.

It is apparent that on this voyage the time-keepers were regarded as the every day means by which longitude was to be found—at least four times as many observations were taken by this method than by lunars—and that lunars were already being regarded as a means of checking the clocks rather than as the daily means of finding the longitude at sea. Mr. Lyons summarised the position in his report, "observations of the distances of the Moon and Sun or Stars may be useful to inform us if the timekeepers have suffered any considerable change in their rate of going. For if the longitude deduced from the moon differs above two degrees from that found by the watches, it is reasonable to imagine that this difference is owing to some fault in the watch, as the longitude found by lunar observations can hardly vary this quantity from the truth; but if the difference is much less, as about half a degree, it is more probable that the watch is right, since a small error in the distance will produce this difference".

In spite of the experiences with the timepieces on the voyages of Captain Cook and Captain Phipps the Board of Longitude continued to offer rewards to those who should discover any method for finding longitude either by timekeeper or by improving the lunar tables or any other method. Various Acts of Parliament were passed to this effect until 1818. During this period several British clock-makers improved upon Harrison's chronometer and received rewards from the Board.

[1] A Voyage Towards The North Pole, Constantine John Phipps, 1774.

This period may be considered as the testing time between the lunar and chronometer methods for pride of place at sea. Captain Cook on his third voyage, which began in 1776, carried chronometers and used them with excellent results, so did Lieutenant Bligh, in 1787. John Meares in his voyages, in 1788-89, from China to the North-West Coast of America was supplied with them and expressed the opinion that "there are many recent instances of very fatal accidents which have happened to vessels, during the regular monsoons, from the want of these very useful instruments".[1]

Captain George Vancouver, in his voyage of discovery to the North Pacific 1791-95, was provided with two chronometers by the Board of Longitude, one of which had accompanied Captain Cook on his last voyage, when it proved to be extremely reliable. Two extracts from Captain Vancouver's account indicate the state of the best instructed nautical opinion during the closing years of the nineteenth century.[2]

12th April, 1791. Took good lunars which gave a mean result of 4 sets taken by me 12° 24′ W. 4 sets by the Master 12° 30′ W.: the chronometer at the same time showing 12° 9′. As I considered the latter nearer the truth the lunar appeared to be 15′-21′ too far West.

26th April, 1791. Several sets of lunar distances Mean result 16° 21′ 32″ W. By chronometer 16° 31′ 15″ W., and as there could be no doubt of the latter being nearer the truth the result of the lunar observations appeared to be 9′ 43″ too far to the East. On the other side of the moon my lunar observations were 15′ to the West of true longitude as proved on our making Madeira.

The early years of the nineteenth century witnessed the growing popularity of the chronometer and even the most conservative of text book writers at last felt compelled to recognise its existence and use. The captain of a man of war was allowed 1 chronometer on going on foreign station if he applied for it and he was also free to supply a second one himself.[3]

It was natural that there should be a conflict of ideas over the lunar and chronometer methods, and a different point of view between the observatory ashore and the ship at sea. What the navigator requires is a time carrying machine—a time-keeper, which will give him the time of the standard meridian and to which he can refer his own local time calculated from his observations. The functions of the astronomer and the navigator are different and complementary in the operation of finding longitude at sea with speed and accuracy.

Even the best chronometer or any other mechanical device may fail,

---

[1] *Meares Voyages*, by John Meares, 1790.

[2] *A Voyage of Discovery to the North Pacific Ocean and round the World*, Captain G. Vancouver, 1798.

[3] *Falconer's Marine Dictionary*, 1815.

but the stars have their ordered movements which are unaffected by a lack of oil, violence of a ship's movement or fluctuations of temperature.

It is possible that the reluctance of the Board of Longitude to accept Harrison's principles without exhaustive and lengthy trials was not solely the result of blind pedantry or intellectual conservatism. They had a duty to perform to the seaman unversed in astronomical science and to guard him against the disasters which would inevitably follow if blind and uninstructed reliance were placed upon a machine, of whose limitations he was unaware.

Cook, Phipps, Bligh, Meares and Vancouver were of the ablest navigators of their time, but to each of these there were hundreds of shipmasters, sailing the seven seas successfully by the old methods, who had still to learn the possibilities and limitations of the new methods.

On any view, however, the Board's treatment of Harrison was prevaricating and ungenerous and, to the maritime world in general, tediously slow in making possible the finding of longitude at sea.

Andrew Mackay, whose work *The Theory and Practice of finding the Longitude at Sea or Land*, was one of the best of its kind in the early nineteenth century, wrote in 1810, "If a chronometer could be constructed so as to go uniformly when placed in every different position and under different degrees of heat then would this method of finding the longitude at sea be a most valuable acquisition to the navigator. Indeed some of our ingenious countrymen have brought this art to a degree of perfection formerly unkown; and every person acquainted with the principles of watch-making must highly admire the accuracy of Harrison's timekeeper. Those made by Meares, Arnold, Kendal, Earnshaw, etc., are also excellent; but it is to be hoped that instruments of this kind may be still further improved, and may be afforded much cheaper than at present for the high price alone is a very great objection to them and very much prevents their being more generally used".

Such was the position 74 years after Harrison had made his first chronometer and nearly 100 years since the establishment of the Board of Longitude.

By degrees, during the first half of the nineteenth century improved chronometers by many makers, became abundant, and a good instrument could be bought for considerably less than £50.

Lieutenant Raper, in 1840, expressed the view that it was high time the chronometer was found in every vessel other than a mere coaster, provided those to whom it was entrusted were qualified to make a proper use of it. Employed merely as a check even one chronometer could not fail to be of great service, but too firm a reliance would lead to the dangerous error of relaxing that vigilance which the known uncertainty of the dead reckoning kept perpetually alive.[1]

---

[1]*The Practice of Navigation*, by Henry Raper, 1840.

At the time Raper wrote these words every well found vessel of any pretensions carried and used chronometers and, in the East India Company's ships, lunars were taken more as a hobby than a necessity. Their officers were indulging, too, in stellar observations, a refinement in those days made possible by the chronometer. After a long voyage every prudent navigator realised that his chronometer had accumulated some error which he could and often did discover within a minute or two by taking a lunar. Where doubts existed or the land was known to be near, either through reaching soundings or exchanging longitudes with another ship, preferably outward bound, he navigated with the care demanded by the situation and seldom failed to reach his port.

When ships ran ashore after long voyages it was not usually because their chronometers had accumulated large undetected errors, but because of carelessness or over confidence. Commander Walker, R.N., who thoroughly investigated the behaviour of the magnetic compass in iron ships during the middle of the nineteenth century probably expressed the true view when he wrote, "The general use of chronometers, the correctness of our logarithmic tables for practical astronomical purposes; the accuracy of our astronomical and mathematical instruments used for naval purposes, have left us little to desire for all the purposes of practical navigation, so long as *the state of the weather* will allow us to make astronomical observations. But the possession of good instruments, charts, and books has made navigation so easy and accurate in *clear weather*, that the necessary care and attention, under ordinary circumstances, to the *helm*, *log*, *lead* and *lookout* have been sadly neglected by the majority of seamen. The result has been, that worse dead reckonings are now kept than ever were kept before. The general adoption of iron into the construction and equipment of ships, deranges the compass courses and a record is made on the log board of courses that the ship never steered; that is, the log board only shews a compass course, instead of the magnetic course, uninfluenced by the local magnetism of the ship or her cargo".[1]

The decline of the sailing ship and the rise of the steamship during the nineteenth century, with the resulting shortening of voyages; the establishment of visual time signals in all the principal ports during the latter half of the century, and the refinements in the mechanism of the chronometer greatly reduced the errors in the finding of longitude at sea. Provided the sky was clear enough for observations to be taken the navigator could hold on his course, knowing his position within as many miles as his forbears often knew within degrees.

One source of error remained. To find the time at ship the hour angle of the observed celestial body had to be calculated, that is the angle at the

---

[1] *The Magnetism of Ships*, by William Walker, 1853.

elevated Pole between the observer's meridian and the meridian passing through the body. In the spherical triangle formed by these two meridians and the zenith distance the measures of the three sides are known from (1) the declination of the observed body, taken from the Nautical Almanac, (2) the observed altitude of the body and (3) the latitude of the observer. From these known quantities the angle at the pole is calculated. The accuracy of (1) is not in doubt, (2) depends upon the accuracy of the observer but (3), unless recently determined, depends upon the accuracy of the dead reckoning which, after a few days of overcast sky or fog, may be in considerable error. It is evident, therefore, that the accuracy of the longitude by chronometer depends largely upon the accuracy of the assumed latitude unless the observation is taken on the Prime Vertical, which is a special case. This source of error was not fully appreciated in the earlier years of the nineteenth century either by text book writers or navigators, and it is possible that many chronometers were blamed for a bad landfall or disaster when undue reliance had been placed upon the dead reckoning latitude.

Commander Walker, in 1853, quoted an example of this which is sufficient to illustrate the point. H.M.S. *Challenger* was wrecked on the coast of South America in consequence of placing too much confidence in her latitude. She had not obtained an observation for her latitude for two days; her latitude by dead reckoning was thirty-four miles in error and this latitude being used for working sights obtained for her chronometer, the computation gave a longitude *one degree* to the westward of the ship's position.

Sumner Lines.—A way to obviate this error, and also make the navigator independent of the meridian altitude at noon for his latitude, was fortuitously discovered by a careful and able American mariner, Captain Sumner, in 1837. It was not the result of a long investigation into a method for the overcoming of difficulties but it was the kind of discovery that could only be made by a man well versed in his subject and who fully appreciated the theory as well as the practice of finding longitude at sea by chronometer.

After his discovery the method was investigated by officers of the American Navy, and others, who reported that it was mathematically correct. In 1843, Captain Sumner published his conclusions, and described his experience as follows:—"Having sailed from Charleston, S.C., 25th November, 1837, bound to Greenock, a series of heavy gales from the Westward promised a quick passage; after passing the Azores, the wind prevailed from the Southward with thick weather; after passing Longitude 21° W. no observation was had until near the land, but soundings were had not far, as was supposed, from the edge of the Bank. The weather was now more boisterous and very thick; and the wind still Southerly; arriving about midnight, 17th December within

LAUNCHED IN 1832

AND STILL WELL AHEAD

WRITTEN by men who know the ropes and read all round the globe between Greenland and the Antarctic, the *Nautical Magazine* needs no introduction to seafarers, shipping people and marine enthusiasts of any nationality. Its subscribers, some of whom were avid readers long before many modern countries were on the map, are found under every flag, afloat and ashore. If you are not yet one of them, now is the time to sign on. The first issue came out over 150 years ago, and there is still no better bargain anywhere for only 90p a month; or £14·16 (U.K.), £14·76 (Overseas) a year, mailed, free to any address on earth, even to the South Pole.

Right from the windjammer reign of Britain's sailor-king William IV, through the succeeding steam age of Queen Victoria, and into our own era of atomic ships, the *Nautical Magazine* has been the voice of the experienced navigator. It still is, more than ever. And not only of masters, mates, apprentices and pilots, but engineers, radio officers, pursers, stewards, the deck crowd and the black gang. The independent voice of all those whose life is the sea and whose know-how is the key to the world's commerce. So you are welcome to write letters to the Editor—who will print them gladly—on any apt subject under the sun, moon and stars, provided you keep your temper. Your views will be read by owners, builders, marine superintendents, examiners and navigation teachers, for they are all among our subscribers, as well as old-timers who have swallowed the anchor but keep abreast in our correspondence columns. Regular letter-writers and readers prefer the three-year subscription for only £41·00 (U.K.), £43·00 (Overseas), which saves money and time. Many much-needed reforms in the Merchant Service stem from the pages of the *Nautical Magazine*, which was founded by Rear-Admiral A. B. Becher, the foremost hydrographer of his day, and who was also its first editor for 39 years until he retired in 1871. And the Admiralty got so much information out of the *Nautical Magazine* for its own early survey records that it used to grant the editor £100 a year, that is, £50 from Naval Funds and £50 from the Mercantile Marine Fund. Today our sheet-anchor is the subscription at £14·16 (U.K.), £14·76 (Overseas) a year from men—and women, too—who know a good thing when they see it.

So the *Nautical Magazine* started serving the Merchant Marine eight years before the very first Cunard liner *Britannia* left Liverpool on her maiden voyage to Halifax and Boston. And since that time it has had only seven editors before the present one, who is the son of the sixth editor.

It was in the editorial epoch of the founder, Rear-Admiral Becher, that the *Nautical Magazine* brought new ideas to the shipyards and was active in exposing a lot of dirty work, not least in marine insurance, thanks to its alert readers and writers. Among these we find James Ballingall, a Scottish shipping surveyor who ended in Australia and who was the first witness called upon to give evidence before the House of Commons

40 miles by dead reckoning, of Tusker Light; the wind hauled S.E. true, making the Irish Coast a lee shore; the ship was then kept close to the wind and several tacks made to preserve her position as nearly as possible until daylight; when nothing being in sight she was kept on E.N.E. under short sail with heavy gales; at about 10 a.m. an altitude of the sun was observed and the chronometer time noted; but having run so far without an observation, it was plain the Latitude by dead reckoning was liable to error and could not be entirely relied on.

"Using, however, this latitude in finding the longitude by chronometer it was found to put the ship 15' of longitude East from her position by dead reckoning which in latitude 52° N. is 9 nautical miles; this seemed to agree tolerably well with the Dead Reckoning; but feeling doubtful of the latitude the observation was tried with a latitude 10' farther North, finding this placed the ship E.N.E. 27 nautical miles of the former position it was tried again with a latitude 20' N. of the Dead Reckoning; this also placed the ship still further E.N.E. and still 27 nautical miles further; these 3 positions were then seen to lie in the direction of Small's Light.

"It then at once appeared that the observed altitude must have happened at all the three points and at the Small's Light and at the ship at the same instant of time; and it followed that Small's Light must bear E.N.E. if the chronometer was right. Having been convinced of this truth, the ship was kept on her course E.N.E. the wind being still S.E. and in less than an hour. Small's Light was made bearing E.N.E. ½ E. and close aboard. The latitude by Dead Reckoning was erroneous 8 miles; and if the longitude by chronometer had been found by this latitude, the ship's position would have been erroneous 31½ minutes of longitude too far West and 8 miles too far South. The ship had, from current tide or error of log overrun her reckoning 1 mile in 20."[1]

Had Captain Sumner not plotted his calculated longitudes on his chart and had it not so happened that when he obtained his observation of the sun it was directly abeam to starboard it is possible that he would have failed to appreciate that he was sailing on a position line which led him directly to the Smalls. But he was obviously a man of prudence, knowledge and quick intelligence and with the picture on the chart before him realised that the straight line upon which he was sailing was in fact part of a very large circle of equal altitude of the sun.

The principle, which he described at length, may be expressed in this way. One half of the earth is always at any instant turned towards any celestial object and, at the centre of that hemisphere or great circle, the object will

---

[1] *A New and Accurate Method of Finding a Ship's Position at Sea*, by Captain Thomas H. Sumner, 1843.

be directly overhead, *i.e.*, in the zenith. At every place which lies on any smaller circle concentric to the great circle the altitude of the object will, at the same instant of time, be the same.

The radius of this circle of equal altitude is usually very large, unless the observed body is near the zenith, and, for practical purposes, a short arc of it may be regarded as a straight line at right angles to the line of bearing.

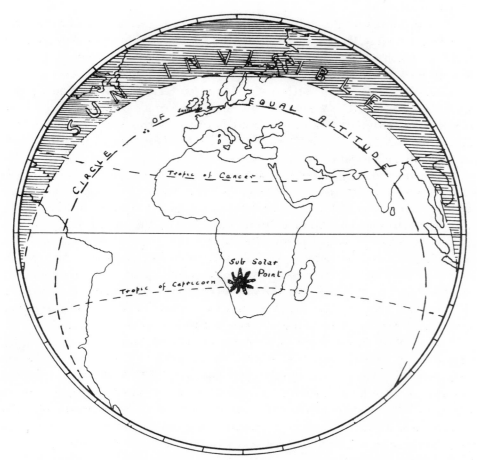

Diagram showing the Circle of Equal Altitude at the time when Captain Sumner observed the Sun on approaching the Smalls, December 17, 1837.

This straight line is called a position line, or in the way in which Captain Sumner used it, a Sumner line. If, said he, another observation of the same object be taken, after an appreciable change in its azimuth, then the two lines of position may be laid off on a chart and a fix obtained in exactly the same

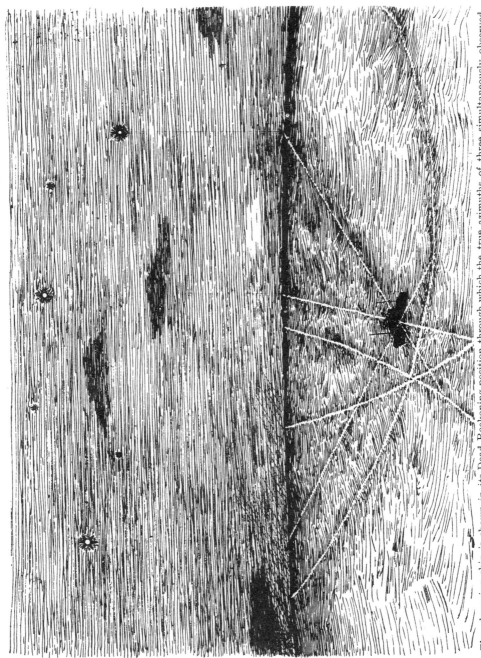

The observing ship is shown in its Dead Reckoning position through which the true azimuths of three simultaneously observed stars are drawn. The Fix of the true position is shown at the intersection of the arcs of the position circles of the three stars. (See Marc St. Hilaire. Page 258)

way as is done by allowing for distance run between two bearings of a terrestial object.[1] The method of obtaining a position line advocated by Sumner was to assume two different latitudes near the dead reckoning position, calculate the corresponding longitudes, and draw a straight line through the positions as he did on his approach to the Smalls, in 1837.

This method became extremely popular during the nineteenth century and a way was devised by which the fix could be obtained mathematically without the graphical solution, but the principle is unaltered.

Marc St. Hilaire.—Another application of the same principle was recommended, in about 1875, by Marc St. Hilaire, in which the dead reckoning position is used. For this position the zenith distance of the celestial body is calculated and compared with the true zenith distance as observed by sextant.[2]

From the dead reckoning position, the difference between these two distances is then laid off in the correct azimuth giving the point on the circumference of the true position circle through which the tangent or position line is drawn.

Simultaneous altitudes of heavenly bodies were also taken during the latter half of the nineteenth century and their position lines obtained by either Sumner's method or that of Marc St. Hilaire according to the preference of the observer. The navigator's necessity for a meridian or ex meridian altitude for his latitude no longer existed, though he seldom neglected an opportunity to obtain it by these means when available. Harrison's chronometer and these additional methods of using it to find both latitude and longitude robbed all other ways of their importance and at last made it possible for the navigator to fix his position whenever the sky was clear enough to see identifiable celestial bodies and the horizon sharp enough for him to measure their altitudes.

---

[1] Known as finding position by Double Altitude.
[2] *i.e* The complement of the True Altitude which is the Observed Altitude corrected in the usual way.

CHAPTER VII.

ELECTRONIC NAVIGATION.

THE new age of navigation—the electronic age—began in the closing years of the nineteenth century. A young Italian named Guglielmo Marconi had become interested in radio and had started experimenting on his father's estate near Bologna. In 1894, using very crude apparatus he succeeded in transmitting over a distance of 9 metres. With further improvements to his aerial system he was able to increase the range to $1\frac{1}{2}$ miles. Very little interest was shown in his work by the Italian Government, indeed, it is said that the Minister of Posts and Telegraphs suggested that Marconi should be admitted to a mental clinic! In 1896, Marconi travelled to London to seek encouragement and financial backing. This move proved successful and he was assisted in his 'wireless' development by Sir William Preece who was chief engineer of the Post Office. In June 1896, Marconi filed his first wireless patent and he began to give successful demonstrations which attracted great publicity. Various balloons and kites were used to obtain greater height for his aerials, Marconi was striving all the time to improve the range of communication. Eventually in a famous experiment he was able to transmit nearly nine miles across the Bristol Channel. The news of this reached Italy and he was invited back by the Italian Naval authorities, the battleship "San Martino" was placed at his disposal and he was able to demonstrate a signal range of 12 miles. Soon after these experiments, Marconi returned to England to set up a wireless station at Poldhu, Cornwall.

In 1899, a wireless station was established at South Foreland and messages could be transmitted to a French station 31 miles away. In the same year, British warships were able to communicate over a distance of 75 miles. In 1900, the Marconi International Marine Communication Company was formed, the purpose being the operation of wireless services between ship and shore stations. It should be pointed out, that at this time, Marconi was only 26. In 1901, Marconi achieved probably his greatest triumph, he managed to bridge the North Atlantic when the letter 'S' in Morse code was transmitted from Poldhu, Cornwall to St. Johns, Newfoundland. It was thought by many at this time that due to the Earth's curvature, radio waves would only have a range of 100 or 200 miles. This achievement had really discovered the presence of various ionized layers in the upper atmosphere which allowed the reflection of radio waves over great distances.

By 1902, Marconi was able to receive messages over 2000 miles at night and by 1910 he could receive messages at Buenos Aires which had been sent from Ireland 6000 miles away. In 1918 the first radio message had been sent to Australia, a distance in excess of 11000 miles.

Perhaps of more importance to the mariner was the transmission of time signals, the first was sent in 1904. This was a great boon, a mariner could now check his chronometer error and without difficulty find his longitude. To some extent, sea life was a little less hazardous, if a ship got into difficulty, assistance could be summoned. In 1912, the S.S. "Titanic" made her maiden voyage across the North Atlantic. In the region of the Grand Banks of Newfoundland, she struck an iceberg and slowly began to sink. The radio was used to summon assistance, but it arrived too late for many.

By 1915, there were 706 coast stations and 4,866 ships throughout the world fitted with a radiotelegraph installation. Many amateur radio enthusiasts had also begun to transmit and this was causing considerable congestion on the airwaves, legislation was required to control this activity.

During World War 1, the main use of radio was in naval vessels. It was realised that bearings could be taken of transmitting ships from two different locations and this would give the ship's position. Use was made of this to keep track of German warships. Radio direction finding was also becoming useful in landfall navigation and coastal navigation. By means of a directional aerial, it was possible to take bearings of coastal radio stations. The most common form of aerial was a loop. When the loop was in line with the radio signal a maximum effect was heard in the headphones, if the loop was now rotated through 90° a minimum signal or null occurred. There is a greater change of signal strength near the null, so the loop was rotated for a nil signal to be obtained. Because of the characteristics of the simple loop a 180° ambiguity arises. Another vertical aerial is then used to resolve the ambiguity, this is called a "sense" aerial.

Sometimes the shore radio station took bearings of the ship and gave the ship the bearing. This was the QTG service, as it involved a charge to the ship it did not prove popular and it has mainly been phased out. Another system was also tried, this involved the use of a wireless beam which rotated at a given speed. As it passed due North a particular signal was transmitted, an observer would be timing the interval between the "North" signal and the time of minimum signal strength. This interval when compared with the time of one complete rotation would give the bearing. Although it was tried for a number of years it was not used by many ships.* The most popular system was the

* **Note.**—At the present time, rotating pattern radiobeacons are used only in Japan. They enable a ship to determine her true bearing from the transmitter without the use of direction-finding apparatus. A directional array of aerials produces a pattern which is rotated. The rotation begins with two nulls north and south of the station and proceeds clockwise emitting a series of dots. Every tenth dot has a change of tone to assist counting. Usually the number of dots counted when multiplied by two will give the true bearing or the reciprocal bearing of the station. It is necessary to consult the Admiralty List of Radio Signals Vol. 2 to see the calibration table for each station.

ship's own direction-finder. This did lead to a number of accidents as ships "homed" in on light-vessels. Mariners are now warned of the dangerous consequences of this technique.

Radio bearings cannot be plotted directly on a Mercator chart because they are Great Circles and an allowance must be made for the convergency of the meridians. (Approximately this correction in minutes is found by $\frac{1}{2}$ the difference in longitude in minutes $\times$ the sine of the mean latitude). When coasting within 25 to 30 miles of the station the correction is very small and can be ignored. Of more importance is the quadrantal correction. This is an error which is due to induced currents being set up in the ship structure. As the electromagnetic wave strikes the vessel, alternating currents occur in the hull, rigging and other conductors.

This gives rise to an error which is a maximum at 45° to the ship's fore and aft line. In order to ascertain this error it is necessary to calibrate the D.F. set by taking visual and radio bearings of a radio transmitter. This calibration is always carried out during daylight hours to avoid the "night effect".

At night, there can be considerable fading in the signal strength, because of interaction between sky and ground waves. Near sunset and sunrise, very large changes are taking place in the ionosphere and reception can become erratic.

Radiobeacons are provided at many coastal stations. Full details of transmissions, call-signs and frequencies used are given in the Admiralty List of Radio Signals Vol. 2. The stations are frequently grouped so that cross-bearings can be obtained when the ship is making landfall. In the past, co-operation was needed with the Radio Officer, he would take the bearing whilst the navigator would note the ship's head. In later D.F. sets, this was not required as the D.F. set had its own gyro compass and bearings could be read directly.

Some skill is required to obtain the aural null and Merchant Navy Officers must satisfy the Department of Trade examiner, when taking examinations, that they are competent to obtain bearings. The latest type of D.F. sets are fully automatic and it is relatively easy to obtain bearings. Signal strength is indicated on a meter and more and more navigators are making use of this aid to navigation.

Consol.—In World War 2, the Germans utilized a rotating electronic beam called Sonne, to give guidance to aeroplanes and ships. After the war, the system was modified and improved by British scientists, it was given the name "Consol". It is a long range, short base line, hyperbolic system which operates in the 250-350 kHz frequency range. A transmitting station consists of three aerials which are only about 3 wavelengths apart. Because of this short baseline, beyond about 25 miles the hyperbolic position lines can be considered great circles with negligible error. The system is thus a directional one. The radiation of each station consists of alternate dot and dash signals. During the "keying", the pattern rotates. The equisignal between the dot and dash-signals moves through one sector, the sector is about 15° in width. On the boundary between each sector a pattern of 60 dots or 60 dashes can be heard. But on any other bearing, the count of 60 is divided between the dots and dashes. During the reception of the equisignal, they cannot be distinguished and the missing count is equally distributed, e.g. suppose a count of 24 dashes and 30 dots was received and six signals were lost in the equisignal period, the corrected count would be 24+3 = 27 dashes and 30+3 = 33 dots. It is possible to convert this count to a Great Circle bearing by consulting tables in the Admiralty List of Radio Signals Vol. 5 or the Admiralty Consul Charts.

The Consol system should not be used for coastal or landfall navigation, because the accuracy is not good enough for this purpose. A mariner relying on Consol whilst coasting could easily find himself ashore. For example, it is possible for the bearings from the Stavanger Consol station to give a position line as much as 12 nautical miles in error. Thus it is primarily an ocean aid to navigation intended for aircraft. It is rarely used by deep sea navigators. The stations transmitting in Europe are:

Stavanger, Norway call-sign **LEC** on frequency 319 kHz (940 m wavelength)
Ploneis,   France   call-sign **FRQ** on frequency 257 kHz (1167 m wavelength)
Lugo,   Spain   call-sign **LG**   on frequency 285 kHz (1053 m wavelength)
There are also two stations on the Russian Arctic coast and two stations in northern Norway.

Under favourable conditions the coverage area can be about 1,000 miles by day and 1,200 to 1,500 miles by night over water. The greatest errors tend to occur between 250 and 400 miles from the transmitter, this is due to interference between ground waves and sky waves at night. The system cannot be used when within 25 miles of the transmitter.

The Americans have their own version of this system, it is called Consolan and it operates in the same way. The dot and dash signals give a Great Circle bearing of the transmitter. There is only one station, situated at San Francisco, a range of 1,000 to 1,400 miles over the sea is given and bearing accuracy of about 0·3° by day and 0·7° by night can be expected. It is not usable when within 50 miles of the station.

Radar.—The use of a radio echo for the detection of targets is not new, as long ago as 1904 a German engineer named Christian Hulsmeyer took out a patent on a radio detection system, but due to technical limitations at this time, it came to nothing.

In 1922, the Italian engineer Guglielmo Marconi presented a paper on

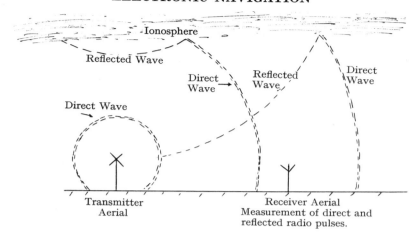

Figure shows Ionospheric Research.   Circa 1925.   The Pulse transmissions are used to determine
the height of the reflecting layer.

radio detection and scientists began to investigate this topic.   In that year, the
United States Naval Research Laboratory were able to detect the passage of a
target between the transmitter and a separate receiver.   Although the target
could be detected, the distance was unknown.   The transmission of a very short
pulse of radio energy was required.

In 1925, the U.S.A. began work on pulse modulation, this technique was
being used to measure the height of the various ionized layers in the upper
atmosphere.   It was several years before it was applied to radar.   In 1930, a
researcher working on direction finder equipment noted that there was an increase in signal strength when an aircraft passed between his receiver and the
transmitter.   The U.S. Naval Research Laboratory followed up this discovery
and by 1932 were able to detect aircraft at distances up to 50 miles from the
transmitter.   Radar research was also being carried on at this time in the U.K.,
Germany and France.   With the increasing power of aeroplanes, it was
realised in the U.K., that we were no longer insulated from a European conflict by the protection of the British Navy and the obstacle of the English
Channel.   Fleets of marauding bombers would be able to invade our airspace
and rain down death and destruction.   The race was now on to produce an air
defence system.   The detection of enemy bombers became a top priority.
Work began under the direction of (Sir) Robert Watson-Watt to design and
erect experimental radar equipment at Bawdsey in Suffolk.   Very fortunately,
these early experiments proved successful and they led to the establishment of
a chain of radar stations just prior to the outbreak of World War Two.   Undoubtedly, these radar stations greatly helped the Royal Air Force to overcome their strong adversary and win the Battle of Britain in the dark days of
1940.

Although the priority was for air defence, the Admiralty were very keen to obtain radar equipment which would enable the Royal Navy warships to seek out enemy ships in conditions of poor visibility. Radar could also be used to give warning of approaching aircraft. The first prototype equipment was fitted in the battleship "Rodney" and the cruiser "Sheffield" in 1939.

It should be pointed out that the U.K. were not alone in having radar equipment, indeed, at the outbreak of World War Two the German radar was

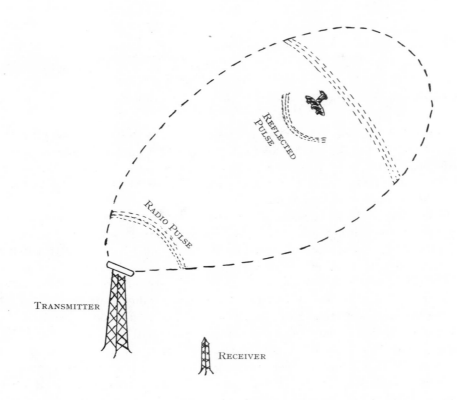

EARLY AIR DEFENCE RADAR. The transmitter has a wide beam-width. A separate receiving aerial would detect the bomber reflection on an "A" scan cathode ray tube.

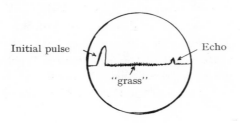

superior. In the 1930's. Germany was very actively engaged in radar research. By 1939, they had developed a system called "Freya" which would give early warning of approaching aircraft and a ship detection system soon followed. By mid 1940, a superior radar called "Würzburg" had been developed, this would give position with sufficient accuracy to direct anti-aircraft fire. At this time, the "Würzberg" was superior to British radar, it used a frequency of 600 MHz. Scientists on both sides of the conflict were striving to narrow radar beams to improve bearing accuracy. It was realised that a solution lay with the use of a higher frequency but there was no radar valve available which would give sufficient power output. At this critical moment, Messrs. Randall and Boot working in laboratories of Birmingham University developed a valve of revolutionary design. This was the multicavity magnetron.

This valve was able to produce 20,000 watts at a frequency of 3,000 MHz. This was a tremendous improvement in radar technology, the power output together with the very high frequency used would lead to the detection of a very small target, there was also a big improvement in bearing accuracy, the radio energy could be concentrated into a narrow beam. The discovery of the magnetron and the development of micro-wave radar was kept a closely guarded secret, until the Germans shot down a British plane which carried this equipment. The Germans realised the Allies were using micro-wave radar and they began to develop their own magnetrons and micro-wave radar.

For security purposes, the radar working in the 3,000 MHz was given the "S" prefix. This designation is still used today. At a later stage in the war, the U.S. and British laboratories in collaboration developed an X-band bombing radar, which operated in the 10,000 MHz range, the shorter wavelength gave even greater definition. However, at the end of 1943, a U.S. bomber carrying an X-band radar crashed in Holland and revealed its secrets to the Germans. This mishap came too late to affect the outcome of the war.

In 1941, the U.S. were able to develop an aircraft radar which would detect the presence of surface vessels. This could be used to detect U-boats on the surface when recharging batteries. With improved centrimetric radar, escort vessels could locate U-boats making night surface attacks on convoys. Undoubtedly, the use of radar helped the Allies win the Battle of the Atlantic.

In the early stages of World War Two, a large number of small Royal Navy craft were using a radar set which worked on a wavelength of about $1\frac{1}{2}$ metres. It was a very crude set by today's standards, but it did give surface warning of other craft, it could also be used for some elementary navigation. The aerial had a horizontal beam width of about 40° and it could be rotated by hand to give an indication of the bearing of the target. A skilled radar operator could only find the bearing of an isolated target to ±5°. The very wide beam width made the radar echoes of land targets difficult to interpret. To obtain approximate position fixes some use was made of radar beacons which had been located at coastal stations for the use of Allied aircraft.

When micro-wave radar became available, the application of Plan Position Indicator (PPI) completely changed the radar display. In PPI radar, a radial trace sweeps across the cathode ray tube in time with the rotation of the aerial. The ship is at the centre of the PPI and as the trace passes over targets the returning radar echo "paints" an image on the phosphorescent screen. This gives an afterglow so that a map-like display of coastal targets is presented. Of course, the quality of the echo will depend on the height and reflective properties of the target. At this time the primary purpose was the detection of enemy shipping and to determine gunnery range and bearing. Navigation was purely secondary. Radar helped to detect and track the "Bismarck" in the Denmark Strait leading to her eventual destruction. Radar also played a part in the sinking of the "Scharnhorst" during darkness at a range of six miles.

The use of radar for navigation received special attention when preparations were being made for the invasion of Europe. It was necessary for the assault craft to cross the English Channel under the cover of darkness. They would need to keep formation and they would need to land on the designated beach, therefore it was necessary to fit navigation craft in each assault group with a centimetric radar. Trials were carried out and predictions of PPI displays of Normandy beaches were made. These proved very helpful to the D Day landings in June 1944.

In the autumn of the same year, the Allies became heavily dependent on the supply of war materials through the port of Antwerp. This meant that ships would have to navigate the difficult passage of the River Schelde. It has many shoals and is often shrouded in thick fog during winter months.

The new 3 centimetre radar was tried by R.N. navigators and they carried out a radar survey of the passage. This involved taking PPI photographs at frequent intervals so that prominent features would be recognisable. A few months later blind pilotage of the River Schelde became possible.

In 1945, as the war was drawing to a close, consideration was given to the needs of the Merchant Navy so that radar could be properly utilized in peacetime. Discussions were held with the interested parties and a performance specification was issued by the Ministry of Transport. Trinity House Pilotage Authority began to fit radar reflectors on buoys, these effectively raised the radar detection range from 2 miles to about 6 miles. Attention was also focussed on certain desirable features of the radar. New circuits were designed to minimize the effect of "sea clutter". (This is unwanted echoes from the sea waves which tend to obscure the centre of the PPI.)

Because of the rapid strides that had taken place during the War, it was thought necessary to hold a Conference on Radio Aids. Accordingly, the first

International Meeting on Radio Aids to Navigation was held in London in May 1946. Radar development and its future was a major feature of these discussions. A second meeting soon followed in the U.S. in May 1947.

Manufacturers in the U.K. and the U.S. now began volume production of radar sets for commercial use, but in the interim, a large number of Merchant ships were permitted to use the ex-naval Type 268 radars.

The use of radar in those early days tended to give some ship-masters extra confidence in fog and a number of well publicized "radar assisted collisions" occurred. This was often due to an excessive speed in fog or the lack of plotting. Navigation colleges in the U.K. soon added Radar Observer Courses to their curriculum, at first the course was optional, but it soon became an essential part of the deck officer certificate of competency. In the early 1960's radar simulators became available. A deck officer could now practice collision avoidance without leaving the safety of the classroom. Targets could now be simulated to move across the PPI at varying speeds and the navigator could plot and then alter course to avoid a hazardous close quarters situation. Similarly, it is now an integral part of the examination for First Mate and Master. Five day courses are run in most navigation colleges.

Radar technique is constantly improving. Early radar sets had a "Head Up" display and relative bearings were taken of other targets. If own ship altered course, the PPI display tended to blur as targets moved across the screen to the new relative bearing. This difficulty was overcome by incorporating a gyro repeater and the radar display could now be stabilized with a "North Up" display. This greatly improved coastal navigation, bearings of other ships became much steadier too. But this did not relieve the need to produce a relative motion plot to ascertain the course and speed of other ships. When there are several targets it becomes rather difficult to cope with the plotting. To reduce the work-load on the navigator, True Motion Radar was developed. In this type of radar set, the ship proceeds along the radar screen (PPI) at the set speed input, the speed input can be set manually or derived from a log impeller. The true course and speed of other ships is given by their trace on the PPI, the traces of other ships can be recorded by using a chinagraph pencil on a plastic reflection plotter. The great advantage of the True Motion radar is that fixed objects appear stationary on the display, provided that the set and drift of any tidal stream or current is correctly allowed for by the use of the appropriate controls.

Because own ship moves along the display, it becomes necessary to re-set the ship position so that the radar view forward is not restricted. On some sets this will occur automatically, otherwise a warning is given to the navigator to re-set own ship. True Motion radar is ideal for making a river or estuarial passage in fog, it is relatively easy for the navigator to monitor the ship's progress along the channel, buoyage and other navigational marks can easily and quickly be recognised by reference to the chart. At one time Chart Comparison Units were manufactured, these enabled the navigator to simultaneously view the chart and the PPI, however these devices have not proved very popular.

The latest development in radar technology is the evolution of Collision Avoidance Systems. These systems incorporate mini-computers and microprocessors which will calculate the course and speed of targets on the PPI, other information such as time and distance to closest approach is available. In some systems the operator can select the targets, in other systems the targets are automatically acquired and tracked. A collision risk alarm can warn the navigator if another ship is coming too close for comfort. Trial avoidance manoeuvres can be simulated to see if they are feasible. The provision of Collision Avoidance Systems should prove to be of great value to the navigator provided they are properly used and their limitations are known. Training on these sophisticated radar sets has recently commenced.

As a result of the 1974 Safety of Life at Sea Convention there has been international agreement to require the fitting of a basic radar set on vessels over 1,600 gross tons. In 1976, proposals were introduced to require the fitting of a dual radar installation on vessels of 10,000 gross tons and upward. In 1980 the dual radar installation was agreed by the IMCO Navigation Safety Sub-Committee and it is now being formalized. Radar is the mariner's most powerful navigational tool and the possible loss of use could lead to a disastrous collision or grounding. In this respect, oil tankers are of special importance, the rapid increase in the size of tankers has led to the potential risk of a 250,000 ton oil spill. Indeed, some tankers are now in excess of 500,000 tons.

The pulse technique which had been used to develop radar was also used to develop Gee and Loran. Gee was developed in Britain in 1940 to meet the needs of the bomber force. At the same time the U.S. also developed a hyperbolic navigation system called Loran. This is an acronym derived from *long range navigation*.

Gee.—This operated in the 20 to 85 MHz frequency and was limited to line of sight distances. The hyperbolic position lines were determined by the measurement of the time difference between the reception of synchronised pulse signals from two or more stations. The transmitting stations were 70 to 80 miles apart, they were usually arranged in a group of four. One of the four stations was the master and controlled the pulses from the other three slaves. The stations transmitted at the same frequency but at different pulse rates. The aircraft receiver was fitted with a cathode ray tube which showed these pulses and by electronic magnification the pulses could be exactly matched and the time difference in micro-seconds measured. This time difference measure-

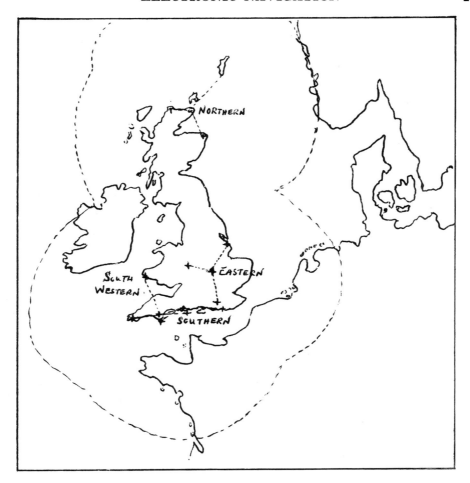

United Kingdom Gee Chains and extent of coverage for 15,000 feet height.

ment gave a hyperbolic position line. It would then be necessary to measure the time difference for another slave to obtain a fix.

Although used mainly by aircraft, it was used successfully by the Royal Navy.

Loran.—In 1941, the Massachusetts Institute of Technology began work on Loran and by 1942 the first stations were established in the North Atlantic. In the following year the system was extended to the Pacific. The original system, now called Loran A, operated in the frequency range 1,750 to 1,950 kHz. The master and slave stations were between 200 and 400 miles apart and because of the better propagational properties, ground wave coverage extended to 700 or 800 miles. By night, skywaves extend the range to approximately

1,400 miles but the results are not so reliable. Skywaves are reflected from various ionized layers in the atmosphere and their reception tends to fluctuate. At the limits of coverage, the signals can be difficult to interpret due to multiple echoes. It is most important that the observer only measures the time difference between ground waves from each station or the One-Hop-E skywave from each station.

The Loran "A" receiver would have a cathode ray tube display with a top and bottom trace. The operator would set the channel frequency and the pulse repetition rate, he would be able to detect the master and slave pulses and these could be drifted along the trace until they jumped onto the "pedestal", a lock button would be operated. The signals would then be successively magnified (Mode 2) and then superimposed so that the leading left hand edges of the pulses were exactly coincident. The reading in microseconds would then be noted. If ground waves were received, they would need no correction, but skywaves would need a small time correction before plotting on the Loran chart. A certain amount of skill was required to operate this equipment especially at night when skywaves predominate. By day, when within range of ground-waves it is relatively simple to operate but it takes a few minutes to obtain a fix.

Loran "C".—In 1957, the U.S. developed a superior Loran system and called it Loran "C". It still used pulsed transmissions but they were on a much lower frequency of 100 kHz. This lower frequency gave improved stability to the radio wave propagation and also extended the range. Ground wave ranges of 800 to 1,200 miles are typical, a very high position fixing accuracy is achieved when within ground-wave range. The accuracy of the fix will depend on the angle at which the hyperbolae intersect.

The Loran "C" pulses can also be received as sky-waves. This can cause problems when the sky-waves contaminate the ground-wave signal but it is taken care of by the Loran "C" signal format and the receiver design. When

Typical Loran ''A'' display on Cathode Ray Tube

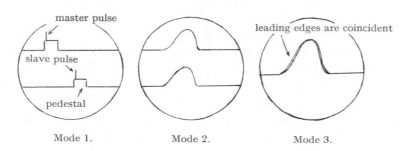

Mode 1.   Mode 2.   Mode 3.

beyond reception of the ground-wave, fixes can be obtained by using sky-wave signals, but it is necessary to apply a correction given by tables published by the U.S. Defense Mapping Agency.   Corrections are also printed on the Loran "C" charts.

The latest Loran "C" receivers employ micro-processors and automatically convert the time differences to a Latitude and Longitude display.

Decca Navigator.—This is a short range hyperbolic navigation system which was developed in World War Two.   It was used by minesweepers im-

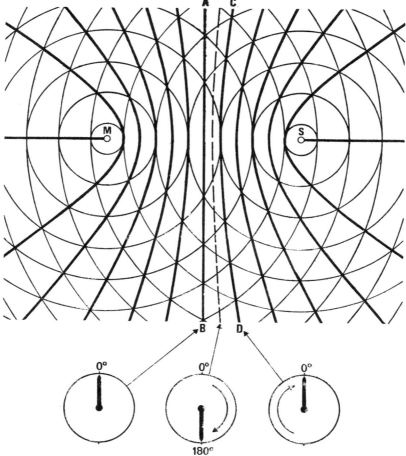

The figure illustrates a hyperbolic pattern which is formed by phase-locked continuous wave signals from Master and Slave stations.   The concentric circles represent successive wavelengths.   The space bounded by two adjacent hyperbolae on which the signals are in phase, e.g. AB and CD is termed a "Lane".   As a ship sails across a Lane the Decometer will rotate through 360°.   By convention the Decometer will turn clockwise for movement from Master to Slave.

mediately prior to the Normandy landings in June 1944, to ensure the accuracy of the swept channels. From a position S.E. of the Isle of Wight a number of channels were swept of mines. Each channel only had a width of 400 to 1,200 yards so precise navigation was needed.

Decca became available for commercial users in 1946 when the first chain of transmitters was opened.

The Decca Navigator system consists of a Master station and three slave transmitters. Ideally, the slaves are situated symmetrically around the master station at distances of 70 to 80 miles. Each station transmits continuous wave signals in the frequency range 70 to 130 kHz. The stations transmit on different frequencies but each is harmonically linked. To identify the slave stations they are designated purple, red and green. The hyperbolic patterns on the Admiralty charts are similarly coloured.

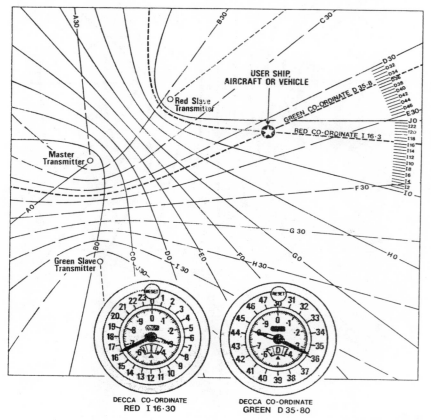

Courtesy Racal-Decca Ltd.

The figure shows a position fix obtained by reading two Decometers and after application of any fixed error, the intersecting hyperbolae give the position.

Decca Track Plotter.

The Decca receiver aboard ship receives the C.W. transmissions and compares their phase difference. In order to do this, the signals are multiplied to give a comparison frequency. The phase difference is indicated on a phase meter or "Decometer" which is calibrated to read to ·01 of a phase. When the lane fraction pointer has moved through 360°, the ship will have moved through one lane. The width of a lane is quite narrow, being half a wavelength on the base-line. Considering the frequencies used on the English 5B chain we have the Master on 85 kHz and the Red slave on 113·33 kHz the comparison frequency is 340 kHz, this corresponds to a wavelength of 880·2 m and the Red lane width on the base-line is 440·1 m. As the Decometer can be read to ·01 of a lane, the theoretical accuracy is 4·4 m. The Decca Navigator Co. publish accuracy contours for the areas covered and it is no exaggeration to say that fixes accurate to within a ship's length are possible in daylight when more than a hundred miles away.

There are certain fixed errors in the system, due to the slight difference in propagation of the radio wave in certain areas, but these errors are published in data sheets. Of more importance is the possibility of "lane slip", this may be likened to a watch with a correct minute hand but the possibility of a slip in the hour hand. This may occur at the extremity of coverage or due to inter-

The Mark IV Decometer unit (18 × 7 × 11 inches overall).

Mark 5 Receiver.

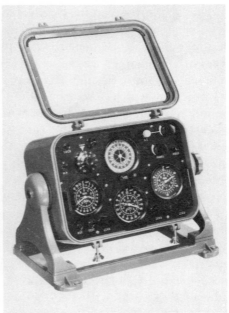

Mark 12 Receiver.

Mark 21 Receiver.

(Courtesy Racal-Decca Ltd.)

ference at night between skywaves and groundwaves. In earlier sets this problem was partly overcome by the transmission of a coarser pattern which was indicated on a separate Lane Identification Meter.

The present Decca Navigator (Mk 21) employs a Multipulse Technique, this greatly improves the stability of the receiver under difficult conditions, the ambiguity of the system is no longer a problem, though care should be used when first entering the Decca Chain coverage. The Decca Navigator system is an ideal landfall and coastal aid to navigation. The simplicity of operation and the reliability is highly regarded by European navigators. The number of chains is continually being extended, there are upwards of fifty chains in use or under construction. It is a pity that due to the U.S. commitment to the Loran "C" system that it is not favoured on the U.S. coast. Decca is mainly used in North European waters, South Africa, Newfoundland, Nigeria, Persian Gulf, India, Bangladesh, Japan and N.W. Australia.

The photographs show the continuous improvement that has taken place in the Decca Navigator system. The first commercial model became available in 1946, this was the Mark IV. It did not have the benefit of lane identification and it was used by ships whose routes were wholly within the Decca coverage. It was normally a single chain receiver which could be supplemented by a unit

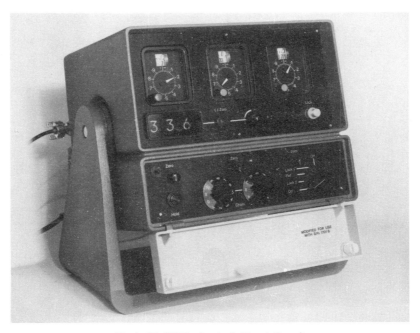

Mark 21 (With Control Panel Open).

(*Courtesy Racal-Decca Ltd.*)

which gave operation with the three British chains. This equipment was soon superseded by the Mark V which had the advantage of lane identification. In the late 1950's an improved method of lane identification was evolved, this was the present "Multipulse" technique. It allowed quicker inter-chain fixing and gave better stability at long range. The Mark 12 with Multipulse became available in 1962 and is still giving sterling service. The present model is the Mark 21 which was introduced in 1971. As a result of the application of transistors, the equipment has become much smaller. The receiver, power unit and display is housed in a single trunnion-mounted unit. The major difference being the digital read-out of the Multipulse Lane Identification, the Decometers now only have a fraction pointer with the lane numbers being displayed in a window above. If any faults should occur they can be quickly solved by changing plug-in printed circuit boards.

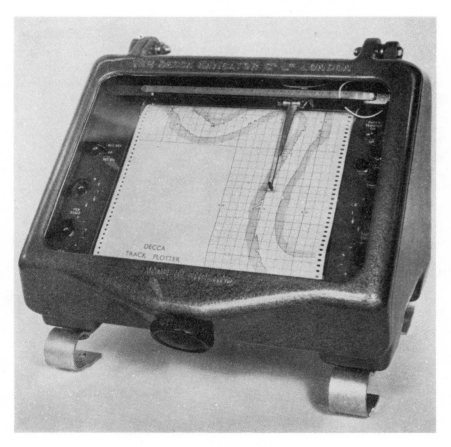

Decca Track Plotter.   (*Courtesy Racal-Decca Ltd.*)

For specialized application a Decca Track Plotter can be used. The information from the Decca Navigator causes a pen to trace out the ship's position on a special chart, at the same time a complete record of the track made good is produced. This would be of great value to hydrographic surveying as lines of soundings are taken. The Decca Track Plotter is frequently fitted on cross Channel ferries, it enables them to safely enter estuaries in poor visibility by following a pre-determined track. In conjunction with fish-finding equipment, the Track Plotter enables the fishing vessel to re-visit the site of previous prolific hauls, the positions of wrecks can be plotted on the chart and this can prevent the nets and other gear from becoming snagged on obstructions.

The Navy Navigation Satellite System (Transit System).—The space age began in 1957, when Russia launched the first satellite, called Sputnik 1. The Applied Physics Laboratory of John Hopkins University in the U.S. were intrigued by the Doppler frequency shift of the radio signals and they realised that the process could give a navigator his precise position if the satellite orbit was precisely known.

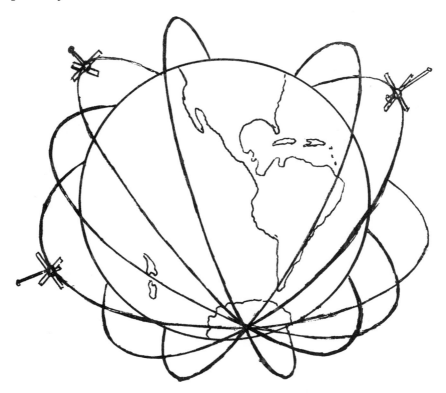

The Transit Satellites in circular polar orbit around the Earth. Height approx. 580 nautical miles.

The Transit system was funded in December 1958 and became operational in January 1964. At first it was for military purposes only, primarily for the navigation of the Polaris submarines to ensure accuracy of any launching of nuclear warheads. In July 1967, the U.S. Government released the system for commercial purposes. Since that time there has been a very rapid growth by commercial users.

The system is operated by the U.S. Navy, it consists of 5 satellites in circular orbits about 1,075 km high (580 miles), these satellites circle the Earth every 107 minutes and provide a "birdcage" within which the earth revolves. Whenever a satellite passes above the horizon there is an opportunity to obtain a position fix by measuring the Doppler shift in the radio signals transmitted by the satellite.

The headquarters of the system are at Point Mugu, California with tracking stations in Maine, Minnesota and Hawaii. Each time the satellite passes within range of a tracking station the Doppler frequency shift in the 150 MHz and 400 MHz transmissions is monitored. This data is then sent to the headquarters computing centre where the satellite orbital data and future movement is predicted. The computer centre then sends a navigation message to the injection stations in California and Minnesota. At the next transit, the navigation message is injected into the satellite memory bank. Each satellite receives a new message every 12 hours. As the satellite orbits the Earth, it retransmits this message at two-minute intervals. The message contents together with the Doppler counts enable the user to determine his position very accurately.

On the ship, a very sensitive receiver is required, because the satellite only has a 1 watt power output. As the satellite rises above the horizon, preferably between 10° and 75° altitude, the receiver "locks on" and receives the orbital parameters together with the Doppler count. This process requires from 10 to 16 minutes, during which the satellite travels 4,400 to 7,000 kms, providing a good baseline. During the satellite pass, the ship's motion should be accurately known. A small computer will then process the information and give a digital read-out of Latitude, Longitude and time of fix.

Initially the cost of this equipment was very high, but with improving technology and the mass production of microprocessors there has been a gradual fall in prices. Models are even produced for yachts. There has been a constant evolution in equipment. With integrated circuits and micro-engineering the equipment has become much more compact.

Besides producing navigational fixes, the latest equipment will give a continuous display of the dead reckoning and time. The dead reckoning is of course, based on the last Transit fix and the automatic speed and heading input. The computational facilities can also be used to solve other navigational

Magnavox MX 1105 Satellite/Omega Navigator.

problems, e.g. Great Circle courses and distances or rhumb line courses and distances to selected way points. By comparison of fixes with the dead reckoning, the set and drift of ocean currents can be found.

When first released for commercial purposes only dual channel receivers (150 and 400 MHz) were available and the equipment was very expensive. In 1971 a single channel receiver was developed. This only received on 400 MHz and gave an RMS error of 88 metres for a stationary observer. The majority of ship installations fit into this category, the dual channel receiver measures and compensates for ionospheric refraction and typically gives a RMS error of 27 to 37 metres.

At the present time, Transit is the only navigation aid which has world-wide availability, it is not affected by weather and its accuracy is equal to that of short range radio-location systems. Because of its simplicity and reliability, it has become very popular with mariners.

The Transit system has one disadvantage, this is the waiting time between fixes. Because of launch imperfections and different precession rates, the satellites are not symmetrically spaced. This can sometimes give a waiting time of 12 hours to an observer at the Equator, this could still be six or seven hours waiting time in higher latitudes. The United States Navy plan to decrease this time interval by launching an improved NOVA satellite to "fill the gap". The newer satellites should have several advantages. Atmospheric drag will be eliminated and as a result the orbital data will retain its accuracy for up to one week. The satellite will have an on-board computer and with a larger memory bank the computer will give orbital information for ten days before requiring an up-date. The transmissions will be twice as strong as the current satellites.

The Navstar/Global Positioning System.—The Navstar/GPS system is a satellite-based navigation system that will give extremely accurate three dimensional position fixes and timing information to users anywhere on the Earth's surface. The GPS system is being developed by the United States for military purposes, this would be primarily for weapon delivery systems but it is hoped that like the Transit system it will become available for commercial users.

The GPS system will have 24 satellites in circular 10,900 mile orbits. These orbits will be in three planes with an inclination of 63°, each plane will contain eight satellites. This satellite constellation will ensure that at least six satellites are always in view and on average nine will be above the observer's horizon. The satellites will have a design life of 5 years but this will probably be extended as the system improves. Power is supplied by solar panels that will track the sun, nickel cadmium batteries will be available for eclipse operation.

The satellites will transmit radio signals on frequencies of 1,575 MHz and 1,227 MHz. The signals will contain orbital data and timing signals from the atomic clock that each satellite carries. The clock has a stability of the order of 1 part in 10^{13}. The ground Master Control Station will ensure that the clocks are synchronized. If the users also had precision clocks they could make range measurements of the satellites and so determine their position. However, users will not require these precision clocks, the position will be obtained by measuring the independent range difference from four satellites. The simultaneous reception of four navigation signals will give three independent range difference equations which will be used to define the observer's position in three dimensions. A ship, of course, only requires two dimensions.

In addition to the Master Control Station, the satellites will be supported by remote monitoring stations located on U.S. controlled territory. The monitoring stations will receive the radio signals and the information will be sent to the MCS for processing and computing of future satellite orbit. This information will be injected into the satellite memory bank for subsequent transmission.

The GPS system is currently undergoing operational testing and evaluation by the United States.   In the early 1980's it is hoped to have 9 to 11 satellites in orbit and by the mid 1980's it should reach the full capability with 24 satellites in orbit.

At this time it is too early to give the performance standards but it is computed that the horizontal positional accuracy will be 7·6 m for 90% of the time.   Hopefully, this incredible accuracy will be available to all mariners.

T

INDEX